D1075414

WINDS AND TURBULENCE IN STRATOSPHERE,
MESOSPHERE AND IONOSPHERE

WINDS AND TURBULENCE IN STRATOSPHERE, MESOSPHERE AND IONOSPHERE

Proceedings of the NATO Advanced Study Institute
Lindau, Federal Republic of Germany, 18 Sept. - 1 Oct. 1966

Sponsored by

NATO Science Committee

Edited by

K. RAWER

Ionosphären-Institut, Breisach, Germany

1968

NORTH-HOLLAND PUBLISHING COMPANY — AMSTERDAM
JOHN WILEY & SONS, INC. — NEW YORK
(Interscience Publishers Division)

© North-Holland Publishing Company – Amsterdam – 1968

No part of this book may be reproduced in any form by print, photoprint, microfilm or any other means without written permission from the publisher

Library of Congress Catalog Card Number 67-26464

Publishers:

NORTH-HOLLAND PUBLISHING CO. – AMSTERDAM

Sole distributors for U.S.A. and Canada:

Interscience Publishers, a division of

JOHN WILEY & SONS, INC. – NEW YORK

SCARBOROUGH
COLLEGE
LIBRARY

PRINTED IN THE NETHERLANDS

PREFACE

In 1965, the NATO Science Committee's Panel on Radio-Meteorology recommended the holding of a Study Institute on phenomena of winds and turbulence in the upper atmosphere, upto a height of 120 km approximately. In earlier years the Panel on Radio-Meteorology had been almost exclusively concerned with tropospheric propagation and meteorological studies. Now however the Panel, and in particular its chairman, P. Misme, felt that the relationship between mesospheric and lower ionospheric phenomena merited greater scientific interest.

An Advanced Study Institute was organised along these lines by the undersigned. It was held at Lindau on Lake Constance, in the south-western corner of the Federal Republic of Germany, on 18 September - 1 October 1966. The meeting was sponsored by the NATO Science Committee and its grant number 1-1966.

In accordance with the objectives envisaged by the Panel on Radio-Meteorology, the participants who were invited came mainly from two fields of research: meteorologists studying the upper atmosphere, and scientists working on radio-propagation and ionospheric investigations. The standpoints of theoretical and tropospheric gas dynamics were represented by two invited speakers, Professor Bolgiano and Professor Gille.

The organisers of the meeting feel that the choice of disciplines was a happy one. The lively interchanges showed that there are many open questions for discussion between these disciplines, particularly with regard to heights between the upper stratosphere and lower ionosphere. At the present time, the direct information available about this intermediate region, the mesosphere, is scanty. With increasing efforts to obtain more data, one may expect a growing demand for a broader theoretical treatment of phenomena occurring in this height range.

With one exception, the following papers are a complete report of the meeting. We felt that the discussions should also be recorded, though we omitted some points of clarification which were subsequently embodied in the printed papers. There were two half-day discussions which are also presented in condensed form.

We hope that this volume will be useful to scientific workers in both disciplines as an introduction to this field which is related to both. We also hope that it will provide an incentive to further research.

K. Rawer

Breisach, 1 February 1968

CONTENTS

ATMOSPHERIC STRUCTURE BETWEEN 30 AND 120 KM

Diego FEDELE and Antonino ZANCLA

Ministero della Difesa Aeronautica,
Servizio Meteorologico, Roma, Italy

Abstract. After an examination of the layers in which the atmosphere is divided, effects of solar, atmospheric and terrestrial radiation are considered as well as the composition of the atmosphere up to 120 km. Winds in the upper atmosphere and predominant zonal circulation are dealt with according to new experimental data.

Résumé. Après avoir examiné les différentes couches de l'atmosphère, les effets du rayonnement solaire, atmosphérique et terrestre sont étudiés ainsi que la composition de l'atmosphère jusqu'à l'altitude de 120 km. Nous examinons ensuite les vents de la haute atmosphère et les zones de circulation prédominante suivant les dernières données d'expériences.

1. UPPER ATMOSPHERE STRUCTURE

The term 'Upper Atmosphere' is commonly used to designate the earth's atmosphere above some explicitly or implicitly definite altitude. However the choice of altitude to separate 'Lower Atmosphere' from 'Upper Atmosphere' or 'Middle Atmosphere' from 'Upper Atmosphere' is not uniform.

According to definitions recommended by WMO the principal layers, in which the atmosphere is divided, are denoted by 'spheres' and their tops by 'pauses' (figs. 1, 2).

Approx. height (km)	Layer	Upper boundary
0 - 10 (polar)	Troposphere	Tropopause
0 - 16 (equatorial)		
Tropopause - 55	Stratosphere	Stratopause
Stratopause - 80	Mesosphere	Mesopause
Mesopause upwards	Thermosphere	

The region above about 80 km may be generally referred to as the ionosphere when discussing ionization, the chemosphere when discussing dissociation, or the thermosphere when discussing temperature structure. The lower boundaries of each of these regions may not be the same but the usage will be obvious from the context.

Some details of the atmospheric structure and principal physical features of this region of the atmosphere and their variability (which is considerable), will be given below.

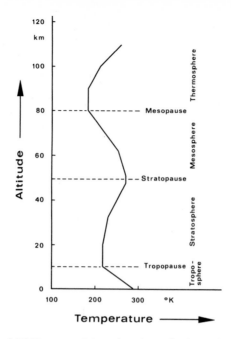

Fig. 1. Standard WMO nomenclature for atmospheric regions up to 120 km.

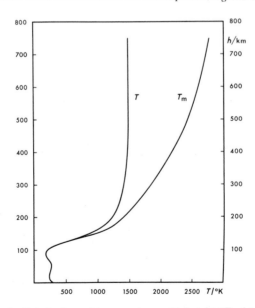

Fig. 2. Approximate distribution of temperature with height (T = kinetic temperature; T_m = molecular scale temperature).

Approximate mean values of pressure, temperature, density, number density, mean free path and molecular weight at a number of levels are given in table 1 taken from the US Standard Atmosphere (1962). This publication lists these quantities at a large number of levels up to 700 km in metric and English units and also values of other useful parameters, e.g. acceleration due to gravity, speed of sound, scale heights, particle speed, collision frequencies, coefficients of viscosity, thermal conductivity etc. Above the levels given, variations of pressure, temperature and density from day to night become significant. The mean values in table 1 refer to mid-latitudes only and up to about 100 km are reasonably well substantiated. Above 120 km, however, more recent work suggests that the quoted temperatures are somewhat low (see CIRA 1965).

In order to understand the reasons for the temperature structure shown in table 1 we first have to consider the direct absorption of solar radiation by the upper atmosphere. This depends on the latter's chemical composi-

Table 1
Atmospheric structure. Mean mid-latitude values.

Height (km)	Pressure (mb)	Temperature ($^{\circ}$K)	Density (kg m^{-3})	Number density (cm^{-3})	Mean free path (cm)	Molecular weight
10	2.65×10^2	223	4.14×10^{-1}	8.60×10^{18}	1.96×10^{-5}	28.96
20	5.53×10	217	8.89×10^{-2}	1.85×10^{18}	9.14×10^{-5}	28.96
30	1.20×10	227	1.84×10^{-2}	3.83×10^{17}	4.41×10^{-4}	28.96
40	2.87	250	4.00×10^{-3}	8.31×10^{16}	2.03×10^{-3}	28.96
50	7.98×10^{-1}	271	1.03×10^{-3}	2.14×10^{16}	7.91×10^{-3}	28.96
60	2.25×10^{-1}	256	3.06×10^{-4}	6.36×10^{15}	2.66×10^{-2}	28.96
70	5.52×10^{-2}	220	8.75×10^{-5}	1.82×10^{15}	9.28×10^{-2}	28.96
80	1.04×10^{-2}	181	2.00×10^{-5}	4.16×10^{14}	4.07×10^{-1}	28.96
90	1.64×10^{-3}	181	3.17×10^{-6}	6.59×10^{13}	2.56×1	28.96
100	3.01×10^{-4}	210	4.97×10^{-7}	1.04×10^{13}	1.63×10	28.88
110	7.35×10^{-5}	257	9.83×10^{-8}	2.07×10^{12}	8.15×10	28.56
120	2.52×10^{-5}	349	2.44×10^{-8}	5.23×10^{11}	3.23×10^2	28.07
130	1.22×10^{-5}	534	7.59×10^{-9}	1.66×10^{11}	1.02×10^3	27.58
140	7.41×10^{-6}	714	3.39×10^{-9}	7.52×10^{10}	2.25×10^3	27.20
150	5.06×10^{-6}	893	1.84×10^{-9}	4.11×10^{10}	4.11×10^3	26.92
160	3.69×10^{-6}	1022	1.16×10^{-9}	2.62×10^{10}	6.45×10^3	26.66
170	2.79×10^{-6}	1106	8.04×10^{-10}	1.83×10^{10}	9.23×10^3	26.45
180	2.15×10^{-6}	1156	5.86×10^{-10}	1.35×10^{10}	1.25×10^4	26.15
190	1.69×10^{-6}	1206	4.35×10^{-10}	1.01×10^{10}	1.67×10^4	25.85
200	1.33×10^{-6}	1236	3.32×10^{-10}	7.82×10^9	2.16×10^4	25.56

tion but at the same time it also modifies it. The second major term in the energy balance of the stratosphere and mesosphere is terrestrial (atmospheric) radiation. Whereas the solar absorption takes place mainly in the ultra-violet part of the spectrum and is largely independent of temperature, the infra-red emission increases rapidly with the temperature of the atmospheric constituents. Hence as a first approximation the air temperature at any latitude and altitude up to about 100 km will adjust itself to a value where these two factors are broadly in balance and the temperature distribution will tend to follow that of the energy absorbed from solar radiation. As a result we find a high temperature region around the 50 km level (ozone absorption of the solar beam) and lower temperature around the 20 and 80 km levels where the direct absorption is comparatively small. The high temperatures in the thermosphere above 100 km are, in part at least, due to direct absorption by molecular oxygen. The energy balance at these higher levels is different, the main constituents for infra-red emission at the levels below (CO_2, O_3 and H_2O) being dissociated and additional terms which are small below 100 km becoming significant. These include corpuscular bombardment (particularly at high latitudes), conduction especially from the solar corona, release of chemical energy, joule heating, dissipation of hydromagnetic waves and infrasonic waves etc., but their magnitudes at the different levels are not known with certainty and it is difficult to assess their relative importance in the energy balance. At all these levels, however, solar ultra-violet absorption appears to be important and in the outer regions above 200 km high correlations between solar illumination (as well as solar activity) and atmospheric density are found indicating a great deal of solar control.

Unbalance between the resultant heating rates at different latitudes will supply the primary driving force for the atmospheric circulation. The circulation will also redistribute the various constituents concerned in the radiative processes. If, however, an accurate independent estimate could be made of the various energy terms by using observations of temperature, composition etc., the effective heat sources and sinks might, in principle at least, be specified. If so, they could be used in the thermodynamic equation and, with the help of the equations of motion and the continuity equation, the resultant circulation could be found. In practice it has not yet been possible to specify these heat sources and sinks sufficiently well ($1^{\circ}K$/day heating has about the same effect as a subsidence of 0.1 cm/sec) and other difficulties have become apparent such as the specification of the respective roles of mean and eddy motions in the stratosphere and mesosphere and that of viscous forces towards the 200 km level, so that progress along these lines has so far been very limited. A knowledge of the field of solar radiation at each level is fundamental to all such progress and therefore this subject and infra-red radiation in the stratosphere and mesosphere will be discussed first. Subsequent sections will be concerned with the composition of the atmosphere and atmospheric circulation.

2. SOLAR RADIATION

Following recent rocket and satellite experiments using ultra-violet spectrometers, photon counters, scintillation counters and ion chambers, the spectral energy distribution for the quiet sun is now reasonable well known for wavelengths up to the visible and beyond, as is also the general depth of penetration into the atmosphere of the solar beam at different frequencies (fig. 3) for given solar zenith angles.

The principal features are (I) that X-rays ($\lambda < 100$ Å) reach levels of about 60 to 120 km and wavelengths of 100-200 Å probably 120-160 km above the earth's surface. (II) Wavelengths of 200 Å to about 1000 Å have the least penetration and only reach about 150-200 km above the earth's surface. (III) Between 1000 and 2000 Å, except for the important Lyman radiation at 1215 Å and some other lines between 1100 Å and 1300 Å which reach 60-90 km, the heights reached are about 90-120 km above earth's surface. The solar curve falls from a roughly equivalent 5000 ^{O}K black body level at 2085 Å to 4900 ^{O}K at 1800 Å and 4750 ^{O}K at 1500 Å. (IV) Between 2000 Å and 3000 Å the penetration is limited by the ozone layer between 30 and 70 km. Most of the near ultra-violet and the visible of course, up to 7000 Å, reaches the surface while the infra-red at longer wavelengths suffers variable absorption by the minor constituents, mainly in the troposphere.

Previous data on the absorption of the solar beam between 30 and 100 km by molecular oxygen and ozone in wavelengths between about 1000 Å and the visible do not appear to have been modified substantially in the last few years and the state of knowledge is broadly as given in Murgatroyd's (1957) review. For completeness fig. 4 from Murgatroyd and Goody (1958) is given to illustrate the following principal features:
1) maxima of heating occur around 50 km due to absorption by ozone and

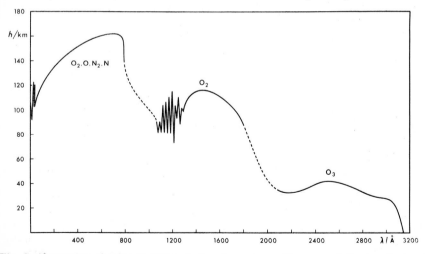

Fig. 3. Absorption of solar radiation in the atmosphere. The curve indicates the level at which the intensity of solar radiation is reduced to e^{-1} (after Friedman).

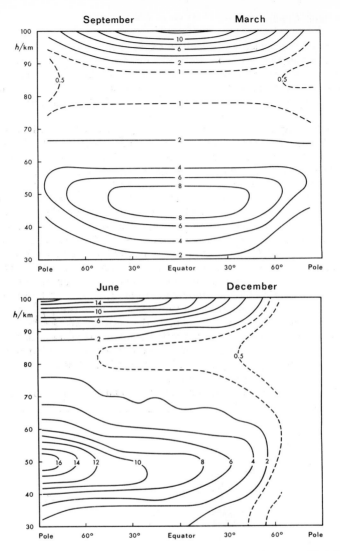

Fig. 4. Temperature change caused by solar radiation as function of height and latitude (Numerical indication in °K per day) (after Murgatroyd and Goody).

around 100 km due to absorption by molecular oxygen with a minimum
around 80 km.

2) at the solstices maximum heating occurs at the summer pole, it is zero at
the winter pole. At the equinoxes the maximum is at the equator with minima at the poles. In general the heating decreases and the altitude of the
maximum increases as the solar zenith angle increases.

Considerable progress has been made recently in the study of absorption of infra-red solar energy at lower levels (35 km to the tropopause), but this has been limited by lack of knowledge of the gaseous concentrations of the minor constituents particularly water vapour (N_2 and O_2 have no significant absorption in the infra-red). Most workers have assumed a 'dry' stratosphere, i.e. with a humidity mixing ratio of about 3×10^{-6} and a constant CO_2 mass mixing ratio of about 4.5×10^{-4}. Considerable data on absorption coefficients for pressure ranges applicable to the lower stratosphere are now available from laboratory work. In addition extensive spectroscopic observations of the infra-red solar spectrum have been made from aircraft flying in the stratosphere and also some of lower resolution from balloon ascents. The most recently available absorption data for the bands of importance:

H_2O: 6.3, 3.2, 2.7, 1.9, 1.4, 1.1, 0.9 μ ;
CO_2: 15, 4.3, 2.7, 2.0, 1.6, 1.4 μ ;
O_2: 1.27, 0.76 μ ;
CH_4: 3.3 μ ;
N_2O: 4.5 μ

have been reviewed by Haughton (1963). The results of recent calculation usually agree within $\pm 30\%$ and show that between 10 and 30 km the mean heating rate due to the solar absorption in the infra-red is of the order of a few tenths of a degree K per day. At these levels this is of the same order as the heating due to absorption in the ultra-violet by ozone; the latter predominates at the higher levels and the former is more important near the tropopause. In the infra-red the absorption due to CO_2 is the most important in the stratosphere while that due to H_2O increases greatly as the height decreases and becomes dominant lower down in the troposphere. Infra-red absorption of the solar beam, although insignificant compared with the ultra-violet absorption by ozone between 30 and 60 km, again probably becomes an important factor between 60 and 80 km and this should be incorporated in later calculations for this altitude range.

3. TERRESTRIAL AND ATMOSPHERIC RADIATION

Information on the field of long-wave radiation (upward and downward fluxes and their divergences) in the stratosphere has accumulated steadily in the last few years. Some direct measurements are available up to the ceilings of aircraft and balloons by radiometers, and instrumental developments and results have been reported from a number of countries. In addition to their use in photographing the cloud systems below, satellites have also carried radiometers to measure in different frequency ranges the incoming and outgoing streams of radiation. So far this work has given more information on the troposphere than on the stratosphere but further experiments have been designed to use these types of measurement to obtain information on the composition and structure of the stratosphere and mesosphere including temperatures in the ozone layer.

It will of course be desirable ultimately to base our knowledge mainly on measurements but in spite of the recent impressive developments in techniques and their applications most of our information on the global fields of radiation above the tropopause is still based on the results of theoretical computations.

For the stratosphere as a whole the most detailed calculations so far available are those of Ohring (1958). His radiation budget covered the region tropopause to 55 km and equator to pole at the solstices and equinoxes and included the effects of solar absorption by ozone and infra-red cooling by O_3, H_2O and CO_2. The latter was the most important cooling agent, H_2O also producing cooling, but the overall effect of the 9.6 μ O_3 band was to produce heating. In the lower stratosphere there was again a heat source at low latitudes and a sink at high latitudes. In the upper part of the stratosphere (21-55 km) there were also radiation excesses in low latitudes and deficits in high latitudes for most of the year, but an excess in high latitudes in late spring and summer. These distributions would be consistent with temperatures generally decreasing polewards at these levels except during the summer when the gradient would reverse, as indeed is observed. It appears likely from these results that in the upper stratosphere there is a transport of excess energy from the summer hemisphere to the winter hemisphere.

Data covering still higher levels are very sparse and few calculations giving latitudinal distributions appear to have been made for levels above 90 km although specimen results describing the temperature structure of the thermosphere are available. Computations of radiative equilibrium temperature in the upper stratosphere and mesosphere have been made by Gowan (1947) and more recently by Leovy, and Murgatroyd and Goody (1965) have attempted to find the principal radiative heat sources and sinks between 30 and 90 km at the solstices. These latter authors calculated the heating due to solar absorption by molecular oxygen and ozone and the long-wave emission in the 15 μ CO_2 and 9.6 μ O_3 bands, the contributions due to other constituents, e.g. H_2O, being assumed to be negligible. Their results suggest that at these levels the departure from radiative equilibrium is small ($<$ 2^{O}K per day) from 60° latitude in the summer hemisphere to 30° latitude in the winter hemisphere. In higher latitudes, however, considerable departures were found with several degrees K per day heating in the summer and comparable cooling in the winter. As in Ohring's work these results indicate an excess of heat in the upper stratosphere and also in the mesosphere in summer and suggest the necessity of a transfer between hemispheres at these levels. Similarly to the finding of Brooks (1958), heating by infra-red convergence in the 15 μ CC_2 band in the region of minimum temperatures (the summer polar mesophere in this case) was found to be an important factor. For use in simplified dynamical calculations based on the above distributions of radiative sources and sinks Murgatroyd and Singleton (1964) produced fig. 5 which is a synthesis of the above results with those of Ohring.

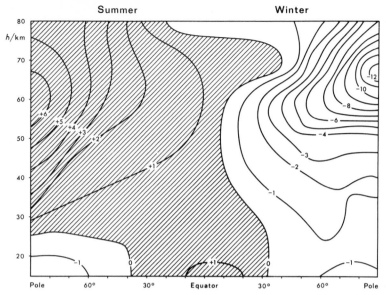

Fig. 5. Radiative heating (+) and cooling (-) as function of height and latitude. (Numerical indication in °K per day.) (after Murgatroyd and Singleton.)

4. COMPOSITION

4.1.

The region from the mesopause to the lower ionosphere is one in which the relative amounts of the various atmospheric constituents changes considerably. This has several important consequences such as the change in mean molecular weight M (which affects such quantities as the speed of sound, the hydrostatic distribution etc.), and also affects considerably the radiation field. In addition to changes from molecular to atomic states following dissociation by solar radiation and also changes from the various consequential chemical reactions, the composition is also affected above about 100 km by diffusive separation. Above this altitude atomic oxygen becomes progressively more dominant until about the 800 km level, above which the lighter gases helium and hydrogen in turn become the main constituents.

Most of the major features up to about 200 km at least can be explained in terms of the chemistry of an oxygen-nitrogen atmosphere. The sun's ultra-violet radiation produces considerable dissociation of oxygen and also of the minor constituents above about 70 km. Recombination takes place following three-body collisions and photochemical equilibrium is approached. At some heights this is rapid and at others rather slow so that the resulting distribution of the various constituents is dependent of atmosphere motions, mixing and diffusion as well as the photochemical processes. A large num-

D. FEDELE and A. ZANCLA

Table 2a

A selection of calculated values of concentrations of the different constituents at different local times of the day (temperate and low latitudes) from Harris and Priester (1962). Murgatroid Technical note No. 70 WMO.

04 00 h

Height (km)	T (^{O}K)	Molecular weight	$N(N_2)$ (cm^{-3})	$N(O_2)$ (cm^{-3})	$N(O)$ (cm^{-3})	$N(He)$ (cm^{-3})	$N(H)$ (cm^{-3})
120	355	27.46	5.80×10^{11}	1.20×10^{11}	7.60×10^{10}	2.50×10^{7}	4.36×10^{4}
140	632	26.55	8.94×10^{10}	1.54×10^{10}	2.04×10^{10}	1.17×10^{7}	2.34×10^{4}
160	804	25.74	2.93×10^{10}	4.45×10^{9}	9.71×10^{9}	8.08×10^{6}	1.78×10^{4}
180	914	24.94	1.24×10^{10}	1.71×10^{9}	5.63×10^{9}	6.40×10^{6}	1.53×10^{4}
200	987	24.13	5.99×10^{9}	7.49×10^{8}	3.59×10^{9}	5.40×10^{6}	1.38×10^{4}

10 00 h

Height (km)	T (^{O}K)	Molecular weight	$N(N_2)$ (cm^{-3})	$N(O_2)$ (cm^{-3})	$N(O)$ (cm^{-3})	$N(He)$ (cm^{-3})	$N(H)$ (cm^{-3})
120	355	27.46	5.80×10^{11}	1.20×10^{11}	7.60×10^{10}	2.50×10^{7}	4.36×10^{4}
140	629	26.45	8.89×10^{10}	1.53×10^{10}	2.04×10^{10}	1.17×10^{7}	2.35×10^{4}
160	845	25.75	2.80×10^{10}	4.27×10^{9}	9.27×10^{9}	7.70×10^{6}	1.69×10^{4}
180	1029	25.01	1.18×10^{10}	1.63×10^{9}	5.19×10^{9}	5.74×10^{6}	1.36×10^{4}
200	1175	24.33	5.87×10^{9}	7.49×10^{8}	3.29×10^{9}	4.64×10^{6}	1.17×10^{4}

14 00 h

Height (km)	T (^{O}K)	Molecular weight	$N(N_2)$ (cm^{-3})	$N(O_2)$ (cm^{-3})	$N(O)$ (cm^{-3})	$N(He)$ (cm^{-3})	$N(H)$ (cm^{-3})
120	355	27.46	5.80×10^{11}	1.2×10^{11}	7.6×10^{10}	2.5×10^{7}	4.36×10^{4}
140	652	26.55	8.70×10^{10}	1.50×10^{10}	1.98×10^{10}	1.13×10^{7}	2.27×10^{4}
160	916	25.81	2.76×10^{10}	4.23×10^{9}	8.87×10^{9}	7.17×10^{6}	1.57×10^{4}
180	1130	25.15	1.21×10^{10}	1.70×10^{9}	5.06×10^{9}	5.14×10^{6}	1.24×10^{4}
200	1293	24.54	6.33×10^{9}	8.29×10^{8}	3.30×10^{9}	4.32×10^{6}	1.07×10^{4}

18 00 h

Height (km)	T (^{O}K)	Molecular weight	$N(N_2)$ (cm^{-3})	$N(O_2)$ (cm^{-3})	$N(O)$ (cm^{-3})	$N(He)$ (cm^{-3})	$N(H)$ (cm^{-3})
120	355	27.46	5.80×10^{11}	1.20×10^{11}	7.60×10^{10}	2.50×10^{7}	4.36×10^{4}
140	658	26.56	8.70×10^{10}	1.50×10^{10}	1.97×10^{10}	1.12×10^{7}	2.24×10^{4}
160	900	25.82	2.83×10^{10}	4.35×10^{9}	9.07×10^{9}	7.30×10^{6}	1.59×10^{4}
180	1080	25.14	1.25×10^{10}	1.76×10^{9}	5.26×10^{9}	5.56×10^{6}	1.30×10^{4}
200	1210	24.49	6.49×10^{9}	8.45×10^{8}	3.44×10^{9}	4.59×10^{6}	1.14×10^{4}

22 00 h

Height (km)	T (^{O}K)	Molecular weight	$N(N_2)$ (cm^{-3})	$N(O_2)$ (cm^{-3})	$N(O)$ (cm^{-3})	$N(He)$ (cm^{-3})	$N(H)$ (cm^{-3})
120	355	27.46	5.80×10^{11}	1.20×10^{11}	7.60×10^{10}	2.50×10^{7}	4.36×10^{4}
140	651	26.56	8.79×10^{10}	1.52×10^{10}	1.99×10^{10}	1.13×10^{7}	2.27×10^{4}
160	858	25.80	2.90×10^{10}	4.44×10^{9}	9.39×10^{9}	7.64×10^{6}	1.67×10^{4}
180	994	25.06	1.27×10^{10}	1.77×10^{9}	5.51×10^{9}	5.98×10^{6}	1.41×10^{4}
200	1083	24.34	6.42×10^{9}	8.22×10^{8}	3.59×10^{9}	5.04×10^{6}	1.26×10^{4}

Table 2b

Calculated variations of constituents from day to night (for late 1960 period) after Kallman–Bijl and Sibley (1963).

Height (km)	T (°K)	Molecular weight	$N(N_2)$ (cm^{-3})	$N(O_2)$ (cm^{-3})	$N(O)$ (cm^{-3})	$N(A)$ (cm^{-3})	$N(He)$ (cm^{-3})	$N(H)$ (cm^{-3})
Day-time								
100	205	28.24	8.08×10^{12}	1.90×10^{12}	5.33×10^{11}	9.63×10^{10}	5.40×10^{6}	8.40×10^{6}
120	332	26.60	3.96×10^{11}	6.25×10^{10}	8.75×10^{10}	4.71×10^{9}	2.40×10^{7}	4.89×10^{6}
140	666	25.34	5.28×10^{11}	6.91×10^{9}	2.05×10^{10}	3.58×10^{8}	9.92×10^{6}	2.33×10^{6}
160	935	24.40	1.72×10^{10}	2.01×10^{9}	9.35×10^{9}	8.34×10^{7}	6.31×10^{6}	1.61×10^{6}
180	1042	23.56	8.20×10^{9}	8.78×10^{8}	5.85×10^{9}	3.05×10^{7}	5.18×10^{6}	1.41×10^{6}
200	1100	22.76	4.35×10^{9}	4.29×10^{8}	3.98×10^{9}	1.26×10^{7}	4.51×10^{6}	1.31×10^{6}
Night-time								
100	210	28.10	1.24×10^{13}	2.86×10^{12}	9.58×10^{11}	1.48×10^{11}	8.34×10^{6}	3.60×10^{6}
120	313	27.34	6.04×10^{11}	1.38×10^{11}	9.94×10^{10}	5.86×10^{9}	3.70×10^{6}	2.10×10^{6}
140	490	26.32	7.45×10^{10}	1.51×10^{10}	2.11×10^{10}	4.00×10^{8}	1.86×10^{6}	1.26×10^{6}
160	689	25.12	1.77×10^{10}	3.06×10^{9}	8.00×10^{9}	5.94×10^{7}	1.13×10^{6}	8.61×10^{5}
180	809	24.04	6.45×10^{9}	9.90×10^{8}	4.20×10^{9}	1.51×10^{7}	8.52×10^{5}	7.12×10^{5}
200	900	23.02	2.79×10^{9}	3.87×10^{8}	2.49×10^{9}	4.81×10^{6}	6.91×10^{5}	6.24×10^{5}

ber of chemical reactions between the neutral and ionised products of the
photochemistry also takes place. As a result of all these effects both theoretical considerations and preliminary measurements indicate that the distribution of the various elements is neither the same in different seasons
nor even by day and night, when the dissociating radiations are not present.
Tables 2a and 2b indicate the type of change expected throughout the day.

There are of course considerable quantitative differences between these
two tables and these indicate the uncertainties in our knowledge of conditions at the various levels. The details of even the mean distributions are
not well know but fig. 6 indicates their order. A good deal of the data listed
is based on theoretical considerations but some measurements are available from rocket experiments using mass spectrometers, or by measuring
the change in the ultra-violet solar spectrum during the ascent.

4.2. *Major constituents*

(i) The major consituent, nitrogen, is not easily dissociated by solar
radiation, although atomic nitrogen may be produced above 100 km following dissociative recombination after ionisation by X-rays and solar ultra-
violet wavelengths $\lambda < 800$ Å. Some is also formed by Lyman alpha radiation down to about 75 km. The final distribution at these levels will be
largely dependent on vertical mixing and diffusion processes.

(ii) Oxygen is dissociated by ultra-violet radiation mainly between 1300
and 1760 Å (Schumann continuum) and recombination in collisions leads to
a photochemical distribution of atomic oxygen, molecular oxygen and ozone.

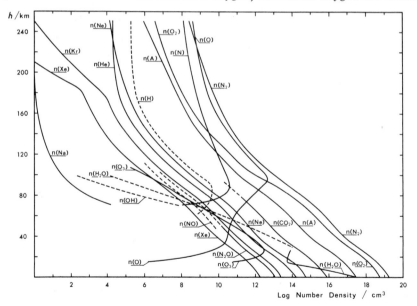

Fig. 6. Vertical distribution of atmospheric constituents (from 'Handbook of Geophysics').

Below about 30 km this is approached very slowly and the ozone distribution is well known to have features determined by the general circulation, such as the maximum in spring and at high latitudes which is not in accordance with the (equilibrium) predictions of photochemical theory.

Between about 30 and 70 km the approach to photochemical equilibrium is rapid and it is virtually reached in day-time. (It is attained fastest at approximately 55 km where the sum of the *odd* atomic oxygen particles O and O_3 is at a minimum.) At night the amount of ozone increases considerably and a secondary ozone maximum is expected at about 70 km especially in summer. The main ozone maximum mixing ratio is at about 35 km and the amounts above about 80 km and below 10 km are very small.

Measurements of ozone amounts above the level of the maximum have been obtained from rockets borne ultra-violet spectrographs and it appears likely that further data will soon be available from dawn and dusk 'grazing ray' determinations by satellites.

The photochemical theory predicts a rapid change completely to the atomic form above 100 km. Local equilibrium, however, is again approached very slowly (the effective solar temperature is only about 4700 $^{\circ}$K at 1300 Å) and it has been shown that the resulting distribution is greatly modified by atmospheric motions. Direct measurements by mass-spectrometers on rockets have confirmed the presence of molecular oxygen up to altitudes of at least 180 km (it is about 65% dissociated at 130 km) and atomic oxygen at levels well below 100 km.

4.3. *Minor constituents*

(i) Chemical reactions also occur between the various nitrogen and oxygen molecules and atoms. The 'D' layer is thought to be due to ionisation of nitric oxide, NO by solar Lyman alpha radiation. Representative concentrations of NO molecules are probably

$$10^9 \ cm^{-3} \text{ at } 65 \text{ km}, \ 10^8 \ cm^{-3} \text{ at } 80 \text{ km and } 10^7 \ cm^{-3} \text{ at } 95 \text{ km}.$$

(ii) It is largely agreed that water vapour is present in rather small concentrations (mixing ratio $\sim 3 \times 10^{-6}$) in the lower stratosphere. There is a controversy, however, whether it remains at about this amount up to the limit of balloon sampling (~ 30 km) or whether it increases with height to a value of 20 to 50 times this amount, as results of different measurements do not agree. The only natural clouds observed above the tropopause are at 20-30 km in winter at high latitudes (mother-of-pearl-clouds) and at about 80 km in summer also at high latitudes (noctilucent clouds). The weight of evidence is that they are both of water substance although the latter may be dust. Water is also dissociated towards the top of the layer and in the various resultant chemical processes with oxygen and ozone H, HO_2 and OH appear, the presence of the latter being confirmed in the light of the night sky. The photochemistry has been discussed by Bates and Nicolet (1950) who showed that the relative proportion of hydrogen increases very rapidly between 75 and 95 km. Hesstredt (1964) has recently made calculations of possible water vapour distributions in the stratosphere and mesosphere taking into account the photochemistry and the motions as far as they can be

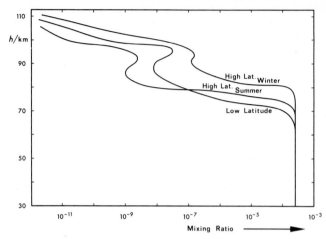

Fig. 7a. Mixing ratio of water vapour and air in a static atmosphere, for different
latitudes and seasons (after Hesstredt, 1964).

inferred at present. His results suggests that above 70-80 km the water
vapour amounts decrease very rapidly (four orders of magnitude in 10 km).
Winter values are substantially greater than summer values in a static atmosphere but upward motions in summer and subsidence in winter can reverse this distribution (figs. 7a, 7b). In summary, however, our knowledge
of the distribution of water vapour above the lower stratosphere is very
limited and there is urgent need of accurate measurements.

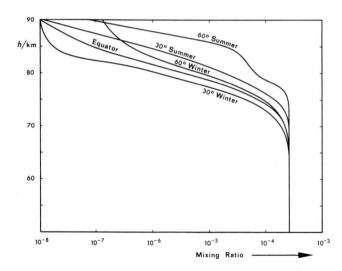

Fig. 7b. Mixing ratios water vapour/air in a non-static atmosphere, taking account
of motions (for different latitudes and seasons) (after Hesstredt, 1964).

(iii) The situation is not much better for the various constituents involving carbon. In the lower stratosphere carbondioxide CO_2, carbonmonoxide CO, and methane CH_4 are important in radiation calculations and are considered to be well mixed with concentration of about 320, 1.1 and 2.4 parts per million by volume respectively. Dissociations again occur towards the 80-100 km level and that of CH_4 may be of particular interest since it could, through the release of its hydrogen and subsequent reactions with oxygen, result in a source of water vapour in the mesosphere.

(iv) Little is known about the amounts of the inert gases argon, neon, xenon and krypton at these levels but direct sampling of the former from rockets indicates that they probably have constant mixing ratio in the stratosphere and that some diffusive separation occurs in the lower ionosphere (15-20% at 100 km or so). Helium which is also found in appreciable amounts in the lower atmosphere may increase significantly in relative amount towards the top of the layer and probably hydrogen also.

4.4. *Other constituents: Aerosols*

In addition to the gaseous constituents discussed above, particles are found at most levels and these have an importance in such fields as optical phenomena, as scatterers, absorbers and emitters of radiation in different wave bands, in certain chemical reactions, acting as possible condensation of freezing nuclei or are used as tracers of atmospheric motions.

Other trace substances found in the stratosphere and mesosphere may be of tropospheric or extra-terrestrial, mainly meteoric, origin.

5. WINDS IN THE UPPER ATMOSPHERE *

Substantial effort has already been expended on establishing a climatology of the wind in the vertical over some places. Generally, such studies include seasonal or monthly mean profiles. The frequency of occurrence of excessive vertical wind shear has also been determined. In a few cases there have been studies of persistence or, conversely, the maximum rate of change of wind at a given level.

Rocketsonde reports from Australia, Canada, Japan, Sardinia, USA, USSR are available in the Meteorological Rocketsonde Network (MRN). In the meridional temperature analysis observed wind shear statistics are useful.

A convenient method of following the seasonal changes and determining the existence of superimposed transient disturbances in the vicinity of an MRN station is to combine its observations in time-height cross sections. Miers (1963) and Morris and Miers (1964) have presented a number of such sections to show the nature of the wind reversals between winter westerlies and summer easterlies that occur in the transitional months. In the fall of 1962, as shown at White Sands (fig. 9), the transition from easterlies to westerlies was regular, progressing downward in September and October at an average rate of one km/day.

* The meteorological definition of direction is used in this and the following contribution; it is opposed to that normally used at ionospheric heights.

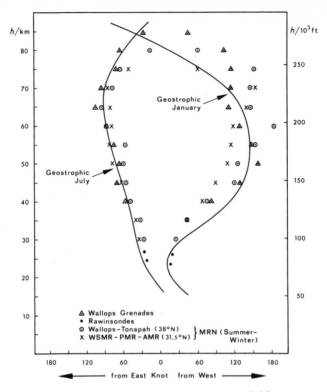

Fig. 8. Zonal wind components. Geostrophic components (solid lines, computed hy-
drostatically from supplemental atmosphere temperatures at 30°N and 45°N) are
compared with zonal components of seasonal average observed winds (coded points);
information for 31.5°N is compiled from data at White Sands Missile Range (WSMR);
Pacific Missile Range, Point Mugu (PMR); and Atlantic Missile Range, Cape Ken-
nedy (AMR) (from Cole and Kantor, after Teweles).

Faust (1963) combined the available reports for stations in the latitude
zones 21° - 38° N (southern stations) and 58° - 65° (northern stations) respectively (fig. 10) to show the annual trend of the zonal component. At the
lower latitude, the 'equinoctial' reversals begin earliest in the highest
layer and work slowly downward. The changeover is more nearly simultaneous with altitude in the north and is affected much earlier in the season,
particularly in mid-stratosphere near 30 km.

In a somewhat different fashion, Appleman (1963) has presented the annual cycle for the southern stations. The standard deviation of the resultant
wind is also presented to show the much larger variability of the winds in
the winter months, notably January. However, the percentage variability
remains large in the equinoctial changeover when the absolute variability
shows no pronounced minimum even though the monthly mean zonal wind-
speed passes through zero.

Webb (1962) and others have discussed the great usefulness of combining

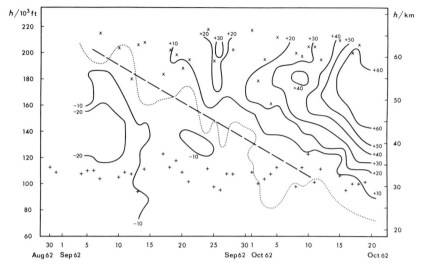

Fig. 9. Zonal wind components; White Sands, New Mexico, fall 1962. West wind positive numerical indication in m/sec (after Miers).

temperature and wind information in determining the sonic structure of the high atmosphere. In a wintertime situation with strong westerlies (fig. 11) Diamond (1963) shows that an eastward-propagating soundwave would encounter a marked vertical increase in sonic speed (defined here as the sum of the speed of sound computed as a function of air temperature and the wind-velocity component in the direction of interest; in the case eastward) and thus be strongly refracted back toward the earth. For this particular situation the westward moving wave would encounter a nearly uniform vertical distribution of sonic speed and dissipate its energy toward the thermosphere.

Quite naturally, a synoptic meteorologist is anxious to delineate for the first time the wheater systems indigenous to the relatively unexplored layers of the upper stratosphere and lower mesosphere. With so few observations at his command, he must use all of his analytical skill.

By combining several methods of data examination, the analyst attempts to establish a slight redundancy of information as an aid in judging the validity of individual reports. He is also able to make useful estimates of missing values.

The basic steps in the analysis procedure are:

1) Construct a 10 mb (~ 31 km) chart from rawinsonde data supplemented with rocketsonde data.

2) Compute the height of the 2 mb (~ 43 km) surface with the aid of temperature time sections, or lacking these, compute a tentative height by judicious use of supplemental atmosphere.

3) Select rocketsonde winds at the calculated 2 mb height for several days before and after map time.

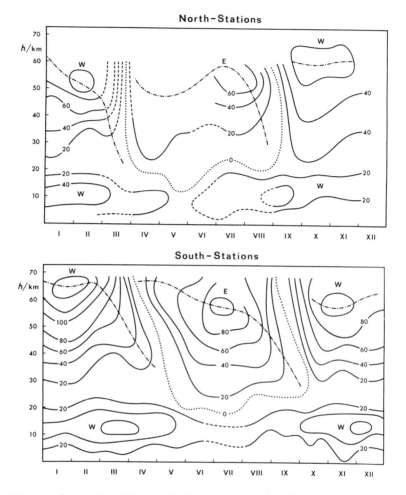

Fig. 10. Annual variation of the zonal wind component, based on monthly means for northern MRN stations (60ºN) and southern MRN stations (30ºN) respectively. Velocity in knot (1 knot = 0.5144 m/sec)(after Faust).

4) Construct contours in geostrophic agreement with the wind estimated for map time.

5) Determine absolute height of contours to give the best fit to observed winds and computed heights (if a final height is substantially different from the tentative one calculated in step 2, discard the latter and proceed again beginning at step 3).

6) Use final 2 mb chart as foundation for the 0.4 mb (~ 55 km) chart with procedure analogous to steps 2-5 above.

Some examples are presented here from among the many sets of anal-

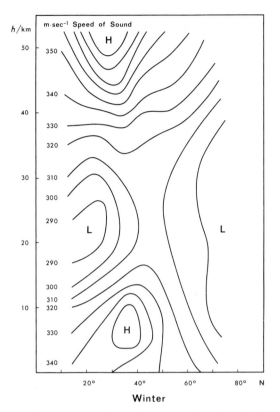

Fig. 11a. Velocity of sound as function of height and latitude. Sonic structure of the atmosphere in winter computed from zonal wind and temperature: for sound propagation from West to East (after Diamond).

yses that have been made for dates with relatively complete coverage of reports from the network.

In the set of charts for 1 December 1961 (fig. 12), the polar vortex is shown at a well developed stage. At 0.4 mb, there are unusually strong west winds that exceed 280 kt at Wallops Island. At the southern stations, winds at 0.4 mb are still increasing with height, indicating relatively warmer air poleward of that station.

On 20 January 1962 (fig. 13) the pattern shows the initial stages of a radical change, particularly at Wallops Island, where the wind has changed to a moderate southern one. At 2 mb, the relatively circumpolar jet stream flow of early December has looped poleward over Alaska and also over the northern Atlantic, leaving a trough of massive proportions over western North America.

A time-height cross-section of temperatures and winds measured by rocketsonde at Ft. Churchill (fig. 14) shows the intrusion of exceptionally

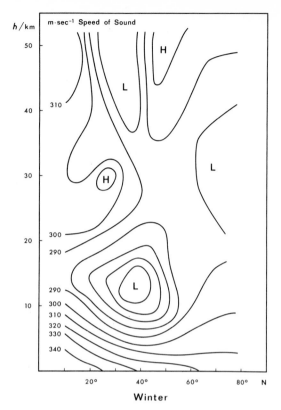

Fig. 11b. Velocity of sound as function of height and latitude. Sonic structure of the atmosphere in winter computed from zonal wind and temperature: from East to West (after Diamond).

warm air leading to a sharp inversion above 37 km on 7 February 1962. Although there is a residual pocket of cool air in the 25 to 30 km layer, the remainder of the sounding down to the tropopause on that day shows anomalously warm conditions. For several days thereafter, conditions at this station tend towards normal, but another high-level warming is indicated on 16 February. An interesting phenomenon is the strong inversion that characterizes these high-latitude sounding particularly in cases where the advection of warm air from the north is indicated by vertical wind shear and mean wind. To account for all observed aspects of the phenomenon, a marked subsidence must accompany the development of a polar anticyclone in the upper stratosphere.

The charts for 7 February 1962 (fig. 15) show that a circulation breakdown is in progress. At this advanced stage, the breakdown appears to be most pronounced near the 2 mb level where a great height pressure area dominates the height latitudes. In the warm air center located over south-

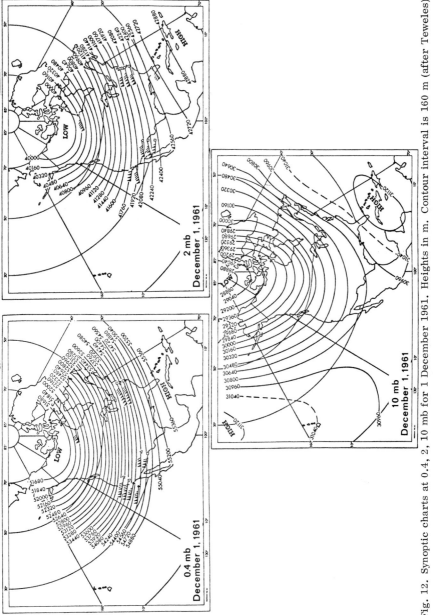

Fig. 12. Synoptic charts at 0.4, 2, 10 mb for 1 December 1961. Heights in m. Contour interval is 160 m (after Teweles).

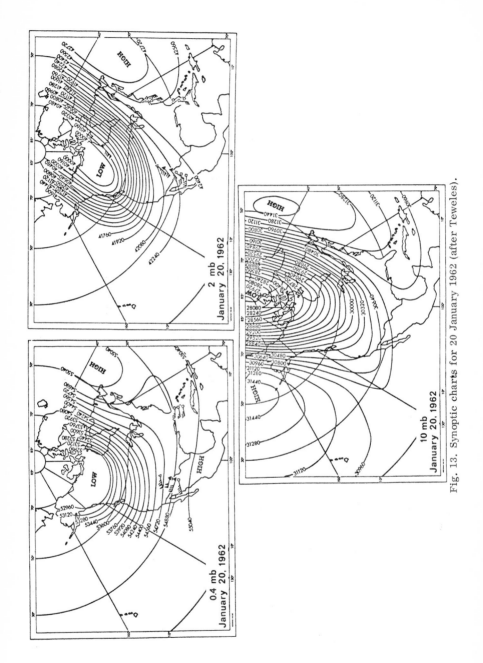

Fig. 13. Synoptic charts for 20 January 1962 (after Teweles).

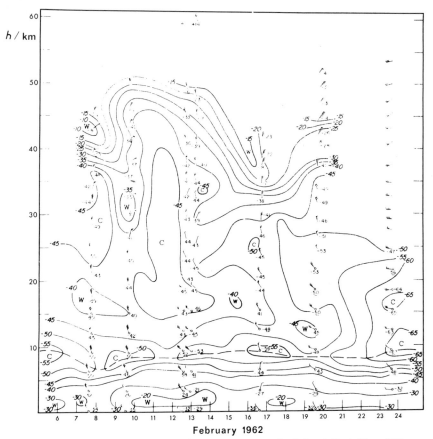

Fig. 14. Time-height cross section of temperatures and winds at Fort Churchill, Manitoba. Temperatures in °C. Winds are plotted with a full barb for each 10 knot and a flag for each 50 knot. Orientation is from the top of the section for North winds and from left for West winds (1 knot = 0.5144 m/sec) (after Teweles).

ern Canada, temperatures are about 30°C above the expected values for that region.

Observed rocketsonde winds are illustrated in time-height cross section from Point Mugu, California (fig. 16). West winds, which exceeded 75 m/s at 35 km, were observed on Friday, 18 January 1963. With resumption of observations on Monday, 21 January, east winds were found above 35 km as a result of the southward expansion of the growing polar anticyclone. Equally abrupt changes were observed over Wallops Island, Virginia during the same weekend. Obviously, during such periods of rapidly changing conditions, observations of at least daily frequency are required.

There are a number of other interesting features in fig. 16. West winds reappear at the top of the sounding on 25 January and progress downward

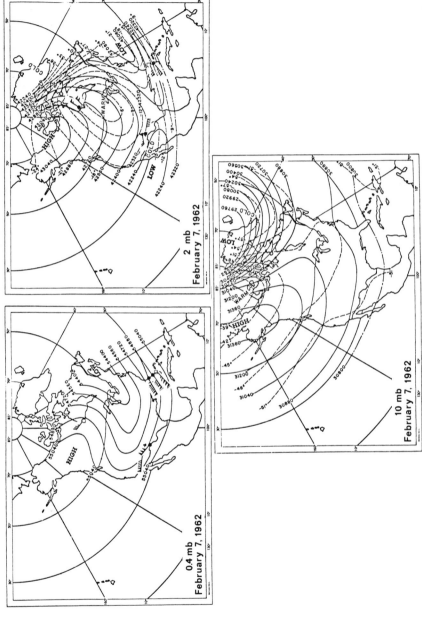

Fig. 15. Synoptic charts for 7 February 1962. Isoterms at 3ºC intervals are shown by dashed lines (from Finger, Teweles and Mason).

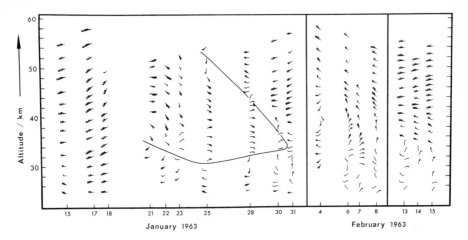

Fig. 16. Time-height cross section of observed rocket sonde winds at Point Mugu, California. Winds plotted as in fig. 14. Region of East winds in January is marked off by solid line (from Finger and Teweles).

until the east winds have been completely excluded on 31 January. This feature is frequently found in cases of this type and suggests that normal cooling and shrinking of the atmosphere at height latitudes constitute the mechanism by which the effects of anomalous warmings are gradually eliminated. The degree of retoration of the initial conditions is shown by the generally strong west winds of mid-February.

6. CONCLUDING REMARKS

Briefly, the major findings based on MRN observations can be recapitulated as follows:

The vertical shear of the zonal winds through the 25-55 km layer requires a generally decreasing temperature in the horizontal from the summer pole across the equator to the winter pole. In the layers above 55 km, the region of the polar night remains warmer than the sunlit regions to the south through the agency of one or more of the recently proposed mechanisms, such as heating by recombination of atomic oxygen, as suggested by Kellog (1962), compressional heating by subsidence in polar regions, or horizontal heat transport by eddies in the mesospheric circulation.

In the layers sounded by the meteorological rocket, diurnal and semidiurnal changes of both temperature and wind have been shown by recent investigations to increase with height, becoming an order of magnitude larger than those at high rawinsonde levels. Haurwitz (1964) in his treatise on subject, discusses diurnal values at MRN levels in perspective with those for higher and lower levels. Whenever rockets are available and as sensors become more accurate, better determinations of diurnal changes ought to be obtained by additional special series of observations, launched at different times of the year and over large range of latitude. One such series, consisting of twenty-two rocketsondes at two hour intervals over a period of two days, was launched at White Sands in February 1964. Meanwhile, for some purposes, network observations, because they are now taken principally at midday, are not completely representative of the daily mean or indicative of conditions at other times of the day.

7. WIND SYSTEMS ABOVE 100 KM

In the treatment of macroscopic motions at heights above 100 km atmospheric gas must be considered as a mixture of ionized and neutral components. Up to the lower E region (i.e. up to 100-110 km) the ionized component is carried by the existing drift of the neutral air. The relative density of the latter is so great that the ionized component cannot be moved easily by the electrodynamic forces. In the F region, that is at heights above 160 km, it is comparatively easier to move the electrons by the electric forces; however, the moving plasma probably does not carry the neutral air with it. In between these two regions, i.e. in the 110-160 km layer, there is a complicated and little known relation between the motions of neutral and ionized particles.

It is obvious that above a certain height the usual meteorological equations of motion as known for the lower atmosphere must be modified to include electrodynamic forces.

The changes of such motion with elevation are rather slow. In the 110-130 km layer the direction of the wind is still along the isobars but its scalar value is not any longer geostrophic. Above 130 km the wind begins to acquire a component in the direction of the pressure gradient. If the pressure patterns were purely zonal, the angle between the isobars and the wind direction would be about 10⁰ at 145 km, and 75⁰ at 300 km.

Another important question concerns the height at which the thermal wind relationship in the form known for the lower atmosphere ceases to be valid. Some important atmospheric motions are not, of course, thermally controlled; among them tidal effects and internal gravity waves.

Fig. 17 represents the resultant components of the wind near 38⁰N latitude. The curves in the 70-160 km height region are averages for 25 sodium cloud firings mainly from Wallops Island and are based on data points in 5 km intervals. Tests with data at 1 km intervals show that points at every 5 km depict sufficiently well the general character of the curves. Sodium cloud experiments are being continued and newer data may, conceivably, alter the results.

In the 70-100 km layer there is a good agreement between the meteorological observations and the sodium cloud data, although in both cases the averaging of a small number of observations is questionable.

One may list the following salient features indicated by figs. 17a, b, c.
1) Up to 100 km altitude the predominant circulation is zonal, but in the 100-160 km layer meridional components equal or exceed zonal components.

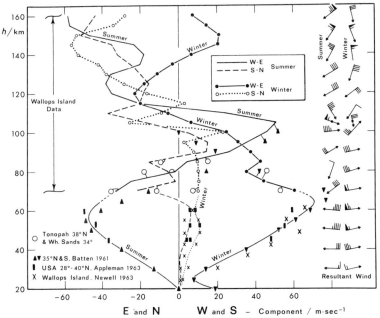

Fig. 17a. Resultant components of the wind near latitude 38°N. Arrows indicate the resultant wind.

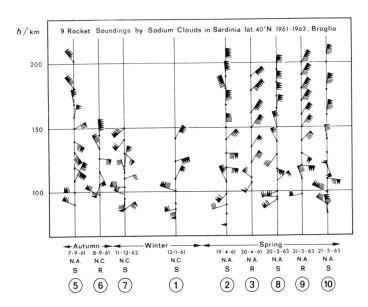

Fig. 17b. Winds are plotted with a full barb for each 10 km/h and a flag for each 50 km/h. They are oriented from the top of the section for North winds.

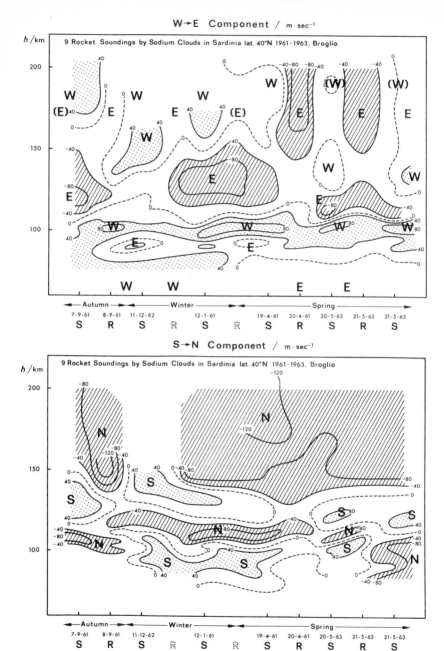

Fig. 17c. Result of rocket soundings by sodium clouds in Sardinia 1961–1963. Numerical indications give speed in m/sec.

2) The radical change of zonal circulation from summer to winter is limited to the stratosphere and the mesosphere.

3) A transitional region exists between 85 km and 110 km with prevailing westerlies in both summer and winter. In summer the winds in this region are mainly from W or NW. In winter winds are from SW, NW, S, NE and N where the order indicates decreasing frequency of occurrence.

4) Another regularity in wind distribution appears above 115 km. In summer the winds between 115 and 180 km are almost exclusively from the NE. In winter they are from the NE between 115 and 130 km, and from the N, NW or NE between 130 and 180 km.

5) Sodium cloud data from other latitudes are still lacking and latitudinal variations in the 100-160 km region, if any, are not known.

Adding vectorially the components from fig. 17, one obtains the resultant winds shown on the right margin of the same figure. Both the resultant winds and the resultant components are misleading at certain heights, due to mutual cancellation of strong components of the opposite sign. This occurs particularly between 95 and 115 km in winter, where the resultant components shown by the figure are deceptively small; considering scalar speed of the wind (cf. fig. 18) one obtains a winter profile strongly peaked at 105 km, similar to the summer profile of the W-E component.

Important features of the motion are revealed by the profiles of the mean scalar speed (fig. 18). These are the absolute values of the velocity vector, regardless of direction. A mesospheric maximum of velocity appears at about 57 km in summer and 64 km in winter. These peaks are controlled by the temperature distribution in the stratosphere and mesosphere. However, a still stronger velocity maximum appears near 105 km. This persistent feature, evident in nearly all velocity profiles, is confined to altitudes 100 to 111 km (except for one case at 95 km). Its average height is 105 ± 4 km (mean and standard deviation) and its mean speed 82 m/sec. At 6 km below and 7 km above this maximum there are two pronounced velocity minima with values smaller by 30 m/sec. Similar but less intense velocity oscillations are observed down to the lowest reach of sodium cloud data (70 km) and up to about 140 km altitude. The inset of fig. 18 illustrates the preference of high velocities to appear at certain altitudes. The curves show relative frequency of velocities equal to and above 80, 100 and 120 m/sec. The principal velocity maximum centred at 105 km is, obviously, an outstanding feature. Above about 110 km the speed generally increases with elevation. This increase appears to be approximately linear and averages 1.8 m/sec per 10 km.

8. VERTICAL WIND SHEARS

Fig. 19 shows the magnitude of vertical wind shears from the sodium cloud profiles at Wallops Island, computed for every km of elevation. The heavy curve represents averages of the individual shears. The light curve shows the extreme shear encountered at a given altitude. Both curves show a peak at 105 km, associated with the principal maximum of velocity. Small

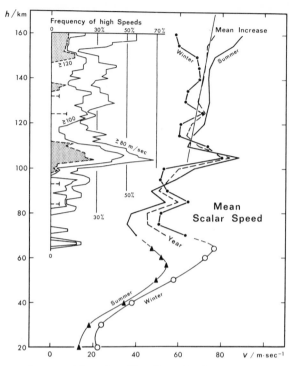

Fig. 18. Mean scalar speed based on 25 sodium cloud experiments from Wallops Island, and frequency of occurrence of speed greater than 80, 100 and 120 m/sec (after Kochanski).

shears in the 136-160 region mark a quiescent zone where velocity oscillations in the vertical are also remarkably small. This shear distribution can be explained by the behaviour of wave motion W and residual motion R. From 70 to 105 km the magnitude of W increases with elevation but the vertical wavelength remains constant and the shears must increase. From 105 to 160 km the values of W decrease, the wavelength increases, R remains nearly constant, and all three effects result in small shears.

The largest extreme shear shown on fig. 19 is 120 m/sec/km. An even larger extreme shear of 140 m/sec/km was observed near 108 km at Hammaguir, Algeria. As is well known, the shear magnitude depends on the vertical interval Δz used in computations. With reference to data from fig. 19 our tests show that this dependence is logarithmic: for Δz of 0.5, 3, and 5 km, the values from the curve labelled 'average' of fig. 19 should be multiplied by 1.45, 0.60 and 0.40 respectively. On the whole, the values of shears shown in fig. 19 are similar to those encountered in the vicinity of the polar jet stream that appears near the tropopause. Common shears near the jet stream are 15 to 30 m/sec/km, frequently 35 m/sec/km. Very occasionally we can expect 50 m/sec/km, and the absolute maximum quoted is 101 m/sec/km.

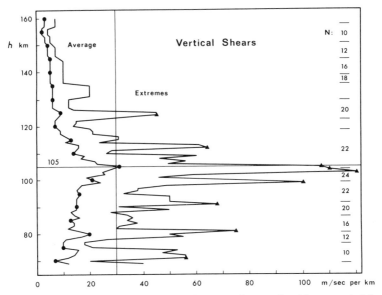

Fig. 19. Magnitude of wind shears based on the same data as fig. 18, computed for $z = 1$ km. The magnitude of the shear is defined as $|\partial V/\partial z|$; this includes the effects of directional changes. N is the number of observations (after Kochanski).

9. VERTICAL MOTIONS

Sparse information about vertical motions in the 70-160 km height region comes from the artificial cloud observations and dynamical considerations. Sodium cloud data indicate relatively infrequent vertical motions of the order of 3 to 12 m/sec. Edwards et al. (1963) quote three cases where vertical motions can be depicted by a straight line drawn through:

- 3 m/sec at   97 km, to + 13 m/sec at 105 km
- 3 m/sec at 102 km, to +   3 m/sec at 109 km
- 4 m/sec at 100 km, to + 12 m/sec at 111 km .

where the negative sign is for a descending motion. In 6 firings, Blamont and Baguette (1961) found the vertical motions on the whole negligible except for two cases, both near 103 km: one of + 6 m/sec, and a second one of - 8 m/sec. Mention only one case of - 4 m/sec, between 107 and 111 km. These data agree well with the concept of internal gravity waves where motions should be nearly horizontal and any vertical motions should be less than 10% of the horizontal component. In the F region, i.e. above 160 km, the deduced vertical movements are about 10 m/sec.

Theoretical considerations of sustained vertical motions yield values of the order of 1 cm/sec. For the mesopause region, downward transport and ensuing recombination of atomic oxygen is thought to be the cause of high mesopause temperature in winter. Kellog (1961) estimates the following downward velocities required to produce chemical heating of 10°K/day:

At 110 km 0.15 cm/sec   At 90 km 0.15 cm/sec
100 km 0.74 cm/sec   85 km 0.7 cm/sec
95 km 0.049 cm/sec

Murgatroyd and Singleton (1961) presented a model of vertical motions in the 20-80 km height region, in which both seasonal and latitudinal variations were taken into account, with vertical velocities of the order of 0.5 to 1 cm/sec. Sudden stratospheric warmings that are known to exist through the 20-60 km layer and perhaps even higher are probably associated with extensive vertical motions but the latter are usually computed only for the lowest region (20-30 km) using map analysis in time intervals of 1 to 3 days; these computations indicate that ascending or descending motions of about 5 cm/sec may appear over areas 1.500 - 2.000 km in diameter.

ACKNOWLEDGEMENT

This short review of our present knowledge of some aspects in upper atmosphere structure is substantially based on sources from WMO Technical Note No. 70 by Murgatroyd, Hare, Boville, Teweles and Kochanski.

REFERENCES

Appleman, H.S., 1963, J. Gepphys. Res.68, 3611.
Bates, D.R. and M.Nicolet, 1950, J. Geophys. Res.55, 301.
Blamont, J.E. and J.M.Baguette, 1961, Ann. Géophys. 17, 319.
Brooks, D.L., 1958, J.Meteorol. 15, 210.
Diamond M., 1963, J. Geophys. Res. 68, 3459.
Edwards, H.D. et al., 1963, J. Geophys. Res. 68, 3021.
Faust, H., 1963, Project cell structure of the atmosphere, Sci. Rep. No. 1, 4th year US Dept. of the Army, European Res. Office,   .
Finger, F.G. and S.Teweles, 1964, J. Appl. Meteorol. 3, 11; 1957, Handbook of Geophysics, Fig. 8-2, p. 8-3.
Gowan, E.H., 1947, Proc. Roy. Soc. A 190, 219.
Harris, I. and W.Priester, 1962, J. Atmos. Sci. 19, 286.
Haurwitz, B., 1964, WMO Tech. Note 58,   .
Hesstredt, E., 1964, Det. Norske Videnskaps, Akademi Geop. Pub. Geophysika Norwegica, Oslo, 25, No. 3.
Haughton, J.T., 1963, A.SiRoy. Met. Soc.89, 319.
Kallmann-Bijl, H.K. and W.L.Sibley, 1963, Planet. Space Sci. 11, 1379.
Kellog, W.W., 1961, J. Meteorol. 18, 373.
Kochanski, A., 1965a, WMO Tech. Note 70, 156.
Kochanski, A., 1965b, WMO Tech. Note 70, 162.
Leovy, C., 1963, Ph. D. Thesis MIT, Boston,   ,   .
Leovy, C., 1964, J. Atmos. Sci. 21, 238.
Miers, B.T., 1963, J. Atmos. Sci. 20, 87.
Morris, J.E. and B.T.Miers, 1964, J. Geophys. Res. 69, 201.
Murgatroyd, R.J., 1954, Quart. J. Roy. Meteorol. Soc. 83, 417.
Murgatroyd, R.J. and R.M.Goody, 1958, Quart. J. Roy. Meteorol. Soc. 84, 225.
Murgatroyd, R.J. and F.Singleton, 1961. Quart. J. Roy. Meteorol. Soc. 87, 372.
Murgatroyd, R.J. et al., 1965, WMO Tech. Note 70, 152.

Ohring, G., 1958, J. Meteorol. 15, 440.
Teweles, S.,1965a, WMO Tech. Note 70, 82.
Teweles, S.,1965b, WMO Tech. Note 70, 97.
Webb, W.L., 1962, J. Appl. Meteorol. 1, 229.

EXPERIMENTAL METHODS IN EXPLORING THE ATMOSPHERE BETWEEN 30 KM AND 120 KM

Diego FEDELE

Ministero della Difesa Aeronautica,
Servizio Meteorologico, Roma, Italy

Abstract. A brief review of methods and techniques for exploring the upper atmosphere is presented. Beyond direct measurements using sounding rockets and gun launched probes, a large amount of indirect measurements can be obtained by means of ground based devices: winds and temperatures from sound propagation or from meteor tracking; density and temperature from light scattering; composition from airglow and aurora.

Résumé. Nous resumons brièvement les méthodes et techniques d'exploration de la haute atmosphère. En dehors des mesures directes par fusées, sondes et obus, on a recu un grand nombre de mesures indirectes à l'aide d'équipements au sol: les vents et les températures peuvent être déduits de la propagation des ondes ou de la goniométrie des météorites. La diffusion de la lumière permet de déterminer la densité et la temperature. Enfin des conclusions concernant la composition sont obtenues de l'observation de phénomènes lumineux et boréales.

1. INTRODUCTION

Our knowledge of upper atmosphere has taken a rapid step forward in the last two decades, due to the rapid development of experimental methods and instruments.

A great effort has been made to extend meteorological radiosoundings to greater heights by balloon up to 30 km and rocket techniques up to about the 65 km level. These are now made as a routine on a synoptic scale in North America.

Besides strictly meteorological measurements, rockets are now used as carriers of instruments such as spectroscopes to measure solar spectrum and atmospheric absorption, or mass spectrometers to measure air composition, photometers measuring heights and intensity in airglow layers.

Beyond direct measurements using high altitude rockets and satellites, a large amount of indirect measurements had been obtained by means of other experimental methods (fig. 1) e.g. anomalous sound-propagation phenomena, observations of the scattered light from search lights and lasers, selective absorption in the ultraviolet spectra of the sun to deduce total ozone and its vertical distribution, visual or photographic tracking of meteoric particles burning in the earth's atmosphere usually at heights of 80 to 120 km, radar tracking of the ionized trails produced by them and so on.

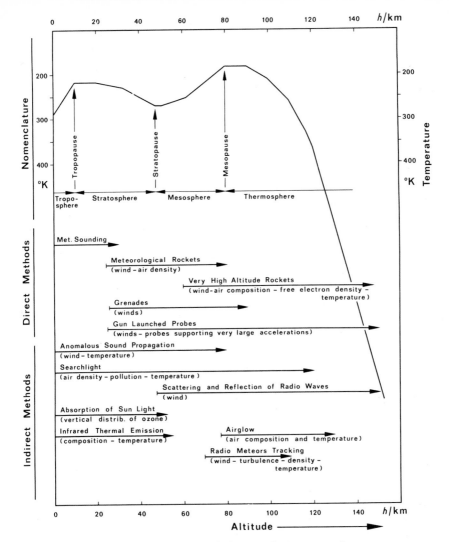

Fig. 1. Experimental methods in exploring atmosphere.

2. EXPLORING ATMOSPHERE WITH ROCKETS AND GUN LAUNCHED PROBES

2.1. *Meteorological rockets*

Since the end of 1958 a network of meteorological rockets has been in operation in North American continent, at first on an intermittent basis, and now on a regular basis. The meteorological rocket is a relatively inexpensive small rocket. Its altitude is now generally limited to about 65 km, owing to the incapability of making sufficiently accurate measurements at higher levels with conventional sensors available at the present time. These soundings do not go high enough to enter the ionosphere but it should be pointed out that meteorological rockets give the parameters of the atmosphere that are of most interest to meteorologists, up to altitudes more than twice as high as those reached by balloons. The increasing adoption of meteorological rockets seems to be inevitable because of the growing need of very high altitude observations for forecasting the circulation of the atmosphere and for observing the areas in which high altitude jet aircrafts of the near future may fly.

A very simple form of meteorological rocket is the simple stage rocket which boosts a small 'dart' containing some radar chaff, or 'window'. An outline of a Loki rocket is presented in fig. 2. Such a rocket can eject a cloud of chaff dipoles at levels up to 80 or 90 km, though in practice the limit is usually about 60 km and these clouds of chaffs can be tracked by a radar as they fall. The rate of fall is rapid at first, and thereafter it slows down as the cloud falls through levels of increasing atmospheric density (fig. 3).

Dipoles disperse during fall and make the cloud a progressively poorer target for the radar to track. The horizontal drift of such a cloud as it falls is an indication of the wind.

The precision of the measurement of the wind by this method is limited by two sources of error. One, which is random, is an error in radar tracking, related to dispersion of chaffs, and the other relates to the degree to which the chaff motion reflects the motion of the wind and is dependent upon the form of the law of fluid resistance which is operating on the particle. The latter source of error may be deduced from vertical velocity. The difference between the observed horizontal velocity v of particles and the horizontal velocity u of the air is given by Rapp (1960):

$$v-u = \frac{w^2}{g} \frac{\mathrm{d}v}{\mathrm{d}z} , \tag{1}$$

where w is the observed vertical velocity of chaffs, g the gravitational acceleration and $\mathrm{d}v/\mathrm{d}z$ the observed vertical shear.

A chaff wind sensing rocket is a relatively economical system, providing ease and simplicity in preparation and launching but the requirement for a good radar makes the use of chaff rockets limited to those sites where there are such radars. The chaff reflector appears to be a good sensor at altitudes above 45 km, but the slow fall rate and the dispersion render it inefficient below that altitude.

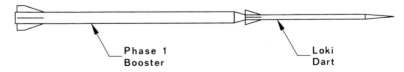

Fig. 2. Outline of a high altitude sounding rocket showing the single-stage which contains radar chaff.

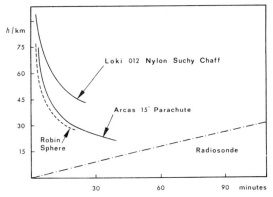

Fig. 3. Rate of fall for chaff dipoles. compared with rate of fall of Arcas 15' parachute. of Robin sphere and with rate of ascent of usual radiosonde-balloon.

Other wind sensors are used successfully with meteorological rockets
to measure wind in heights 25 to 50 km and air density up to 70 km.

An inflatable plastic sphere of about a meter in diameter, containing a
radar reflector ('Robin' sphere) can be expelled from the rocket. When
such a sphere falls it is subject to air drag which depends on the relative
velocity of the sphere and on the air density. Thus when such a sphere is
accurately tracked by radar the drag can be deduced from its rate of change
of velocity and the distribution of air density can be derived. Moreover
wind is measured from horizontal drift of the sphere in the layer through
which it is falling, in the same manner as for falling chaffs. Experience
with these falling spheres in the U.S. indicates that wind measurements
can be made with an accuracy of a few m/s, and densities can be determined
up to 70 km with an accuracy of about 5% (Leviton and Wright, 1961).

The parachute is another wind sensor applicable at levels below 50 km.
Its performance characteristics are quite similar to those of Robin sphere.
Fig. 3 compares altitude versus time for chaff; Robin sphere and Arcas
4.5 m diam. parachute.

An important variation of the meteorological rocket involves a rocketsonde with temperature sensors that is lowered by parachute after the
rocket reaches its peak altitude. A schematic diagram of how it is used is
shown in fig. 4. This rocket sounding system can be operated without the
complex support of a firing range and a high-powered radar, with the use
of a standard or modified 'Rawinsonde' ground station. It has been operated
in the Antarctic, as well as at many other remote sites. A similar approach
was taken in the U.K. for the IQSY and it is understood that meteorological
rocket systems are being developed in France, Poland, West Germany and
Japan. As the cost of such rockets goes down and the reliability goes up it
will be feasible for many weather services to adopt meteorological rockets
on an operational basis.

Such rocket-sondes measure temperature as they fall by direct exposure
of a temperature element, either bead thermistor (USA sonde) or fine wire

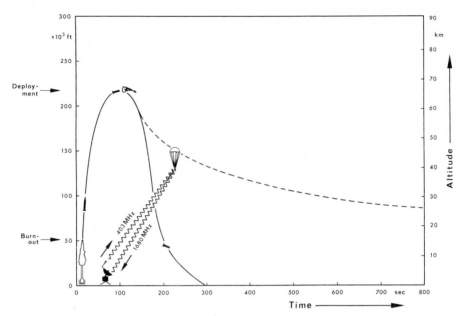

Fig. 4. Schematic diagram of the way the Arcas rocket-sonde is used with a modified
GMD-2 Rawinsonde ground station.

(USSR sonde). The correction factor that must be applied to account for effects of radiation, electrical heating, compressional heating and conduction
through the wire leads is for example of the order of 30°K at 65 km for
Arcas-rocket-sonde. It increases rapidly at higher levels making these
sensors useless for temperature measurements above 65 km. Below these
altitudes, the error decreases to about 8°K at 55 km and to 5°K at 50 km.
The temperature error is always positive; i.e. the temperature sensor always indicates too warm. It is possible to arrive at an indication of the
mean temperature error versus height associated with the bead thermistor
under conditions of a normal meteorological sounding. The maximum variability resulting from deviations from the reference conditions of initial
height, fall velocity, initial support post temperature, solar absorptivity of
sensor, lead wire length, effective infrared radiation temperature, time
constant, power dissipation of bead, yields an accuracy in the temperature
correction of $\pm$ 9°K at 65 km, $\pm$ 5°K at 60 km, and $\pm$ 3.5°K at 50 km (Wagner, 1964). The correction accuracy deteriorates rapidly above 65 km.
However soundings taken in the same geographical region under similar
conditions would present temperature profiles for comparative purpose to
within a degree of one another even at the upper limit of the system.

2.2. *Very high altitude sounding rockets*
    Above 60 or 65 km, wind and density sensors and temperature sensors
of the current meteorological rockets are incapable of giving measurements

of these parameters. Moreover at heights above these levels, measurements of other parameters of the atmosphere are also needed, e.g. atmospheric composition, solar radiation, ionic composition, free electron density. Other methods and techniques are to be applied to provide meteorological and aeronomical parameters at very high altitudes. To obtain densities above 70 km, falling spheres of 18 cm diam. were first used during IGY. Built-in accelerometers telemetered the acceleration as they fell. Other developments along the same line resulted in inflatable spheres with accelerometers giving density to over 100 km. It is to be pointed out that to obtain densities at this altitude it is necessary for the peak altitude of the rocket to be well above 100 km so that the sphere can gain sufficient supersonic speed before it re-enters the region where the density is to be measured. It is also possible to use passive falling spheres. Their acceleration is determined by tracking them from ground with a very sensitive and accurate radar.

A convenient method for determining winds in upper atmosphere is that of measuring the drift of rocket released smoke trails. Above 60 or 70 km to 200 km had been frequently used the technique of ejecting from the rocket a trail of alkali metal vapours that scatter sunlight at twilight. However the latter is restricted to a 20-40 min period at sunset and sunrise, when the trail is sunlit and the sky background is dark enough. A sodium vapour trail can be released from a rocket containing metallic sodium in the form of pellets mixed under high pressure in an iron-oxide aluminium thermite mixture in a stainless-steel cylinder with a vent-tube. At an appropriate time the thermite can be ignited by an electrically fired squib. The yellow brilliant light from the fluorescing sodium cloud can be seen by the naked eye also at distances as far away as 500 km. Observations of these trails are usually made by several cameras on the ground and the winds are deduced by triangulation measurements from the photographs (Egidi, Fea and Fratucello, 1961). In spite of limitations of this technique, a great deal of useful informations has been obtained in this way.

A further prospect is opened by using the glow to determine the temperature at different levels by measuring the broadening of the sodium D lines, produced by Doppler effect. This technique involves a most ingenious method for determining the line shape. While its accuracy is not as great as could be wished, it is one of the few techniques to give temperature in the upper atmosphere to about 400 km directly.

A variation of this method is the tracking of trails that are made luminous at night by a photochemical reaction of the vapour with atomic oxygen. A promising substance for use at night is trimethylaluminium. A trail of TMA can be photographed from 85 to about 160 km. Another substance that glows at night, not quite so efficiently but over a similar range of altitudes, is nitric oxide. Nitric oxide can be released as a trail from a rocket-borne pressurized tank in the 90 to 160 km region. This release results in a continuous spectrum of shorter persistance (150 sec at about 100 km, falling off below and above this altitude), but still sufficient for wind measurements. An advantage of the NO trail is that a lasting glow results in the 90 to 100-km region also, where the aluminium glow is not persistent. Furthermore, the more readily understood mechanism of the NO glow may enable us to estimate the ambient atomic oxygen concentrations. The nitric oxide experiment is a remarkable demonstration of the fact that, at an altitude of about 115 km, oxygen is predominantly in the atomic form.

One of the simplest rocket methods for determining temperature and winds in the high atmosphere is the grenade technique. A sequence of explosions are created one above the other at intervals of several kilometers. The velocity of sound in a gas is given by the equation

$$c = (\gamma R T / M)^{\frac{1}{2}}$$

where M is the average weight of one mol of the gas molecules, T is the absolute temperature, R the gas constant; γ the rate of specific heats a quantity having the values $\frac{5}{3}$, $\frac{7}{5}$, or $\frac{9}{7}$, depending on whether the gas is composed of monoatomic, diatomic or triatomic molecules. For a mixture, the appropriate average is taken. There is negligible change in M with height until 90 km is reached. Even then the change which is due to the conversion of molecular oxygen to the atomic form by the ultra-violet light of the sun, is not great. If the medium through which the sound is being propagated is moving, the actual velocity of sound is that given by the above equation plus the velocity of the medium. Other factors can influence the speed of sound relative to an observer. Thus if the strength of the sound wave is very great so that the pressure oscillation in the wave is comparable to the pressure of the gas, then the velocity is greater than that given by the equation and depends as well on the frequency of the wave. As the shock wave from an explosion travels outwards, its pressure amplitude falls roughly in proportion to the distance covered. In practice this means that only rather near the source of an explosion we need consider any variation of the velocity of sound in a medium like that given above.

In the American experiments the position and times of a series of grenade explosions are determined by photographic and photoelectric observations and the time and angle of arrival of the wave are recorded at some station on the ground. Analysis of the data proceeds in the following way. We know the time of travel and angle of arrival of the sound pulse from, say, the lowest grenade, so provided the ray is not far from the vertical, we can trace it back and find the 'virtual' position of the explosion. To do this, we make use of the known temperature and wind distribution as far as it can be obtained from balloons and we guess the distribution in the interval. This virtual position will not quite coincide with the optical position. It will be displaced sideways, due mostly to the wind, and in height due to the wrong temperature (and hence velocity) having been assumed. From these displacements we can make a correction to our guess about the wind and temperature until we have reduced the displacement to zero. We then carry out the same procedure for the next higher grenade and so on.

The British rocket grenade experiment is a modification of the original American system which is aimed to obtain greater accuracy and also data on the vertical wind strengths. A succession of 18 grenades is released between 30 and 100 km altitude. Their flashes are recorded on accurate ballistic cameras. The direction in which the camera is pointing is obtained by photographing the stars. An array of 9 microphones records the arrival of the sound at points over an area 50 km in diameter, while the instant of firing of the grenades is detected both by photocells in the rocket, making use of the telemetry link, and on the ground. An electronic computer determines the position of each burst from the coordinate on the plates. Analysis of the British experiment is rather different from that of the American experiment since here we only have travel times of the sound to a number of different places but no direction of arrival. Knowing the position of the burst from optical measurement we proceed by guessing a wind and temperature structure to give certain times of arrival. These times are checked against the actual times of arrival and the guess modified until the correct times are obtained. To sort out the effects of the three wind components N-S, E-W and vertical, and the temperature, we require for each grenade good data from four listening stations. Excess stations provide insurance against microphone failure, appropriate ground coverage for grenades over the whole range of height, and a means of estimating accuracy of the results. The guessing procedure approaching by closer and closer approximation to the true distribution of wind and temperature is a laborious process for anyone to perform, but the problem is presented to an electronic computer which makes it easy.

2.3. *Pressure and density measurements*

Rocket-borne pressure gauges are in most cases adaptations of ordinary laboratory instruments. In the region between 2 and 3×10^{-3} Torr Pirani gauges are used (fig. 5), mounted in heavy metal cases which reduce the temperature change during flight to a few degrees. Below 10^{-1} Torr ionization gauges may be employed. In these the ionization of the air in the

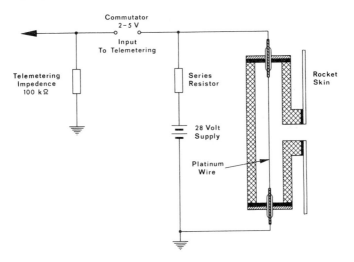

Fig. 5. Pirani gauge, mounted in heavy metal case connected to a hole on the rocket skin.

End View   Section View with Circuit

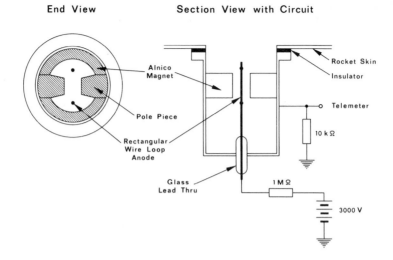

Fig. 6. Schematic view of a Penning-Philips gauge used as a rocket-borne pressure gauge.

gauge by alpha particles (alphatron); by electrons from a cold cathode (Penning-Philips gauge, fig. 6) or by electrons from a heated cathode (thermoionic ionization gauge) is measured.

Pressure gauges are generally located near the rocket tail (A in fig. 7) to measure ambient pressure to about 100 km, and on the nose to measure ambient density. At altitudes above 100 km, pressure and density are generally deduced from pressures measured on the nose cone (B, C in fig. 7). Residual gas around the gauges limits the accuracy in atmospheric pressure measurements above 100 km.

Atmospheric density can be calculated from pressure measured at the nose of a rocket, or, if the rocket is moving sideways, from pressures measured on the sides of the rocket. Two formulas must be used, as follows:

1) the Rayleigh formula at low altitudes (the mean free path being small),
2) a kinetic theory formula at high altitudes.

The Rayleigh equation for rocket velocities greater than the velocity of sound can be expanded into

$$P = \gamma^{-\frac{1}{4}} \cdot \rho V^2 + 0.46\, p + \ldots\ldots \tag{3}$$

Fig. 7. Location of pressure gauges in the rocket.

where P is the nose pressure, γ the rate of specific heats, ρ the ambient density, V the rocket velocity, p the ambient pressure. The first term is large compared to succeeding terms. For $\gamma = \frac{7}{5}$, the quation may be written

$$\left(\frac{\rho}{g\ m^{-3}}\right) = 0.144\ \frac{(P/\text{Torr})}{(V/\text{km s}^{-1})^2} - 0.066\ \frac{(p/\text{Torr})}{(V/\text{km s}^{-1})^2} + \cdots . \tag{4}$$

At high pressures, this equation is valid for the pressure at the nose of a yawless rocket, and it is approximately correct for the pressure change on one side of a rolling rocket moving at right angles to the rocket axis[*].

At high altitudes, where the mean free path of the molecules is greater than the diameter of the rocket, the equation is no longer valid. In this case the change in the pressure in the gauge ΔP as the rocket rolls, can be calculated from kinetic theory, by setting the number of molecules entering the gauge per second equal to the number leaving. The resultant equation is

$$\rho = \frac{\Delta P}{\sqrt{\pi}\ v\ V_\perp}$$

where v is the most probable velocity of the molecules in the gauge and $V_\perp$ is the component of the rocket velocity perpendicular to the gauge opening in A (fig. 7). This equation shows that the charge in the inside pressure, P, is independent of the outside temperature. In these measurements it is assumed that the residual pressures around the rocket or gauges have no effect on the pressure changes.

2.4. *Composition of high atmosphere*

Determination of upper air composition is more interesting at high levels, where gravitational separation of components will occur. No detectable gravitational separation up to a height of 85 km has been found. Turbulent mixing due to winds in the troposphere and stratosphere is sufficient to prevent any detectable change in atmospheric composition.

The method of analysing air samples taken from various heights in sealed bottles, has been applied with some degree of success up to 90 km. For very minute samples the method is useless. Nearly all the oxygen present reacts with the collecting vessel. Furthermore there is tendency to sample the light gases preferentially. This occurs when the mean free paths of the molecules are approaching the diameter of the sampling tube and is due to the fact that the mean velocity of the light gases is greater than that of the heavy gases.

At higher levels air composition is checked by methods of mass spectrometry. The atmospheric gas is passed into a mass spectrometer and actual quantitative analyses are rapidly made during the flight. Conventional magnetic-field mass spectrometers may be used for this purpose when high

---

[*] These equations are valid under particular assumptions of symmetry. They are not strictly applicable to complicated rocket structure and can only be used as a guidance in these cases. Empirical determinations could be obtained using a model in a supersonic wind channel.

precision is needed (fig. 8). When reducing rocket payload is more important, a miniature radio-frequency mass spectrometer is used. In this instrument, ions of the gas to be analysed enter an electric field which im-
parts to them a velocity inversely proportional to the root of their mass.
This velocity can now be measured by means of a variable frequency radio

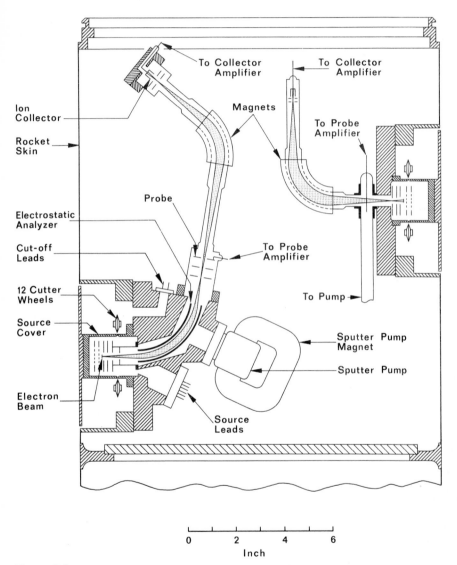

Fig. 8. Schematic view of cross section of rocket showing mounting of two different
mass-spectrometers (Nier et al., 1964).

frequency voltage applied to a series of grid structures. The current con-
veyed by the ions is measured and telemetered to ground, together with the
frequency of the radio frequency. Mass spectrometry is a difficult method
of measurement. The ion source does not produce ions in exactly the same
concentration ratio as that which applies to the gas in the chamber. In addition, we cannot be sure that the gas in the chamber has the same composition as that outside. However, some reasonably good data have been obtained (Schaefer, 1963; Meadows-Reed and Smith, 1963; Nier, Hoffman,
Johnson and Holmes, 1964; v. Zahn et al., 1967).

2.5. *Solar radiation*

High altitude rockets are used as carriers of instruments measuring intensity of solar radiations and selective atmospheric absorption of light.
One of the chief difficulties in carrying out measurements of solar radiation from rockets arise from the lack of stability of the rocket. Any chosen
window in the rocket skin only points toward the sun for a small fraction of
the rocket's life. This is not especially important for the study of the relatively intense radiation just beyond the 2900 Å cut-off, but it is very serious for the shorter radiations which are comparatively weak. Several devices have been introduced to obviate these difficulties. The effective area
of a window may be increased by the use of suitably disposed reflecting
mirrors or diffusing beads. A sunseeker is to be used when a substantial
increase of the intensity of illumination is needed.

To disperse solar radiation, a very fruitful method is the use of a spec-
trograph. From the rocket point of view, this is cumbersome and expensive,
nevertheless, many observations have been carried out using rocket-borne
spectrographs, equipped with suitable photocells or photon counters as energy measuring sensors. The latter are devices rather similar in principle
to the counters which are used in nuclear physics to detect and count fast
particles. Some means have to be introduced so that the counter is only ac-
tuated by radiation of the required wavelength range. This may be done by
placing in front of the counter one or more materials known as filters which
are selective absorbers. Thus a window of calcium fluoride only transmits
ultra-violet light in the wave-length range 1250 to 1350 Å. An example of
this method is the study of the Lyman α radiation from hydrogen at 1216 Å,
which is an important constituent of the solar radiation. It will produce
photoionization of nitric oxide gas, so the detector consists of a small
chamber filled with nitric oxide at 25 torr pressure. But as all radiations
with wave-length shorter than 1100 Å will also ionize NO, the window of the
chamber is made of lithium fluoride which absorbs all these unwanted radiations.

Solar ultraviolet spectroscopy provides the upper air physicist with the
needed information about the high energy solar photons which pass through
the upper atmosphere where they may produce ionization, dissociation, excitation and heating effects. Applications of the knowledge of solar ultraviolet radiation have to do with the formation of the F- and E-layers and the
cause of the high temperature of the earth's upper atmosphere.

Measuring solar radiation absorption spectroscopically as the rocket

moves upward is a relatively simple method to check the vertical distribution of certain constituents, e.g. O_3, O_2, O and N.

2.6. *Gun launched probes*

In principle, many of the rocket-borne instruments could be developed
to be carried by a gun-launched vehicle, even though the accelerations are
extremely large, of the order of 10.000 to 40.000 g.

The payloads that have been used have been packages of chaff that could
be expelled and tracked by radar and tanks of chemicals that could create a
vapour trail. A US Army 12.5-cm gun could fire a 10 kg shell to about 60
km and a 40-cm gun could fire a projectile to over 100 km with a substantial payload (McGill University, 1963).

3. INDIRECT SOUNDINGS FOR UPPER ATMOSPHERE OBSERVATIONS

Prior to the advent of sounding rockets, all the experimental informations that were available on the upper atmosphere above about 30 km came
from indirect observations. These informations have subsequently been
shown to be surprisingly accurate. Even though sounding rockets are now
available, there is still a possibility of further extending some of the indirect sounding techniques, owing to their ability to make routine observations relatively simple and inexpensive compared to the rocket observations.

3.1. *Anomalous sound propagation*

Earlier information on winds and temperatures between about 30 km and
60 km has been derived from studies of the so-called anomalous sound
propagation from large explosions on the ground. As mentioned in section
2.2., the speed of sound is

$$c = (\gamma R\ T/M)^{\frac{1}{2}} + v\ , \tag{5}$$

where v is the wind component along the azimuth of propagation and T the
air temperature. As the composition of the air does not vary appreciably
up to the altitudes under consideration, γ, R and M may be taken as constant, so that

$$c = \text{const}\ \sqrt{T} + v \tag{5a}$$

Gradients in speed of propagation along a path, generally cause the ray to
bend and a ray is also bent by changes of the wind component normal to the path
of propagation. The sound waves from an explosion that go into the upper
atmosphere are bent upwards as they move through the troposphere toward
colder temperatures, and above this, as they progress into the stratosphere
towards the region of maximum temperature, they are bent back down towards the ground. The effect of high-level winds is to help in bending the
ray downwards when they are increasing with height in the direction of
propagation. The result is the propagation of a sound wave from an explosion for very great distances through the stratosphere and return to the
ground in a particular direction. A number of programs in the past have

employed this in a systematic way to determine conditions of temperature and wind above the tropopause.

The experimental procedure is quite similar to that employed in sounding grenades techniques. The time taken by the sound to travel a known distance from the explosion point to a lattice of microphones is measured. The apparent speed and direction of the sound travel over the lattice are found from the times of arrival at the individual microphones. From these data and wind and temperatures from simultaneous radiosonde, the trajectory of the sound and its time of travel up the top of the balloon ascent can be calculated. The distance and time at higher levels are then found. If some law of variation of wind and temperature with height is assumed, solutions for the speed of sound at different altitudes can be obtained and if simultaneous measurements of this type are made on three or more azimuths, values of wind and temperature may then be calculated from eq. (5a).

The complexity of the computing task and the uncertainties of the assumed law of variation of wind and temperature with height, set a severe limit to the details which can be obtained. Results are, of course, not so satisfactory as those obtained by the technique of rocket-borne grenades. There are obvious advantages in using aerial explosions, since the passage of the ray does not depend on, and is not limited in height by a reflecting layer. Moreover, in grenade technique, a certain number of explosions at selected intervals in height on a near-vertical line, are produced, so that a differential analysis can be done and the analysis itself is simplified and improved in accuracy, owing to the fact that near-vertical rays can be used.

3.2. *Light scattering methods*

When a strong beam of light is sent upwards in the atmosphere we can observe it from the side, owing to the scattering caused by molecules in its path, and also by the dust and haze in its path. Assuming Rayleigh scattering, for a fixed wavelength, the intensity of light scattered at an angle α down from the beam, is

$$I = \text{const } (1 + \cos^2 \alpha)\rho$$

where ρ is the air density. The constant can be found by comparison with radio-sonde observations made at the same time. The method can be used for altitudes from about 10 km to over 120 km, the lower limit being determined by the additional scattering due to dust in the troposphere and the upper limit by the decreasing contrast with the light of the night sky. The latter difficulty can be minimized by modulating the beam. The searchlight techniques may be greatly improved with the advent of extremely high power monocromatic pulsed sources from lasers (Fiocco and Smullin, 1963). Another advantage of the pulsed laser is its ability to be applied in measuring the range as well. One of the problems with this method is the difficulty of distinguishing between scattering from molecules of air and from small aerosol particles of very fine dust observed even in the high stratosphere. Maybe that further improvement in separating the two influences can be obtained by two or more simultaneous scattering measurements with monocromatic light of different wavelengths, considering that Rayleigh molecular scattering depends on the fourth power of wavelength (proportional to λ^{-4}), while dust scattering depends roughly on the first power of the wavelength (proportional to λ^{-1}) for scattering particles larger than 0.2 μ in diameter (Ångström, 1929).

Sunlight scattering can be used to determine the distribution of dust layers by measuring the change in intensity and polarization, at several wavelength, of the skylight, in the direction of setting or rising sun, as the shadow of the earth changes its altitude (Bigg, 1956; Volz and Goody, 1962). In spite of the advantage of not requiring an artificial source, this technique appears to be no longer convenient, owing to limitations and to the difficulty of interpreting the results.

Other investigations involving scattered sunlight measurements concern the distribution and temperatures of some atomic and molecular constituents in the atmosphere above 70 km. Atoms of sodium, potassium and also molecular nitrogen, have strong scattering at resonant lines in the visible or ultra-violet part of the spectrum. Measurements of the variation in intensity of these lines at twilight can give the vertical distribution of the constituents. It is also possible to obtain information on upper atmosphere temperature from the Doppler widths of atomic lines, or rotational temperatures, especially from N_2^+. However, deduced temperatures have to be related to a height of emission and this often cannot be determined accurately. Accuracy of these measurements is hardly better than $\pm 30^\circ K$ and often considerably worse.

3.3. *Airglow and aurora measurements*

'Airglow' is a characteristic emission resulting from a number of photochemical reactions taking place in the upper atmosphere, above 60 km. Dayglow and twilight glow, although many times more intense than nightglow, are more difficult to investigate, due to the presence of scattered sunlight. The spectra obtained at the surface reveal the constituents involved but not their relative abundance. The strongest emissions in the nightglow spectrum are:

that of atomic oxygen at 5577 Å (green line) and 6300-6364 Å (red pair) ,
of molecular oxygen at 2600 and 4300 Å,
of sodium at 5893 Å (yellow D doublet)
and that of hydroxyl radical OH at 6500 and 11 500 Å.

(The last emission is the strongest in the airglow (Murgatroyd, 1965)). Emission heights range from 120 to 200 km for the red pair of atomic oxygen and from 60 to 120 km for the other spectral lines. In addition to the use of airglow spectra to obtain information on composition and chemical reactions which take place in the upper atmosphere, temperatures were deduced from the Doppler width of atomic lines, especially from the oxygen green line, giving the best accuracy, using techniques similar to those employed in analysing sunlight resonant scattering. This technique has led to some interesting determinations of temperature variations at middle latitudes, but it is difficult to apply at high latitudes, due to the interferences of auroral emission. Another difficulty is due to a lack of knowledge of the effective emission heights.

The aurora is a relatively bright emission caused by solar protons and electrons arriving in the upper atmosphere at high latitudes, most frequently about 23° from the magnetic poles. The height of the aurora is from about 90 km to several hundred km. It may be determined by standard methods of triangulation in which photographs of the same display are taken at different stations, separated by 30 km or so. The spectrum of an aurora is quite rich in lines and bands. The green coloration arises from the intense atomic oxygen line at 5577 Å and red coloration is due either to the red pair of atomic oxygen at 6300-6364 Å or to certain bands of N_2. Spectral observations of the aurora can be made with techniques similar to those employed in airglow observations and have been used to infer the composition and reactions taking place in the upper atmosphere.

3.4. *Meteors*

One of the most powerful methods yet found for measuring motions in the upper atmosphere, from 70 to 110 km, is tracking the growth and motion of meteor trails by optical and, more recently, by radar and Doppler techniques. Meteors are fragments of extraterrestrial material entering the earth's atmosphere at very high velocities (10-70 km/sec), which are destroyed in the upper atmosphere. Ordinary shooting stars, which may be seen by a single observer at a rate of several an hour, during particular periods of the year, vary in weight from about 10^{-3} to 10 g. Meteors with smaller weights down to about 10^{-6} g can be detected by radar methods. Tracking their trails optically (usually photographically) or by radio echo methods provide information about winds. Information on atmospheric density and temperature can be obtained measuring their luminosity, deceleration, heights of appearance and disappearance and the ionization they produce. The tracking of the ionised trail by radio methods has proved particularly fruitful and has allowed the separation of mean winds, tidal components and irregular components.

REFERENCES

Bigg, E.K., 1956, The detection of atmospheric dust and temperature inversions by twilight scattering, J. Meteorol. 13, 262.

Chanin, M.L. and R.D.Steen, 1963, Phys. Rev. 132, 2554.

Clark, G. and G.McCoy, 1965, Measurement of stratospheric temperature. J. Appl. Meteorol. 4 (3).

Egidi, A., G. Fea and G. Fratucello, 1961. Misure del vento nella bassa termosfera mediante la tecnica della nube al sodio, Atti Ass. Geof. Italiana, 331.

Fiocco, G. and L.D.Smullin, 1963, Detection of scattering layers in the upper atmosphere (60-140 km) by optical radar, Nature 199, 1275.

Haerendel, G. and M.Scholer, 1967, Space Res. VII, 509.

Kochanski, A., 1964, J. Geophys. Res. 69, 17.

Leviton, R. and J.B.Wright, 1961, Accuracy of density from the Robbin falling sphere, GRD Research Note 73, Air Force Cambridge Res. Laboratories, Bedford.

Meadow-Reed, E.B. and C.R.Smith, 1963, Mass spectrometric investigations of the atmosphere between 100 and 227 km above Wallops Island, Virginia, NASA Tech.Note D. 1851.

McGill University, 1963, Project HARP, Report on the first twelve firings and sta-
    tus as of 30 July 1963, Dept. of mechanical engineering, Report 63-5.
Murgatroyd, R.J., 1965, In: WMO Tech. Note No. 70, 19.
Nier, A.O., J.M.Hoffman, C.Y.Johnson and J.Holmes, Neutral composition of the
    atmosphere in the 100 to 200 km range, J. Geophys. Res. 69, 5.
Rapp, R.R., 1960, The accuracy of winds derived by the radar tracking of chaff at
    high altitudes, J. Meteorol. 17, 507.
Schaefer, E.J., 1963, The dissociation of oxygen measured by a rocket mass spec-
    trometer, J. Geophys. Res. 68, 1175.
Volz, F.E. and R.M.Goody, 1962, The intensity of twilight and upper atmospheric
    dust, J. Atmosph. Sci. 19, 385.
Wagner, N.K., 1964, Theoretical accuracy of meteorological rocket sonde thermis-
    tor, J. Appl. Meteorol. 3, 4.
Von Zahn, U., et al., 1967, Space Res. VII, 1150.

DISCUSSION

Baguette:

La mesure des températures ionosphériques par observation de la lar-
geur Doppler de la raie de résonnance du sodium n'est justifiée que si les
atoms de sodium émis dans l'atmosphère sont en équilibre thermique avec
les composants neutres du gaz atmosphérique. Ceci a lieu si le nombre de
collisions des atomes de sodium avec les particules neutres est suffisamment grand dans un temps suffisamment court (soit l'ordre de la minute)
pour que les mesures puissent avoir lieu après l'équilibre et avant la dis-
parition du sodium. La question a été traité par Chanin (1963) et il donne
les ordres de grandeur des temps d'équilibre.

Fedele:

The collision frequency of the sodium atoms with the atoms and molecules of atmospheric gases is of the order of

$$10^3 \text{ sec}^{-1} \text{ at } 120 \text{ km },$$
$$10^2 \text{ sec}^{-1} \text{ at } 130 \text{ km },$$
$$20 \text{ sec}^{-1} \text{ at } 150 \text{ km and}$$
$$5 \text{ sec}^{-1} \text{ at } 200 \text{ km }.$$

Starting from an initial temperature of 2000°C, the sodium atoms could gain
the equilibrated temperature of the surrounding air particles (within less
than 10°) in a period of time not greater than a few minutes, even at the
upper layers reached by these soundings. The times to reach equilibrium
are longer if the density of the sodium atoms is not small against that of
the air molecules. If the sodium cloud is produced by a thermite generator,
its density is at first great and therefore its cooling is slow. The great initial density presents also some complications when the temperature is
computed from the spectral distribution of the energy (line-broadening by
Doppler effect) because account must be taken of auto-absorption.

In order to avoid this effect, the dispersion of the vapours by means of
explosives is preferable. As the cloud can be observed 20 min or longer, it
is possible to follow the vapour temperature as function of the time and, thus,
determine experimentally the time needed to reach thermal equilibrium.

Rawer:

A question concerning the metal vapour method: Lüst (Haerendel and Scholer, 1967) has observed a separation of neutral and ionized vapour which they attribute to the influence of electrical fields. Could not these forces influence the motion of the cloud so that it would not correspond to the neutral wind only? At which heights could such forces disturb the determination of the neutral wind?

Fedele:

Let u be the mean relative speed of the ionized atoms of charge e and mass m in an electric field E. Then u depends upon the collission frequency f of the atoms with neutral gas particles. Under equilibrium conditions, neglecting the effects of the earth's magnetic field, u is obtained by the relation:

$$u = \frac{eE}{mf}. \tag{6}$$

It does not seem to me that at the levels of vapour dispersion there are any electric fields so strong and collission frequencies so small to cause drifts of the ionized atoms comparable with other errors which occur in measuring wind speed by the method of the vapour clouds.

Before Lüst's experiments, it was usually accepted that up to 120-125 km the sodium cloud motion might represent the motion of the neutral component of the air.

Comparison of simultaneous observations of sodium cloud drifts (partially ionized) and artificial ionization drifts (ionosonde data) in the 100 to 125-km layer (Kochanski, 1964) gives us an indirect check. At greater heights it was not yet possible to specify how much the electrodynamic forces cause deviations between the ionized and visible part of a sodium cloud with respect to neutral air.

Neutral air motion should not only depend on the particle collision frequency but also on the number ratio of ionized and neutral particles which is variable during the experiment owing to diffusion and changes of sunlight.

Experiments like those made by Lüst and his collaborators will probably give a better answer to these questions in the future.

EFFECTS OF SOLAR RADIATION
IN THE LOWER ATMOSPHERE

Barbara KRIESTER
Free University, Berlin

Abstract. The main characteristics of the solar and terrestrial radiation will be considered and a short insight will be given into the mean heat balance of the earth-atmosphere system. Some special features of the circulation which arise through the latitudinal unbalance will be treated and the mean pattern will be shown by using mean maps of constant pressure levels.

Résumé. On étudie les caractéristiques essentielles du rayonnement solaire et terrestre et on résume l'équilibre thermique du système terre atmosphère. Le déséquilibre latitudinal est à l'origine de quelques propriétés particulières de la circulation. Ces particularités sont étudiées et à l'aide de cartes moyennes (à niveau de pression constante) les conditions moyennes sont démontrées.

1. INTRODUCTION

First I want to define how I will use the term "lower atmosphere" in this lecture. To agree with the theme of this summerschool which treats movements and turbulence of the atmosphere between 30 and 120 km, i.e. of the upper atmosphere, the expression lower atmosphere here refers to air just until about 30 km. This includes following the IUGG system of nomenclature for subregions of the atmosphere, the whole troposphere and the lower part of the stratosphere.

Although the troposphere has the most direct thermal interaction with the earth's surface caused by sun heating or cooling it seems to be reasonable to include the lower stratosphere in this discussion considering the striking features of responding to tropospheric movements. Moreover the level of about 30 km is the approximate ceiling of most of the sounding balloons and therefore an instrumental boundary for routine meteorological data and synoptical treatment.

This lecture, however, by no means will give a complete insight into all aspects of the subject but is restricted by considering only some phenomena of general meteorological importance.

2. EFFECTS OF SOLAR RADIATION IN THE LOWER ATMOSPHERE

2.1. *Some characteristics of solar and terrestrial radiation and the mean heat balance of the earth-atmosphere system*

The sun is the principle source of energy available to the earth and its atmosphere. Only through the absorption of the solar radiation and the emission into space of the terrestrial radiation from the earth and atmosphere our planet can receive and lose energy. The solar energy received is converted into internal energy which will be transformed into potential energy, latent heat and kinetic energy. Thus all atmospheric and oceanic motions are derived from solar radiation.

The upper atmosphere derives most of its energy directly by absorption through various atmospheric gases although the energy so absorbed represents only a few percent of the total solar energy reaching the earth's atmosphere. The troposphere in contrast obtaines its energy more indirectly after reradiation or convection from the earth's surface.

It is well known that the annual and diurnal variation of temperature and the recurrence of special circulation patterns are strongly related to the annual and diurnal variation of solar radiation. However, before discussing this problem I want to call to remembrance the main characteristics of solar and terrestrial radiation in the lower atmosphere and its mean heat budget.

The sun is regarded as a black body with a surface temperature of about 6000°K. The radiative laws of a black body are well known both theoretically and experimentically. The main feature is the radiative emission in a continuous spectrum over all wavelengths with an intensity maximum occurring at a special wavelength which depends on the temperature of the radiator. Moreover not only the energy in the appropriate range of the spectrum but also the whole energy increases rapidly with increasing temperature.

The effective output of solar radiation is measured by the solar constant, for which no definitive value exists until now, because its observation is a matter of some difficulties. The most usual value amounts to 1.94 ly min^{-1}, which is a 30-year mean reported by the Smithsonian Institution. To the IGY, however, a value of 1.98 ly min^{-1} was recommended.

The normal flux is the incoming solar flux on a unit area perpendicular to the direction of the radiation. With regard to the effective insolation we have to consider the flux of solar energy per horizontal unit area. This flux received in the upper atmosphere, the so-called undepleted insolation, is a function of latitude and time of the year. The distribution of the undepleted insolation over the earth shows a time-latitude maximum in summer solstice at the pole, which occurs mainly as a result of the long solar day. This fact is well perceptible in the polar stratosphere where the high summer temperatures are caused by continuous insolation.

The direct solar beam however, will be depleted while passing through the atmosphere. Thus the direct insolation at the earth's surface depends on the transmissivity which includes absorption and scattering processes. Scattering has an important influence upon the state of the atmosphere as it partially degrades the solar beam into a diffuse flux of energy, and returns a considerable proportion unused into space. Scattering occurs at the air molecules and this dispersion of radiant energy, the so-called Rayleigh or molecular scattering, is apparent in the whole atmosphere. In the troposphere are two other scattering agents which contribute to the depletion of the direct solar beam. These are water vapor and dust. If the solar beam happens to pass through cloudy skies diffuse reflexion occurs, i.e. scattering by relatively large particles. Moreover, water vapor and dust are the most important constituents of the air which cause absorption in the troposphere. Absorption by ozone occurs in the lower stratosphere producing strong temperature changes. In recent studies attention has been drawn to water vapor and dust content of the lower stratosphere which may contribute to the depletion of the solar radiation in this layer either by absorption or scattering. It must be pointed out that all scattered radiation is also subject to absorption. This fact has to be considered if calculations of temperature changes by absorption are made.

In comparison with the energy flux of 1.94 ly min^{-1} incoming at the upper limit of the atmosphere, only a quarter, i.e. 0.5 ly min^{-1}, will be available to the earth and atmosphere. One now may assume that from this energy a total of approximately 40% is reflected to space, by far the most through clouds and to a little amount through the air and the earth's surface. The ratio of the outward to the inward flux is known as the albedo of the earth. The remaining part of the energy flux is absorbed by the ground.

The daily value of the depleted insolation finally reaching the earth's surface is considerably reduced in all latitudes compared with the undepleted values. The distribution over the earth shows the strongest depletion in the highest latitudes due to the growing of the path length of the solar ray through the atmosphere. The time-latitude maximum now is found at somewhat lower latitudes.

Both the earth and those parts of the atmosphere where absorption of the solar short-wave radiation occurs are emitting radiation in the long-wave range appropriate to their temperature. The terms long- and short-wave radiation arose due to Wien's displacement law. The wavelength of maximum emission at the planetary temperature is 11.5 μ whereas the wavelength of maximum radiation from the sun has been measured at 0.474 μ. The principle gaseous absorbers of the low-temperature radiation are water vapor and carbon dioxide in the troposphere while ozone contributes to a small amount in the stratosphere. These constituents are present in sufficient quantity to absorb, and therefore to emit, a considerable proportion of the terrestrial radiation, which is therefore passed out through the atmosphere from one layer of gas to another. The so-called greenhouse-effect of the troposphere occurs because of the strong absorption of the long-wave radiation by water vapor and also by carbon dioxide.

As this long-wave radiation becomes of main importance at night when short-wave flux is absent, long-wave radiation from the ground level is referred to as nocturnal radiation, irrespective of the time of the day. Temperature changes produced by radiative heating or cooling due to this terrestrial radiation in the mean show a prevailance of cooling in the lowest layers. Thus in order to maintain a local long term heat balance there must be other methods of vertical heat transfer in the troposphere.

These are turbulent and latent heat transfer. The first is caused by vertical mixing of air with different thermal histories and the latter is due to condensation and evaporation. In the lower stratosphere, however, it has been determined that in the mean the wind shear is of one order of magnitude less than in the upper troposphere. This fact indicates that in the stratosphere eddy diffusion of heat occurs only in a small amount. Moreover, to a good approximation no latent heat will occur because of relatively small values of water vapor in the lower stratosphere. It may be generally accepted that the troposphere is a region where heat exchange is predominantly caused by convection and turbulent mixing of air. On the other hand it is stated that the stratosphere is a region where the heat exchange is mainly caused through the process of radiative transfer. The troposphere therefore is said to be in a convective equilibrium while radiative equilibrium exists in the stratosphere.

Let us now consider the mean heat balance of the whole earth-atmosphere-system. That such a condition of equilibrium exists is attested by the fact that there has been no significant change in the mean temperature of the earth and its atmosphere over recorded times. This will be attained by a balance between the radiative heat transfer of incoming solar short-wave radiation and outgoing terrestrial long-wave radiation and the completing actions of turbulent and latent heat transfer.

The planetary temperature derived from this equilibrium amounts to -23ºC. However, all radiative processes mentioned before (such as the depletion of long-wave and short-wave radiation by scattering, absorption, and reflection, respectively) act firstly: to keep the mean temperature of the earth's surface much higher and secondly: to establish colder temperatures in the upper troposphere. The tropopause at a fixed height and with a fixed temperature likewise is assumed to be maintained as a result of thermal equilibrium.

The planetary temperature therefore can be said to be an equilibrium temperature that the earth and atmosphere system must attain with the solar energy in order to keep this planet's internal energy constant. This is true for the whole globe.

However, regarding distinct latitude belts it will be found that there exists a surplus heat energy at low latitudes and energy deficit at higher latitudes. This would lead to an increase in the mean temperature of equatorial regions while in polar regions the mean temperature would decrease. To complete the global heat balance a poleward directed energy transport is necessary which is carried out to a small amount by the ocean currents but in principle by the tropospheric circulation.

It is now an interesting question featuring the general circulation by which this transport may be accomplished. On the other hand it is very important to know the exertion of relatively short term variations of the global heat pattern on the evolution of the general circulation. Moreover, there still remains the important question of how the general circulation would be influenced by irregular changes of the solar emissivity or by variations of the reflectivity of the earth-atmosphere system. The variations of the long-term solar energy flux may arise by a more or less disturbed state of the sun with a major or minor sunspot maximum which indicates more or less emission of ultraviolet or corpuscular radiation. Changes in the reflectivity could occur through variations in the proportion of atmospheric

carbon dioxide or through changes in the planetary albedo due to variations
in snow cover, cloud cover and atmospheric turbidity, the latter being produced perhaps through intense volcanic eruptions. In the following, the
northern hemisphere only will be regarded although there may occur energy
transport across the equator, especially when studying daily or monthly
conditions.

2.2. *Some aspects of the general circulation*

As it was pointed out, the conditions of equilibrium make it necessary to
postulate a circulation in the troposphere - and in the oceans - which transport poleward the total energy of the earth-atmosphere system gained in
latitudes $0-35^o$.

Thus, the circulation established on a rotating longitudinal uniform
earth with a meridional temperature and pressure gradient due to the energy surplus at low latidudes and energy deficit at high latitudes is the so-
called planetary wind circulation. Fig. 1 shows this well known feature:

the polar high,
the subpolar low pressure belt at latitude 60°,
the subtropical high pressure belt at latitude 30°,
the equatorial low pressure belt.

Corresponding to this general pressure distribution we will find the following wind system:

poleward from 60° latitude: light winds mostly from the east,
in midlatitudes: zonal westerlies,
within the subtropical high pressure belt: light winds or calms,
between latitude 30° and the equator: the steady blowing trade winds,
in the equatorial region: again light winds or calms.

This planetary wind circulation, however, by no means shows the real
feature of the general circulation because an important fact is neglected.
Due to the distribution of land and sea over the earth, especially at the
northern hemisphere, modifications arise. They come out clearly when
looking at mean circulation charts. On the other hand by using mean maps
some of the most important features of the circulation are smoothed out
through averaging processes.

Therefore, before discussing some mean maps I want to give a short insight into the two possible transfer mechanisms which are responsible for
the redistribution of surpluses and deficits of heat over the earth. Heat
transfer may be accomplished firstly by meridional cellular circulation and
secondly by quasi-horizontal waves. There is no doubt that such a meridional vertical cell extends approximately between latitude 30° and the equator. In middle and high latitudes a meridional cell may exist but observations indicate that in these latitudes the major part of the heat transfer is
accomplished by quasi-horizontal waves which are superimposed upon the
main westerly flow.

The only variations in the relative magnitudes of heat transport generally accepted are seasonal in origin. Let us now consider the seasonal var-

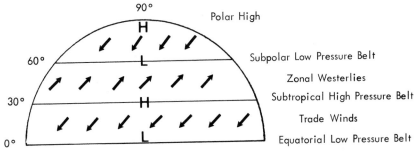

Fig. 1. Planetary wind circulation.

iations in the circulation of the troposphere and stratosphere. The normal January and July maps will be given here since they are more or less representative of the normal winter and summer circulation, respectively. These charts were prepared by Jacobs for the period 1900-1939.

From the mean map of the 1000-mb constant pressure level of January (fig. 2) it is apparent that the pressure belts referred to at the planetary wind circulation consist of cells. Thus, the sub-polar low pressure belt contains two semipermanent low centers, the Aleutian and the Icelandic lows which are located at latitude 50⁰-60⁰. Likewise, the subtropical high pressure belt is characterized by a number of semipermanent high centers of which the Pacific and the Azoric highs exist during the entire year. The anticyclones over the continents of America and Asia are caused by the strong cooling of the land areas which leads to a direct thermal circulation. The interruption of the subtropical high pressure belt by relatively low pressure over the Mediterranian is due to the warm and humid air in comparison with the surrounding area.

The polar region is influenced mostly by the low pressure belt of the midlatitudes. At the Pacific side of the polar region, however, a weak high center is found. The equatorial low pressure belt is shown just at the equator and seems to be cellular in character, too.

Between winter and summer some considerable changes occur. Looking at the mean map of the 1000-mb constant pressure level for July (fig. 3) the following will be seen: the subpolar low pressure belt has filled considerably and shifted poleward, especially in the Aleutian area, where no closed cyclonic circulation is perceptible in July. Likewise, the subtropical anticyclones moved somewhat poleward and are strengthened. The continental areas, however, have relatively low pressure which is essentially caused by the monsoon effect, since there is now an outflow aloft from the warm continents towards the surrounding colder oceanic regions.

The equatorial low pressure belt moved to the north, corresponding to the shifting of the thermal equator, especially over the Arabian and Indian area, due to the strong development of the Indian monsoon low.

At the polar region the anticyclone of the winter is replaced by a low pressure center.

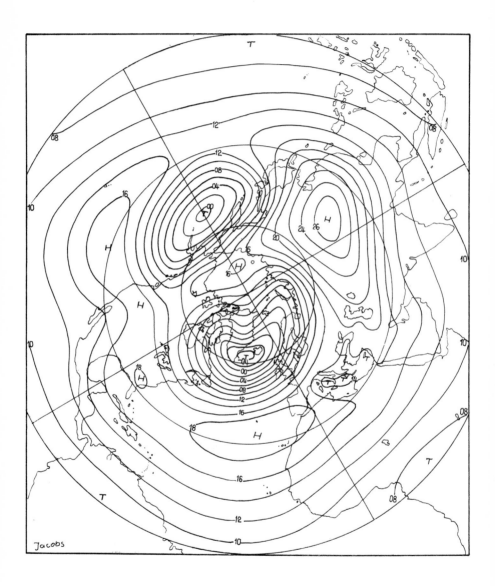

Fig. 2. 1000 mb monthly mean map January 1900–1939 (Jacobs, 1958).

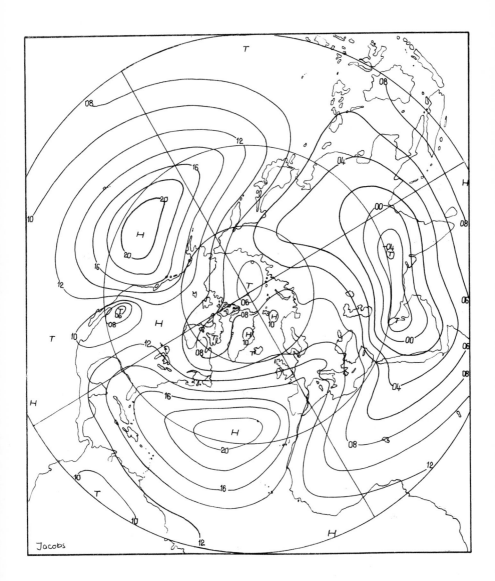

Fig. 3. 1000 mb monthly mean map July 1900-1939 (Jacobs, 1958).

Now let us see, how these circulation patterns change with increasing height. The mean thickness map 500/1000-mb of January (fig. 4) gives an insight into the mean temperature distribution in the lower troposphere in winter. The most interesting features in this season are the two cold centers which are located over Siberia and the Canadian Archipelago. In these areas a minimum of incoming radiation and a maximum of outgoing radiation coincide and give occasion to strong radiative cooling.

In summer, however, as we can see looking at the mean thickness map 500/1000-mb of July (fig. 5), the tropospheric cold center is concentrated almost exactly at the North Pole.

The thermal equator which could be seen in January lying near the geographical equator, has shifted now to the north following the position where the sun stands in the zenith. There are two significant centers of warm air over Arabia and Southwestern America. It is well to be seen from this map that the meridional temperature gradient is considerably reduced compared with that of January. The two cold troughs are replaced from the east coasts of the continents of America and Asia to the oceans.

At the mean map of the 500-mb constant pressure level of January (fig. 6) we see that nearly all of the pressure centers of the 1000-mb level are no longer discernable but that there is a good agreement with the mean thickness map of this month. This is resulting from the hydrostatic principle that the pressure decrease in the vertical is maximum where the density is greatest. Thus, cyclones and troughs tilt toward the colder air, whereas anticyclones and ridges tilt toward the warmer air. The subpolar low pressure centers are therefore found at the 500-mb level over Siberia and Canada and the subtropical high pressure centers at latitudes 10°-20°. In summer, as shown by the mean map of the 500-mb constant pressure level of July (fig. 7), a single cyclone is located over the polar region in the middle troposphere, while the subtropical high pressure centers are displaced to the north to latitudes 20°-30°. The closed cyclonic circulation over India is due to the strong development of the Indian monsoon low.

Corresponding to the weakening of the meridional temperature gradient, the pressure gradient is reduced, such that the zonal westerlies are decreasing from winter to summer season.

In both summer and winter, troughs are located near the east coasts of both Asia and North America, and there is an indication of a trough in central Europe. In summer, there is, in addition, a fourth trough over the eastern Pacific. Within the regions of the East American and the West Pacific troughs the highest pressure gradients occur causing a maximum of zonal wind speed in this level. The westerly component of wind of the mid-latitudinal troposphere increases with increasing height because of the temperature decrease towards north, and an absolute maximum - the so-called jet stream - occurs around the 200-mb level, an altitude around 10 km.

The annual variation of the mean jet stream is such that it reaches its highest mean latitude and lowest speed during the late summer. The maximum wind speed of the winter is about twice as large as in the summer, although in winter often two axes exist. They are referred to as the polar and subtropical jet.

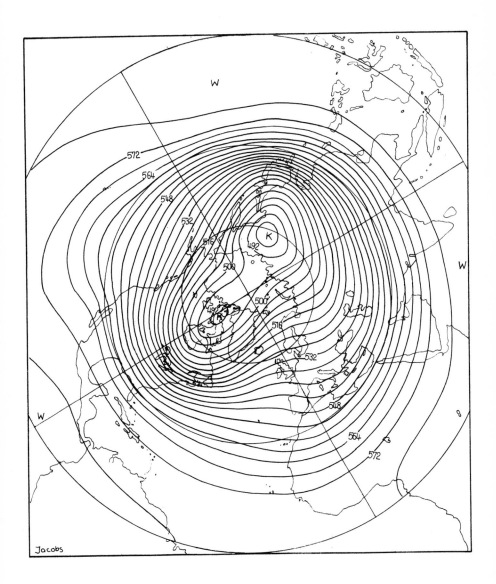

Fig. 4. 500/1000 mb mean thickness map January 1900–1939 (Jacobs, 1958).

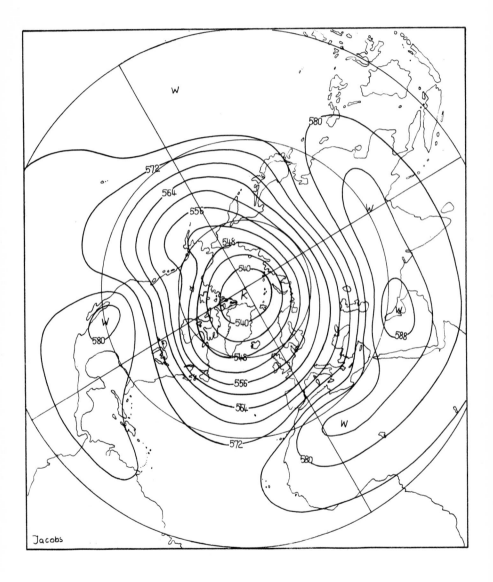

Fig. 5. 500/1000 mb mean thickness map July 1900-1939 (Jacobs, 1958).

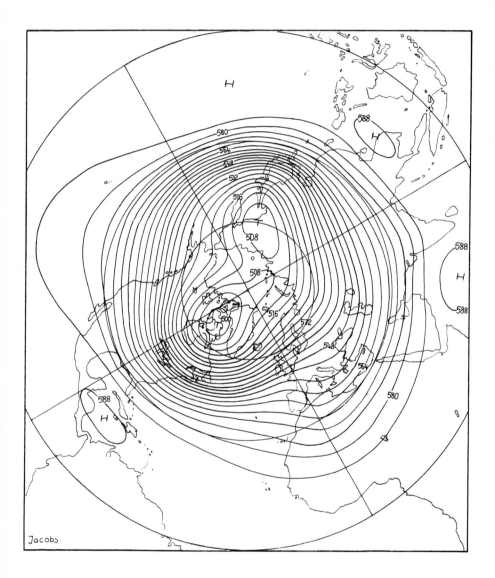

Fig. 6. 500 mb monthly mean map January 1900-1939 (Jacobs, 1958).

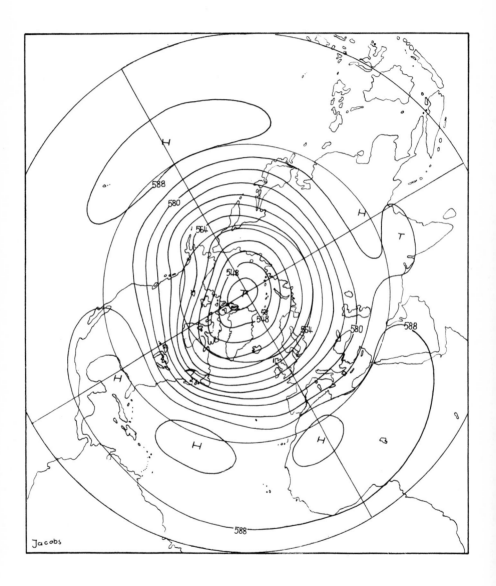

Fig. 7. 500 mb monthly mean map July 1900–1939 (Jacobs, 1958).

Within the elevation range discussed so far all latitudes were in the troposphere, where temperature decreases upward and poleward and the normal west winds of the midlatitudinal troposphere increase with increasing height.

The upper boundary of the troposphere is known as the tropopause.[*] This boundary is sloping upward from the pole where it is found between 6 and 8 km to the equator where it reaches 16-18 km. The 100-mb constant pressure level is found therefore in the troposphere over the tropics and in the stratosphere over middle and high latitudes. The very significant feature of the stratospheric temperature distribution is the reversed gradient in all latitudes with exception of the polar region in winter, as we can see by the mean temperature distribution at the 100-mb level in January (fig. 8). This reversed gradient may be regarded as a large scale compensation, which causes the removal of shorter wavelength disturbances. The basic "long wave structure" of the upper troposphere, however, is preserved, but cold troughs of the middle and upper troposphere are replaced by warm troughs in the 100-mb level, and respectively warm ridges by cold ridges. This leads to a weakening of the zonal westerly winds and a decreasing of the intensity of the pressure centers.

Two exceptions must be considered. As mentioned before at low latitudes the 100-mb level is part of the troposphere. Thus the vertical temperature changes are almost entirely tropospheric and the zonal wind, on the average, increases with height.

The mean map of the 100-mb constant pressure level of January (fig. 9) shows therefore a similar pattern as the 500-mb mean map of the same month, but the East Siberian low being almost entirely compensated through the West Pacific warm area. In summer the temperature gradient at the 100-mb level is completely reverse to that of the troposphere, as shown by the mean temperature distribution of July (fig. 10). Thus the zonal westerlies are considerably weakened and even replaced by easterlies at some latitudes. This is apparent from the mean map of the 100-mb constant pressure level of July (fig. 11).

All these 100-mb mean maps were prepared by Wege and are based on data from 5 yrs. This is too short a period for the establishment of quantitatively reliable normal maps. Nevertheless, the maps illustrate many features that appear to be qualitatively reliable. The same is true for the following mean maps of the 50-mb constant pressure level.

At the 50-mb level the temperature distribution of January (fig. 12) shows a similar pattern to that of the 100-mb level with the meridional temperature gradient opposite to that observed in the troposphere. In the polar region, however, temperature decreases to the north which is the significant feature of the stratosphere in winter. The mean map of the 50-mb con-

---

[*] The definition of the tropopause is based on a significant change of the temperature lapse rate. The WMO has defined the first tropopause as the lowest level at which the lapse rate decreases to 2°C per kilometer or less. At one single sounding it is possible that the lapse rate is decreasing more and then is less again at some higher levels.

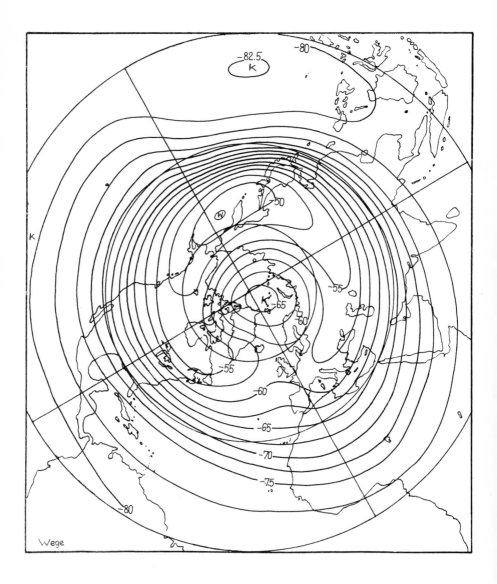

Fig. 8. 100 mb mean temperature distribution January 1949-1953 (Wege, 1957).

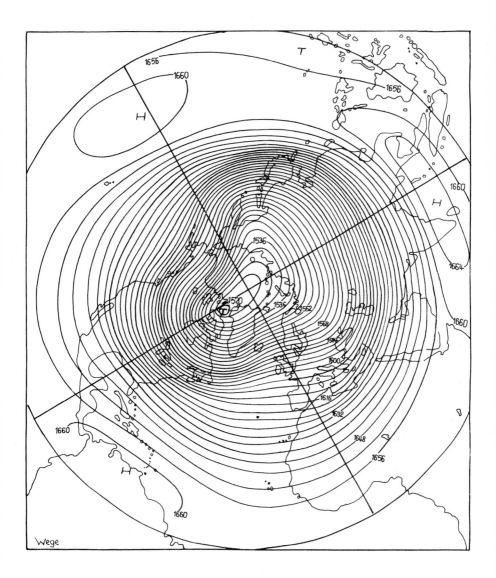

Fig. 9. 100 mb monthly mean map January 1949–1953 (Wege, 1957).

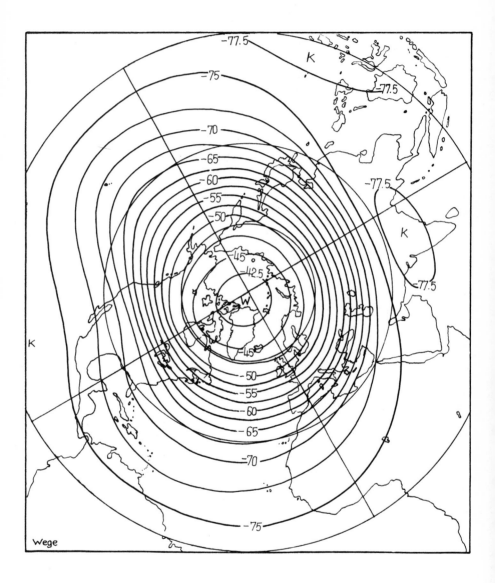

Fig. 10. 100 mb mean temperature distribution July 1949–1953 (Wege, 1957).

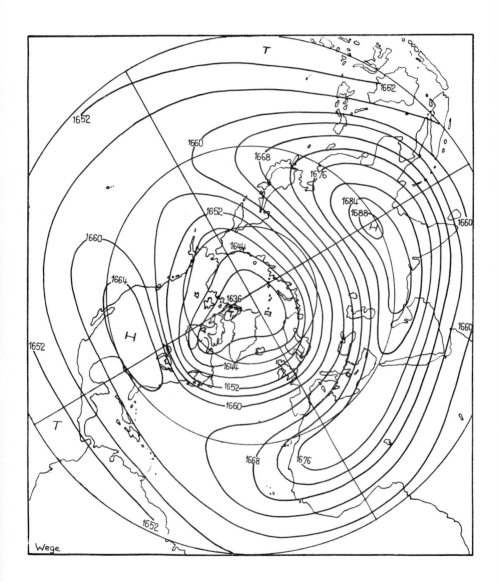

Fig. 11. 100 mb monthly mean map July 1949–1953 (Wege, 1957).

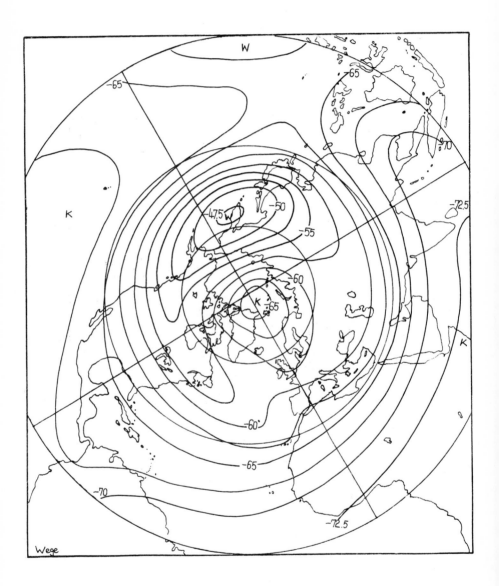

Fig. 12. 50 mb mean temperature distribution January 1949–1953 (Wege, 1957).

stant pressure level of January (fig. 13) shows a cold low centered near the pole and west winds at nearly all latitudes. Within the polar regime these west winds further increase with height accordingly to the poleward decrease of temperature.

In summer highest temperatures in the 50-mb level are found at the pole and show somewhat higher values than in the 100-mb level for the same month, as may be seen by the mean isotherms in 50 mb of July (fig. 14). The mean map of the 50-mb contour values of July (fig. 15), however, shows strikingly different conditions. In the polar region now the highest pressure values are found and the zonal westerlies are replaced at all latitudes by zonal easterlies.

To discuss the circulation at still higher levels one must bear in mind the vertical temperature distribution in the lower stratosphere. In the winter polar regime the temperature decreases upward and becomes very cold at about 30 km. Thus the cold low centered near the pole becomes more pronounced with increasing altitude and is surrounded by a band of strong west winds. This is shown by the 10-mb map of 1 January 1958 (fig. 16). In summer, however, the temperature increases with height and the zonal easterlies at 10 mb have considerable greater speed than at 50 mb, as may be seen by the 10-mb map of 16 July 1961 (fig. 17).

These stratospheric easterlies in summer are suprisingly constant in direction, seldom varying more than 10° or 20° from the east. It may generally be said that the summer circulation pattern of the middle stratosphere is very constant through the whole season and has, moreover, no considerable year-to-year variability. The 10-mb map of a single day, as shown here, therefore appears to represent mean conditions. During the winter and spring months, however, strong variations from year to year may occur which are essentially associated with the phenomenon known as stratospheric warming. This phenomenon varies so much in detail from one year to the next that it is not possible to reproduce a true picture of this circulation pattern by using normal charts or even monthly mean maps. In my next lecture I will discuss this problem of the disturbed circulation in the stratosphere in more detail.

Another remarkable year-to-year variation occurs in the tropical stratosphere making for this reason normal charts completely useless. Studies of the past years have revealed a completely unexpected variation of zonal wind direction in the tropical stratosphere with a period of about 26 months. The main features of this phenomenon, generally referred to as the equatorial stratospheric wind oscillation, are illustrated by a time-height cross section of zonal wind at Canton Island (3°S, 172°W) prepared by Reed et al. (1961), fig. 18. The principal features of the oscillation are:
1) The zonal wind component in the equatorial stratosphere varies between east and west with a period of about 26 months.
2) The phase of the oscillation is the same at all longitudes but varies with height, such that the easterly and westerly currents descend at a rate of about 1 km per month.
3) The amplitude is greatest at the equator and at about 25 km.

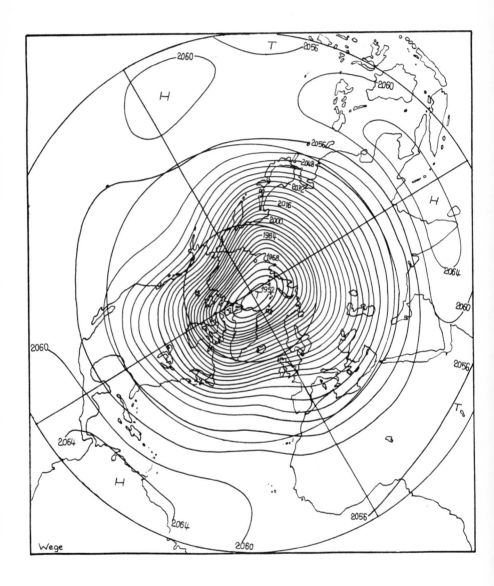

Fig. 13. 50 mb monthly mean map January 1949-1953 (Wege, 1957).

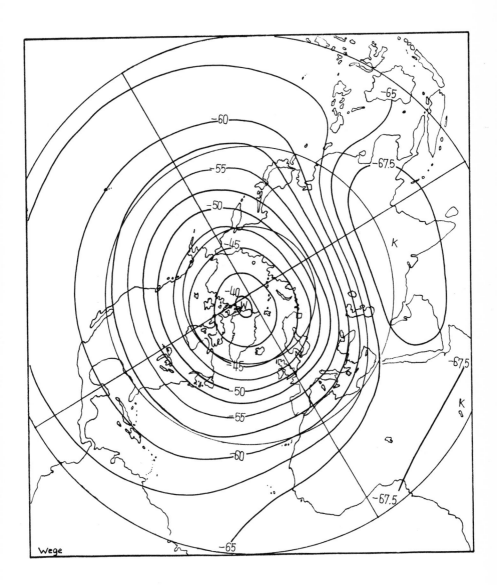

Fig. 14. 50 mb mean temperature distribution July 1949-1953 (Wege, 1957).

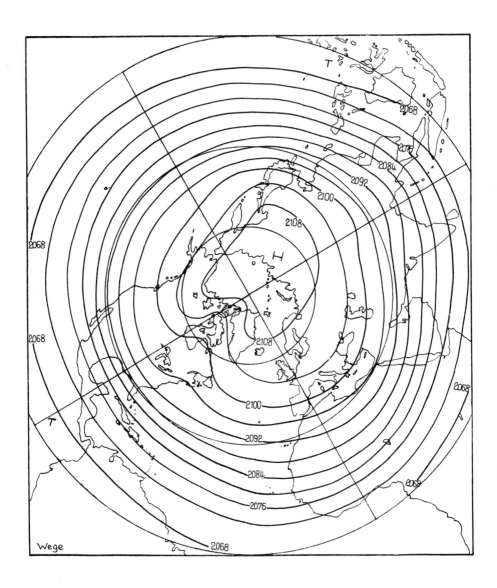

Fig. 15. 50 mb monthly mean map July 1949-1953 (Wege, 1957).

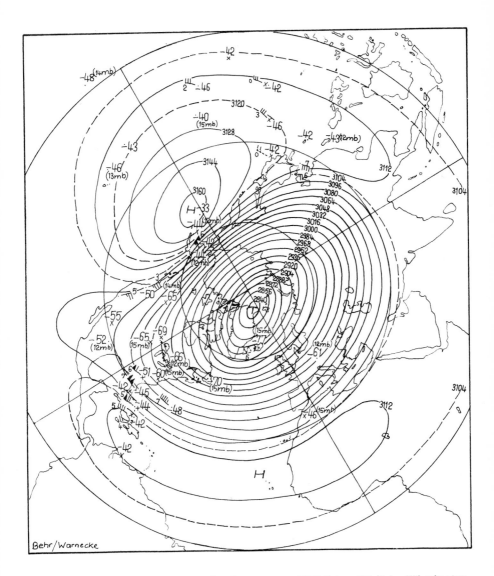

Fig. 16. 10 mb constant pressure level. 1 January 1958 (from: Tägliche Höhenkarten der 10-mb Fläche für das Internationale Geophysikalische Jahr 1958. 1960. Met. Abh.. XIII. (1)).

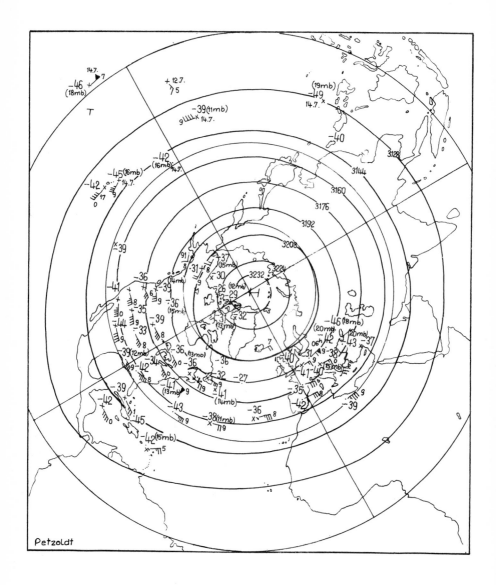

Fig. 17. 10 mb constant pressure level. 16 July 1961 (from: Preliminary Daily Northern Hemisphere 10-mb Synoptic Weather Maps of the Year 1961, 1961, Met. Abh.. XX (3)).

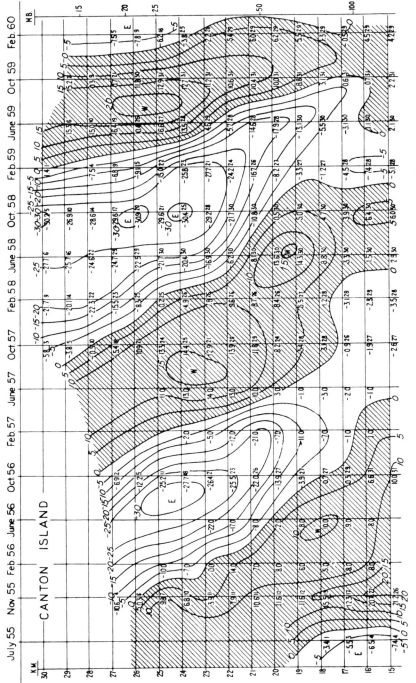

Fig. 18. Time-height cross section of the monthly mean zonal wind components at Canton Island (Reed et al., 1961).

4) The oscillation is nearly indistinguishable near the tropopause and only
   barely detectable at 30°N.*
5) An associated small temperature oscillation exists showing somewhat
   lower temperatures related with easterly winds and higher temperatures
   with westerly winds. This is shown by twelve-monthly running means of
   temperature and zonal wind component at 50 mb over Canton Island prepared by Ebdon (1961) (fig. 19).

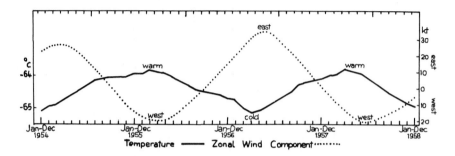

Fig. 19. 12-monthly running means of temperature and zonal wind components at
50 mb at Canton Island (Ebdon, 1961).

There is no satisfactory explanation for the occurrence of this oscillation
until now although there is no doubt that a fluctuation of about 2 years is apparent in many other elements at different sites of the earth and at different
times. There have been made some attempts to lead back the quasi-biennial
oscillation to variations in the solar activity but this, just as well as other
explanations, still remains to be proved.

3. FINAL REMARKS

Meteorologists have been concerned in the past years with many problems connected with the part of the atmosphere I called the lower atmosphere. The scientists who have contributed to studies higher up have been
mostly physicists, chemists, and aeronomers. Although there are always
many problems to solve in the lower atmosphere the research in the next
years must be concentrated to the upper atmosphere. This requires a
strong cooperation of all scientists concerned with atmospheric sciences

---

* The wind oscillation is most pronounced in the equatorial stratosphere but also detectable 30° North and South of the thermal equator. At these latitudes, however,
  there is found no sharp reversal from easterly to westerly winds or vice versa because of polewards increasing amplitude of the annual cycle. Angell and Korshover
  (1962) tried to pursue the wind oscillation into middle and polar latitudes and they
  found some indications of its existence but with a small amplitude only.

because we are all interested in the structure, circulation, and interaction of the atmosphere as a whole.

REFERENCES

Angell, J.K. and J.Korshover, 1962, The biennial wind and temperature oscillation of the equatorial stratosphere and their possible extension to higher latitudes, Monthly Weather Rev. 90, 4.

Asakura, T. and A.Katayama, 1964, On the normal distribution of heat sources and sinks in the lower troposphere over the Northern Hemisphere, J. Meteorol. Soc. Japan, Series II, 42, (4).

Craig, R.A., 1965, The upper atmosphere, Meteorology and Physics (New York).

Ebdon, R.A., 1961, Some notes on the stratospheric winds at Christmas Island and Canton Island, Quart. J. Roy. Meteorol. Soc. 87.

Goody, R.M. and G.D.Robinson, 1951, Radiation in the troposphere and lower stratosphere, Quart. J. Met. 77, 332.

Haltiner, G.J. and F.L.Martin, 1957, Dynamical and Physical Meteorology (New York).

Hare, F.K., 1965, Stratospheric dynamics north of 40°N, Quart.J.Met.91, 390.

Jacobs, I., 1958, 5- bzw. 40jährige Monatsmittel der absoluten Topographien der 1000-mb-, 850-mb-, 500-mb- und 300-mb-Flächen sowie der relativen Topographien 500/1000 mb und 300/500 mb über der Nordhemisphäre und ihre monatlichen Änderungen, Met. Abh., IV, (2).

Johnson, J.C., 1954, Physical Meteorology (Technology Press of the MIT).

Julian, P.R., L.Krawitz and H.A.Panofsky, 1959, The relation between height patterns at 500 mb and 1000 mb, Monthly Weather Rev. 87.

Julian, P.R., 1963, Some correlations of tropospheric and stratospheric pressures and temperatures in mid- and high latitudes, Symp. on Stratospheric and Mesospheric Circulation Berlin 1962, Met. Abh., XXXVI.

Landsberg, H.E., 1962, Biennial pulses in the atmosphere, Beiträge zur Physik der Atmosphäre, 35, (3/4).

Murgatroyd, R.J., 1965, Tracers and transfer problems in the lower stratosphere, Quart. J. Met. 91, 390.

Palmen, E., 1951, The role of atmospheric disturbances in the general circulation, Quart. J.Met. 77, 333.

Reed, R.J., W.J.Campbell, R.A.Rasmussen and D.G.Rogers, 1961, Evidence of a downward-propagating, annual wind reversal in the equatorial stratosphere, J. Geophys. Res. 66, (3).

Reed, R.J., 1963, On the cause of the 26-months periodicity in the equatorial stratospheric winds, Symp. on Stratospheric and Mesospheric Circulation Berlin 1962, Met. Abh., XXXVI.

Sawyer, J.S., 1965, The dynamical problems of the lower stratosphere. Quart. J. Met. 91, 390.

Veryard, R.G. and R.A.Ebdon, 1963, The 26-month tropical stratospheric wind oscillation and possible causes. Symp. on Stratospheric and Mesospheric Circulation Berlin 1962. Met. Abh. XXXVI.

Wege, K., 1957, Druck-, Temperatur- and Strömungsverhältnisse in der Stratosphäre über der Nordhalbkugel, Met. Abh. V, (4).

Williams, G.P. and D.R.Davies, 1965, A mean motion model of the general circulation, Quart. J. Met. 91, 390.

DISCUSSION

Dieminger:

1. The principal difference between the summer pole and the winter pole, as far as the temperature of the mesosphere is concerned, is that over the summer pole the temperature decreases from 290° at 50 km to 170° at 80 km whereas over the winter pole the temperature increases from 230° at 60 km to 270° at 80 km indicating less stable conditions over the winter pole.

2. This discussion brings us back to the basic question whether the control comes from above (solar) or from below (meteorological). The principal difficulty in assuming external control is that the energy of solar events is negligible compared with the energy involved in the "heat engine" of the lower atmosphere. Only a triggering from external events seems possible.

STRATOSPHERIC WARMINGS

Barbara KRIESTER
Free University, Berlin

Abstract. The different types of stratospheric warmings will be classified with respect to their main characteristics. A survey will be given over the stratospheric warmings which occurred since the first one was described in 1952. Connections to the tropospheric behavior and to the 26-month cycle in the stratospheric winds over the tropics will be discussed and finally some theories about causes will be considered.

Résumé. On entrepend une classification des différents types d'échauffements stratosphériques suivant leurs caractéristiques principales. On résume les différents événements d'échauffement stratosphérique depuis la première description en 1952. Les liasons avec le comportement troposphérique ainsi qu'avec le cycle de 26 mois des vents stratosphériques tropicaux sont discutées. Enfin quelques théories concernant les causes éventuelles sont considérées.

1. INTRODUCTION

Since the first explosive stratospheric warming was observed over Berlin in 1952, referred to as the "Berliner phenomenon" by Scherhag (1952), an increase of high level obversational data gave the possibility to investigate the disturbed pattern of the stratospheric circulation and the associated tropospheric behavior over the entire northern hemisphere. In the southern hemisphere the same phenomenon occurs, as was shown in some recent studies by several authors, but is not as well known as in the northern hemisphere due to the lack of data.

As was pointed out in my lecture yesterday the wintertime circulation of the lower stratosphere is dominated by a cold low centered near the pole, which becomes more pronounced with increasing altitude and is surrounded by a band of strong westerly winds. In the summer stratosphere, on the other hand, a warm high center is found over the pole with very constant easterly winds in all latitudes. The temperature differences between summer and winter may exceed 50°C at the 10-mb level in the polar region. As might be expected from the vast difference between the mean patterns for summer and winter, there is also a vast difference between the disturbances of summer and winter. In summer only small-scale, small-amplitude fluctuations of the stratospheric easterlies and temperatures occur, whereas in the winter circulation of the stratosphere intense changes in the thermal and wind patterns may arise which alter drastically the monthly mean patterns from the winter picture presented up to now. In addition, an extreme year-

to-year variability occurs during the months of winter and spring while the
months of summer and autumn have considerably less year-to-year variations. This year-to-year variability of the stratospheric circulation in winter and spring is essentially associated with the stratospheric warmings.

2. STRATOSPHERIC WARMINGS

2.1. *Classification of the different types of stratospheric warmings*

Daily stratospheric charts analyzed for levels up to 10 mb since 1957
have shown that the wintertime and springtime circulation patterns vary in
a complex manner. It is therefore necessary to distinguish between different types of stratospheric warmings. They may be classified into two general categories: midwinter warmings and final warmings. This is in accordance with the classification recommended for stratospheric warming
alerts during the International Quiet Sun Year (IQSY).

The midwinter warmings, moreover, may be divided with respect to
their intensity and extension to large areas of the northern hemisphere into major and minor warmings. Major midwinter warmings at their beginning are associated with a contour pattern change from an intense circumpolar vortex to a pattern of bipolar troughs and associated anticyclones.
Temperature starts to increase usually at the highest level observed near
the boundary of the polar regime in the jet stream along the eastern side of
one or both of the bipolar troughs which extend into middle latitudes. The
warming once established intensifies rapidly and temperatures may reach
$0^{\circ}C$ at the 10-mb level. The region of high temperatures spreads north-
wards, finally reaching the polar region and at the same time penetrates
downward to lower levels. At this stage the bipolar troughs are cut off into
separate cold lows, one or both of which weaken rapidly as they move to
lower latitudes. Over the polar region an anticyclone is established and
easterly winds are found at middle and high latitudes. A complete breakdown of the polar regime is attained. The circulation pattern over the polar
region now shows summer conditions but mostly higher temperatures, as
observed in summer. This circulation reversal ends with cooling of the polar region and a weak cyclonic flow is restored at high latitudes.

Minor midwinter warmings may be associated with several types of circulation patterns. The warmest air is generally associated with an anticyclone but the polar vortex, although sometimes splitted, remains the dominant circulation feature, often displaced, however, from the polar region.

The time of occurrence of these midwinter warmings extends from December through February whereas the final warmings and the accompanying
circulation reversal to summer conditions occur from March through early
May which generally depends on the winter conditions of the same year. This
leads to a classification into late and early final warmings. Late final
warmings occur if the restored polar vortex remains a dominant feature until at least the middle of April. Temperatures then gradually rise and the
polar cyclone slowly weakens until it is replaced by a developing anticyclone.
Temperatures then have reached summertime values.

Early final warmings usually start in the Pacific area. The Aleutian high moves poleward across North America with temperatures exceeding summertime values and reaches the pole in late March or early April, while the polar vortex weakens and moves southward over Asia.

This classification of the stratospheric warmings, however, does not bring out all characteristics of the phenomenon, as may be seen in our further discussion.

2.2. *A survey of the stratospheric warmings observed since* 1951

Since the occurrence of extreme high temperatures in the wintertime stratosphere - first described in 1952 - special attention was paid to this phenomenon by many scientists. For those early years, however, the knowledge of the stratospheric events was considerably limited due to the scarcity of data. It must be pointed out again that the warming starts at the highest levels in the stratosphere and therefore an early recognition of stratospheric warmings depends on the availability of data on a hemispheric scale from very high levels. Radiosonde ascents of the early fifties, however, seldom reached high levels such as the 10-mb level, and the radiosonde stations were restricted to the American and European area of the northern hemisphere. Thus, stratospheric warmings were mostly detected with the aid of measurements of some single stations and could be fuller described only if they occurred over the American area where the radiosonde network was as homogeneous as it is today.

In this way, Scrase (1953) was able to give a hint to a stratospheric warming in 1951 by radiosonde observations over the British Isle. From 5 to 20 February temperatures were observed to be 20^{0} higher than during the remaining part of the winter and easterly winds were established.

In 1952 at least two stratospheric warmings seem to have occurred. The first "Berliner phenomenon" was observed in January when the temperature over Berlin increased to $-23^{0}C$ at the 10-mb level on 30 January. During this warming, however, the stratospheric southwesterlies over Berlin were not influenced and we may be correct to call this nowadays a minor midwinter warming with respect to its extension. In the same year a major midwinter warming occurred in the middle of February, reported by several stations in the western part of the northern hemisphere. This warming led to the breakdown of the polar regime, the polar vortex was split into a Pacific and an Asiatic center and over most of the polar region an anticyclone was established. This may be seen by the map of the 41-mb constant pressure level of 21 February, prepared by Warnecke (1956) (fig. 1). The stratospheric warmings of 1952, ofter referred to as the "Thule phenomenon" and the "Second Berliner phenomenon", seem to be part of this major midwinter warming. The great intensity of this warming is derivable from the radiosonde measurement over Berlin of 23 February: temperature increased to $-12^{0}C$ at the 10-mb level.

In 1953 a minor midwinter warming seems to have occurred over America as observed over Belmar, N.J., but no significant major warming was detectable in this year. Sufficient data from Siberia during this winter are not available to determine the feature of the entire northern hemisphere.

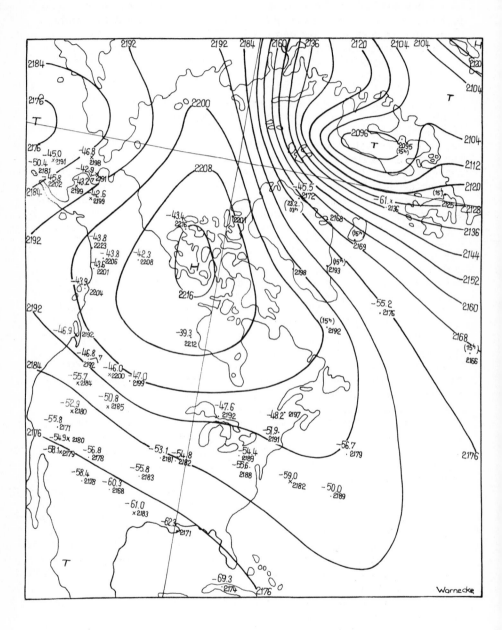

Fig. 1. 41 mb constant pressure level, 21 February 1952 (Warnecke, 1956).

In 1954 one minor midwinter warming was observed over Europe in January. At the beginning of March the temperature rose steadily over the Canadian Arctic until the end of the month. There are some indications of an eastward progression of the warming and the associated anticyclone, finally reaching Europe in the middle of March.

During January 1955 a very early major midwinter warming seems to have occurred, first observed on 1 January over the Canadian Arctic, which led to a closed high over this area. There are only little indications, such as an increasing of temperature over Tromsø in late January, that a complete breakdown of the polar vortex was perhaps attained. The absence of data over the USSR makes it impossible to be certain of this fact. The true return to summerlike conditions, however, may be assumed to have occurred in the middle of February.

For the year 1956 two minor warmings were reported over Europe in January and March and one over the Canadian Arctic in the middle of March. The polar vortex, however, remained over the western European area until the end of April which indicated an extreme late final warming.

In 1957 a remarkable strong midwinter warming occurred which was described in detail by several authors to which I will refer to now. Teweles (1958), Craig and Hering (1959), and Lowenthal (1957) gave studies of this case which could be well pursued because of its initiation in middle latitudes over North America with its excellent radiosonde stations and because of the exceptional magnitude of this warming. It was first observed on 24 January, when large 25-mb temperature rises were reported from the southeastern of Canada but it could be pointed out later that in higher levels the warming had started at least five days earlier. The warm center was situated within the jet stream at the east side of a trough extending into midlatitudes over America. It moved slowly northeastward, intensified, and gradually penetrated to lower levels. On 5 February the radiosonde station in Fort Churchill reported -3°C at the 10-mb level. Extensive changes had taken place throughout the stratosphere. With the formation of a closed high over the Atlantic Ocean and a weakening and southwestward displacement of the Canadian low center the circulation had changed considerably. Teweles (1958) has pointed out that a simultaneous warming occurred in the southeastern part of the trough located over Siberia. In this year the polar vortex was not re-established and an early final warming took place.

1958 was the first year within the International Geophysical Year (IGY) and therefore upper-air data from the USSR were available. It was now possible to superintend the disturbances of the stratospheric circulation on a hemispheric scale. Moreover, since July 1957 the Stratospheric Research Group of the Free University Berlin has analyzed and published daily synoptic maps of the stratospheric mandatory levels up to 10 mb and by means of these maps it was possible to investigate the stratospheric circulation during all winters until today. The following survey will be given by the aid of 10-mb constant pressure maps constructed by this group.

The remarkable strong stratospheric warming of January and February 1958 was studied in detail by Scherhag (1960), Teweles and Finger (1958). Let us look now at a serie of 10-mb maps to determine the development of the disturbed circulation pattern of this winter.

On 24 January (fig. 2) we see the polar vortex beginning to split into two separate cold centers. The Aleutian anticyclone is well developed as usual in this time but an extreme high center is found over Asia Minor associated with a warm center within the strong stratospheric southwesterlies. This anticyclone moved in a northwesterly direction reaching western Europe on 28 January (fig. 3). The polar vortex is now cut into a Canadian and a Siberian cyclone and a high pressure ridge extends across the pole to the Pacific area now including the Aleutian high. On 30 January (fig. 4) the warming has moved further towards the west, high temperatures are now found over the coast of North America and the associated anticyclone covers the entire northern Atlantic. The Canadian cold low has considerably weakened and filled up in the following days while moving to the Pacific Ocean. The Siberian low, however, was cut off again as may be seen on 4 February (fig. 5). The first anticyclone was now a dominant feature of the stratospheric circulation over the American continent while a second warming occurred over southeastern Europe. The warmest temperatures were found again within the jet stream at the east side of the trough. This warm center moved perpendicular to the streamlines toward the north and on 11 February (fig. 6) the circulation was dominated by warm anticyclonic centers over the largest part of the high latitudes. A few days later these high centers began to weaken and a small polar vortex was restored as may be seen by the 10-mb map of 3 March (fig. 7). This polar low center remained a dominant feature until at least the early part of May when an extreme late final warming occurred.

In 1959 some minor midwinter warmings occurred during January and February which all showed a net eastward movement. The most remarkable warming was found in late January over the European area causing a closed anticyclonic flow. The polar vortex, however, was not influenced in any way by those warmings. An early final warming started on 1 March with the Aleutian high migrating eastward and establishing summer conditions in late March.

The strange behavior of the winter 1959/60 was fully described by Labitzke (1962). In the middle of December a warming over the Canadian Arctic occurred due to the eastward shifting of the Aleutian high and the polar vortex was moved to the Europian Arctic. This may be seen by the variations of the contour values of the 10-mb level from 16 to 23 December (fig. 8). This well pronounced Aleutian high remained a dominant feature of the stratospheric circulation until late January and was responsible for the split of the polar vortex. This feature may be seen from the constant pressure maps of the 10-mb and 5-mb level of 8 January (figs. 9 and 10). Over Europe some minor warmings were observed during January through March which were associated with a high center moving from east to west, crossing Europe at least three times. The path of this anticyclone may be seen by fig. 11 prepared by Labitzke. During this period of the westward mi-

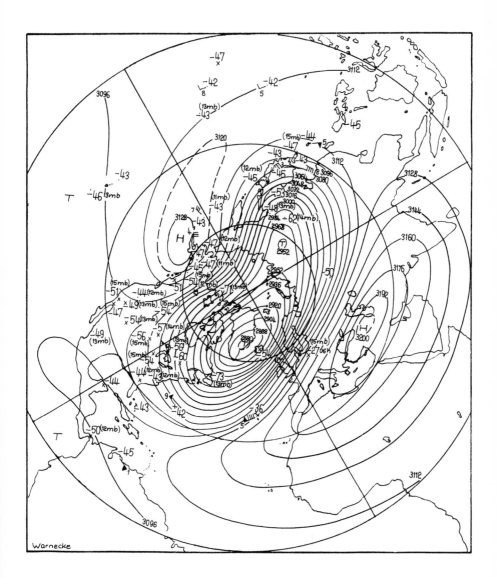

Fig. 2. 10 mb constant pressure level, 24 January 1958 (from: Tägliche Höhenkarten
der 10-mb Fläche für das Internationale Geophysikalische Jahr 1958, 1960, Meteorologische Abhandlungen des Instituts für Meteorologie und Geophysik Berlin. XIII (1)).

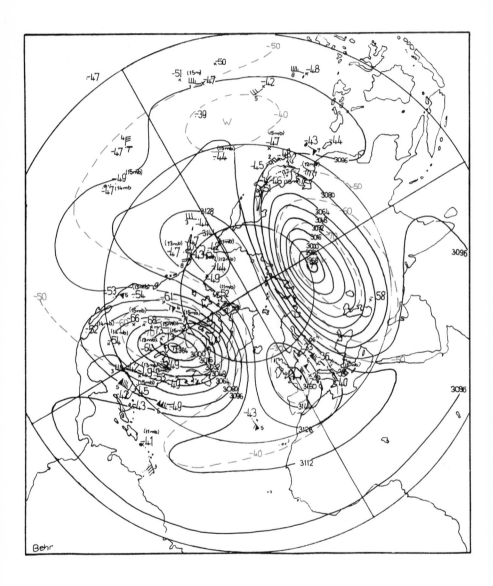

Fig. 3. 10 mb constant pressure level, 28 January 1958 (dashed lines are isotherms)
(Labitzke, 1962).

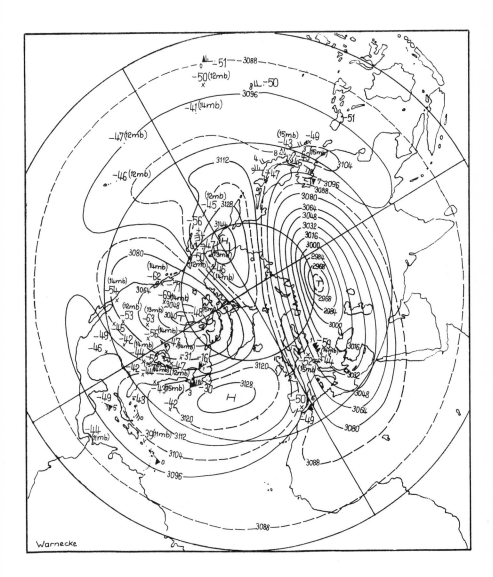

Fig. 4. 10 mb constant pressure level. 30 January 1958 (from: Tägliche Höhenkarten
der 10-mb Fläche für das Internationale Geophysikalische Jahr 1958. 1960. Meteorologische Abhandlungen des Instituts für Meteorologie und Geophysik Berlin. XIII (1)).

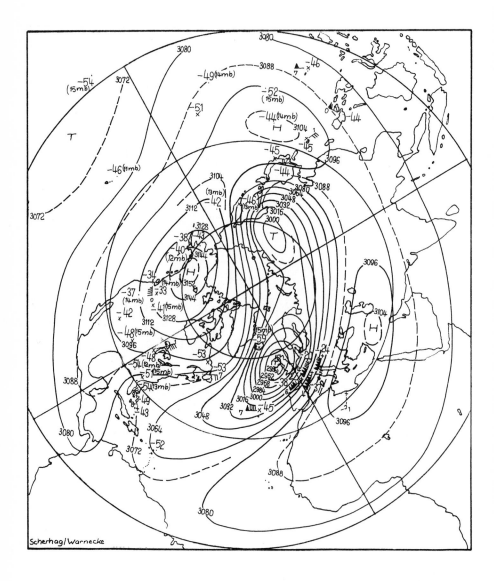

Fig. 5. 10 mb constant pressure level, 4 February 1958 (from: Tägliche Höhenkarten der 10-mb Fläche für das Internationale Geophysikalische Jahr 1958, 1960. Meteorologische Abhandlungen des Instituts für Meteorologie und Geophysik Berlin. XIII (1)).

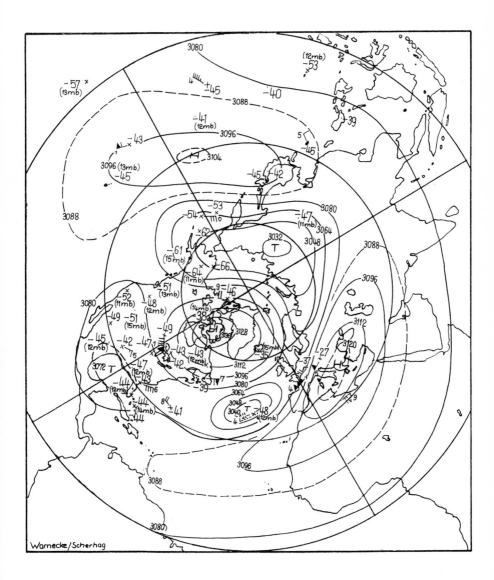

Fig. 6. 10 mb constant pressure level, 11 February 1958 (from: Tägliche Höhenkarten der 10-mb Fläche für das Internationale Geophysikalische Jahr 1958, 1960, Meteorologische Abhandlungen des Instituts für Meteorologie und Geophysik Berlin, XIII (1)).

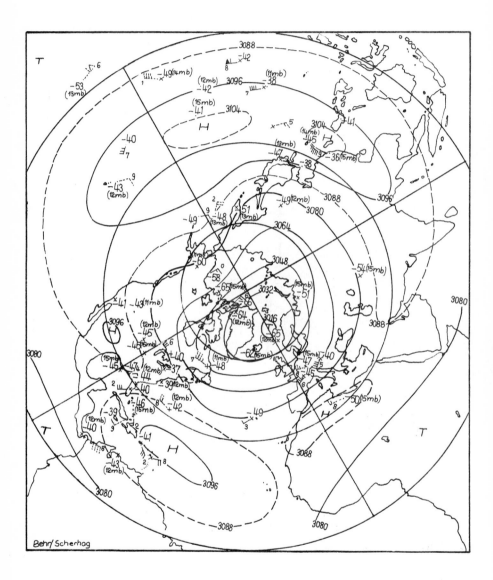

Fig. 7. 10 mb constant pressure level, 3 March 1958 (from: Tägliche Höhenkarten
der 10-mb Fläche für das Internationale Geophysikalische Jahr 1958, 1960. Meteorologische Abhandlungen des Instituts für Meteorologie und Geophysik Berlin. XIII (1)).

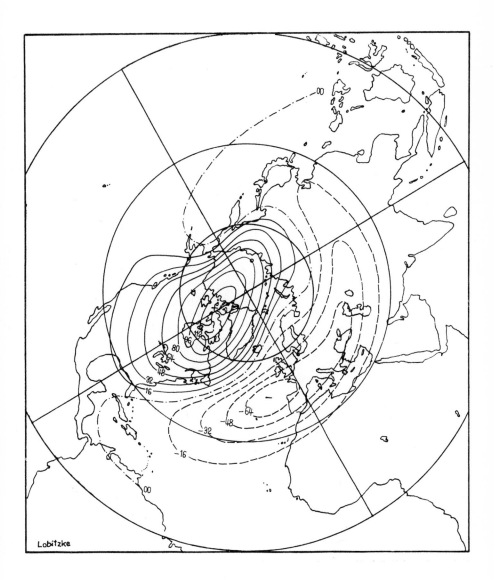

Fig. 8. Variation of the 10 mb contour values, 16 to 23 December 1959 (Labitzke, 1962).

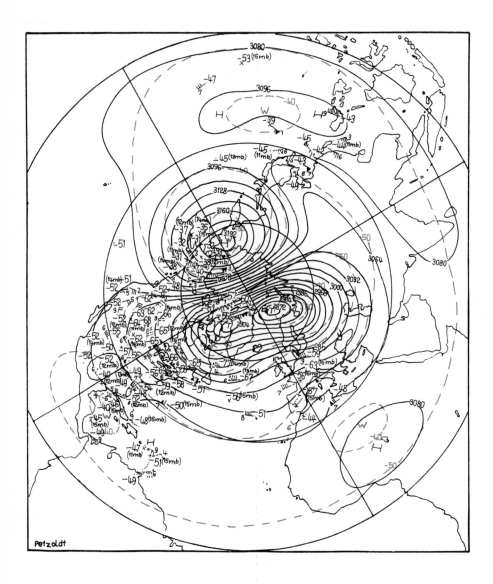

Fig. 9. 10 mb constant pressure level, 8 January 1960 (dashed lines are isotherms) (Labitzke, 1962).

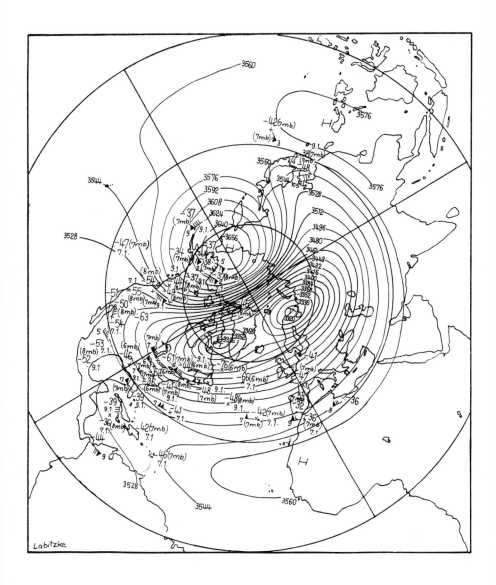

Fig. 10. 5 mb constant pressure level, 8 January 1960 (Labitzke, 1962).

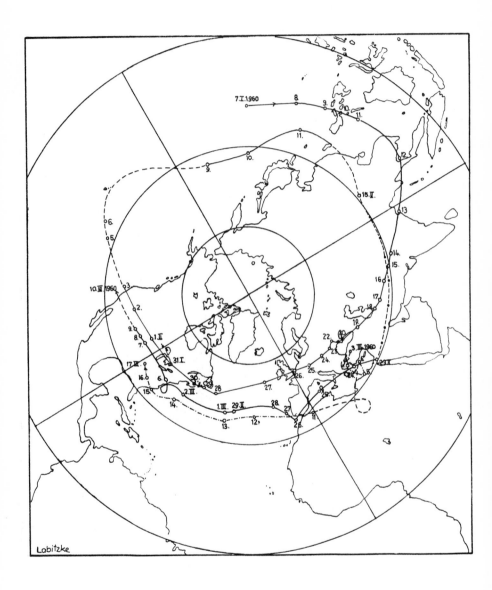

Fig. 11. Path of the 10 mb highs from 7 January to 17 March 1960 (Labitzke. 1962).

grating anticyclone at the boundary of the polar regime the Aleutian high was not strongly marked but initiated a late final warming during April.

In the winter 1960/61 at least two minor midwinter warmings were observed which originated in the strong southwesterlies at the east side of the trough extending to the midlatitudes of America. The associated anticyclones showed a movement from west to east, the first reaching Europe in late December, the second in late January, as may be seen by the 10-mb constant pressure map of 29 January (fig. 12). The final warming of this year occurred very early in the middle of March, caused by the intensification and extension of the Aleutian anticyclone to polar regions.

In 1962 several significant warmings occurred over the Aleutians and over the eastern European areas, but the polar vortex remained the dominant feature of the stratospheric circulation as may be seen by the 10-mb map of 17 February (fig. 13). During early March the polar vortex was cut into two cold lows over the Canadian and Siberian Arctic but no complete breakdown was attained. At the end of March a well pronounced polar vortex governed the stratospheric circulation and a late final warming occurred in this year.

A considerably strong stratospheric warming occurred in 1963 compared with the years before, which is well known through publications by Scherhag (1963) and Finger and Teweles (1964). During the first two weeks of January the circulation pattern of the 10-mb level was dominated by a very cold circumpolar vortex as may be seen by the 10-mb map of 12 January (fig. 14). The first hint to a stratospheric warming appeared at mid-January as this pattern was changed to a nearly bipolar circulation system. A few days later an intense warm center arose at the east side of the trough extending to America as is apparent by looking at the 10-mb map of 20 January (fig. 15). This warm area moved towards the north - perpendicular to the streamlines - and intensified rapidly to about 0°C on 25 January over the Canadian Arctic. At the same time another warm center initially located at the east side of the Siberian trough has intensified and has moved towards the north, joining the Atlantic warm center on 26 January, as may be seen by the 10-mb map of this day (fig. 16). The polar vortex was split already some days before and the associated anticyclones had strengthened considerably. The low centers further filled up while moving to the south and at 29 January (fig. 17) no closed cyclonic flow was detectable over the polar region. This date may be considered to be the culminating point of the circulation changes because in the following days weak cyclonic flow was re-established over the polar region while temperatures began to decrease, although the thermal pattern of high latitudes still showed summertime conditions as may be seen by the 10-mb map of 1 February (fig. 18). Continuous cooling of the polar regions, however, caused further decreasing of the contour values. In the 10-mb map of 9 February (fig. 19) it is well to be seen that the cold low situated over the north European area has strengthened while the anticyclones have weakened, one of which has moved to northwest Canada and remained there the dominant feature of the circulation until late February. A restored vortex, however, was found during the entire month of March over the polar region and a late final warming took place on about 10 April.

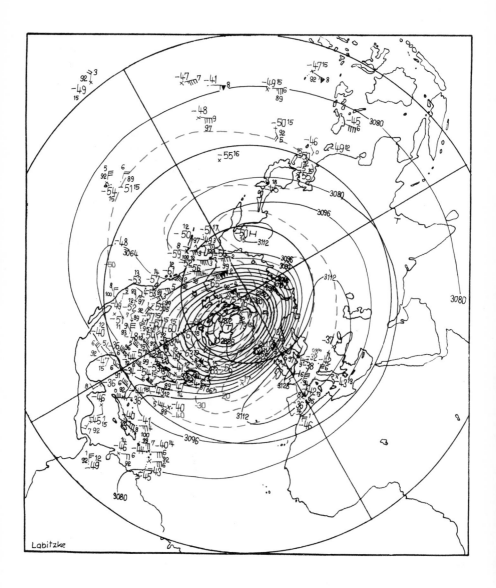

Fig. 12. 10 mb constant pressure level, 29 January 1961 (dashed lines are isotherms)
(Labitzke, 1962).

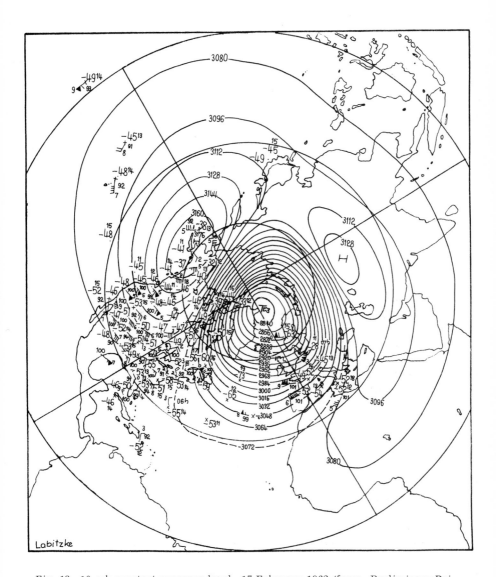

Fig. 13. 10 mb constant pressure level, 17 February 1962 (from: Preliminary Dai-
ley Northern Hemisphere 10-mb Synoptic Weather Maps of the Year 1962, 1962, Meteorologische Abhandlungen des Instituts für Meteorologie und Geophysik Berlin,
XXVI (1)).

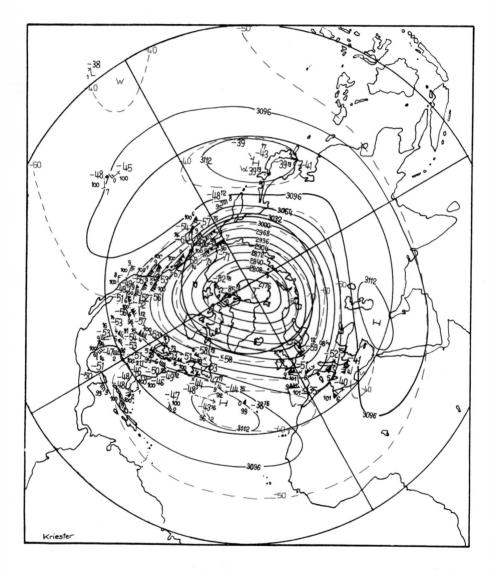

Fig. 14. 10-mb constant pressure level, 12 January 1963 (dashed lines are isotherms)
(from: Daily and Monthly Northern Hemisphere 10-mb Synoptic Weather Maps of the
year 1963, 1963, Meteorologische Abhandlungen des Instituts für Meteorologie und
Geophysiek Berlin) XL, (1).

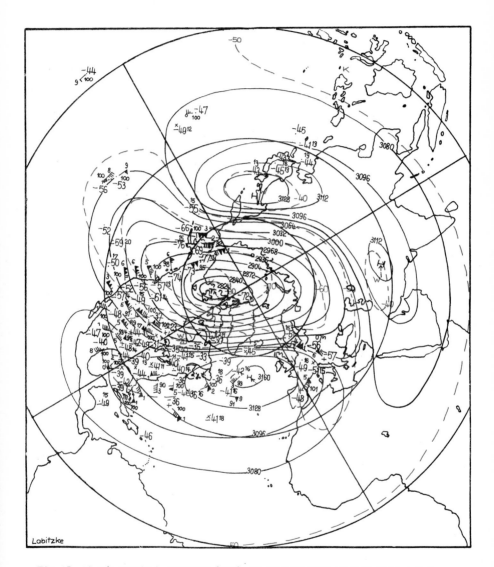

Fig. 15. 10-mb constant pressure level, 20 January 1963 (dashed lines are isotherms) (from: Daily and Monthly Northern Hemisphere 10-mb Synoptic Weather
Maps of the Year 1963, 1963, Meteorologische Abhandlungen des Instituts für Meteorologie und Geophysik Berlin) XL, (1).

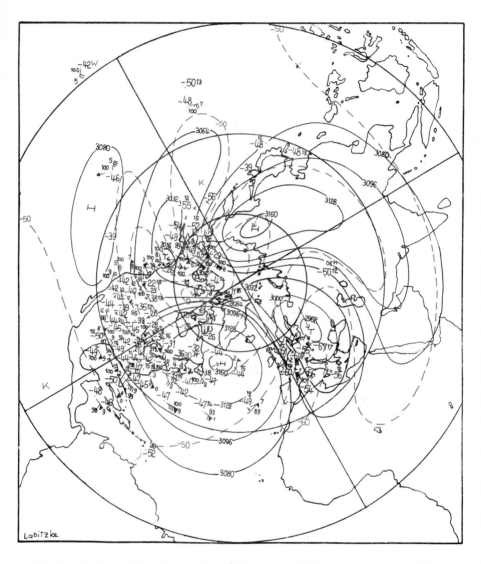

Fig. 16. 10-mb constant pressure level, 26 January 1963 (dashed lines are isotherms) (from: Daily and Monthly Northern Hemisphere 10-mb Synoptic Weather
Maps of the Year 1963, 1963, Meteorologische Abhandlungen des Instituts für Meteorologie und Geophysik Berlin) XL. (1).

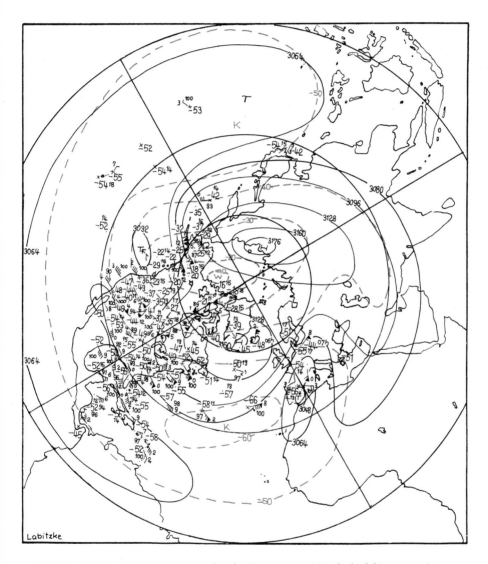

Fig. 17. 10-mb constant pressure level, 29 January 1963 (dashed lines are isotherms) (from: Daily and Monthly Northern Hemisphere 10-mb Synoptic Wheater
Maps of the Year 1963, 1963, Meteorologische Abhandlungen des Instituts für Meteorologie und Geophysik Berlin) XL, (1).

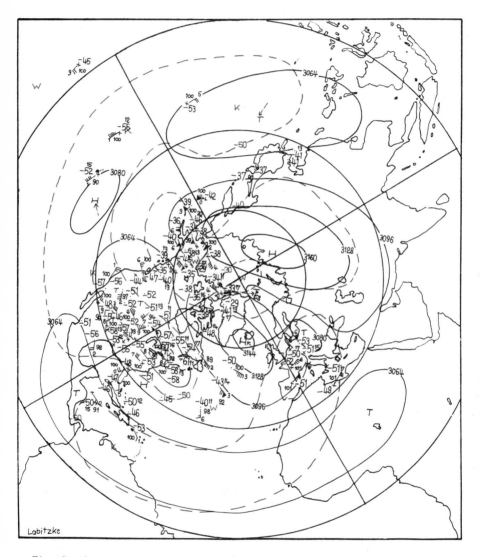

Fig. 18. 10-mb constant pressure level, 1 February 1963 (dashed lines are isotherms) (from: Daily and Monthly Northern Hemisphere 10-mb Synoptic Weather
Maps of the Year 1963, 1963, Meteorologische Abhandlungen des Instituts für Meteorologie und Geophysik Berlin) XL, (1).

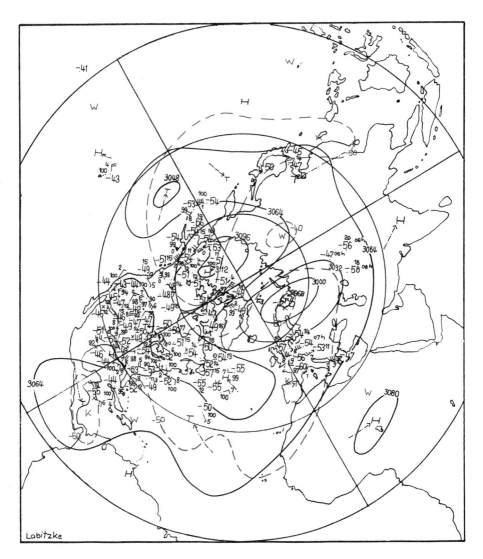

Fig. 19. 10-mb constant pressure level, 9 February 1963 (dashed lines are isotherms) (from: Daily and Monthly Northern Hemisphere 10-mb Synoptic Weather
Maps of the Year 1963, 1963, Meteorologische Abhandlungen des Instituts für Meteorologie und Geophysik Berlin) XL, (1).

In 1964 some minor midwinter warmings occurred over the Aleutian and southeast European area which did not affect the unusually strong developed polar vortex of this year. The Aleutian high was well pronounced during the middle of January showing temperatures increasing up to -25ºC. In late January a warming was observed over central Europe which is shown by the 10-mb isotherms drawn for 31 January (fig. 20). This date seems to be worth mentioning since the Berlin radiosonde station reported a temperature of +1ºC at 3.8 mb (fig. 21) which indicated that at higher levels the warming was more pronounced than in the 10-mb level. The polar vortex, however, remained the dominant feature of the stratospheric circulation until at least early May, when temperature increase arose over the Aleutian region and simultaneously over northern Europe. This led in a short time to the breakdown of the polar regime and the circulation pattern reached summertime conditions in late March.

In 1965 again only some minor midwinter warmings occurred at the boundary of the polar regime. The final warming, however, took place in a very striking manner. It started on about 7 March over the Eurasian continent, then moved to the east. The Aleutian high at this time was only weakly developed but very high pressure was found over the eastern part of the northern hemisphere. The temperature distribution at this early stage may be seen by the 10-mb isotherms of 11 March (fig. 22). During the eastward progression of the warming the polar vortex stayed mainly over the northern European area but was transferred to Canada in the late part of March while the warm air reached the pole. The true reversal to summertime conditions was attained at the end of April.

In this year, however, a completely different circulation pattern was established from those observed in the past years. The polar vortex remained undisturbed while some minor warmings occurred at the boundary of the polar regime. On 30 January, however, the evolution of the breakdown of the polar vortex was introduced by intensification of a warm center situated at the west side of the Aleutian anticyclone. This warm center moved towards the west and the eastern part of the northern hemisphere showed unusually high temperatures during early February while the polar vortex was transferred to the Canadian Arctic. The Aleutian high, even somewhat displaced to the west, was considerably strengthened and started to move towards the pole while the polar vortex moved back to the European Arctic and was split on 23 February. On 26 February, the Aleutian anticyclone reached the pole and the breakdown of the polar regime was attained. The two cold lows were now situated over Central Asia and eastern Canada, the latter being yet strong developed, whereas the Asiatic low filled up. There seemed to have occurred an extremely early final warming. The striking feature of the circulation of this year, however, was the re-establishment of a circumpolar cyclone which stayed over the polar region until early March. Thus, an extremely late final warming took place.

After having studied the different behavior of all stratospheric warmings from the winter 1956/57 until today, a very interesting feature of the stratospheric circulation became obvious. A similar behavior pattern of the

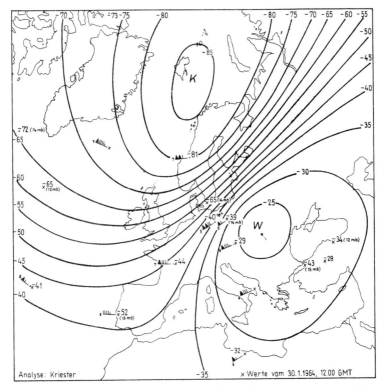

Fig. 20. 10 mb temperature distribution, 31 January 1964 (Mädlow, 1964).

stratospheric midwinter warmings in alternate years with respect to the
origin of the initial warming and the direction of movement of the associated systems was pointed out by Labitzke (1966), who proposed to divide the
midwinter warmings into two types: American and European. Every second
year, the midwinter warmings begin in the stratosphere above the eastern
United States and Canada, whereas in the alternate years the warmings
originate over central and eastern Europe. The movement of the associated
anticyclones at the 10-mb level during periods of midwinter warmings is
shown by fig. 23. In the four years, 1957, 1959, 1961 and 1963 the warmings
originated over the American region and showed a net eastward movement,
but the two major warmings of 1957 and 1963 later spread northward causing a breakdown of the stratospheric polar vortex. In the intervening years
the initial warmings took place over the European-Asiatic region with the
associated highs moving retrogradely. This was well pronounced in the
years 1958 and 1960, but in 1962 and 1964 only a part of the warmings
reached Europe, since the associated anticyclones stayed over Russia and
Asia Minor. The last years, however, brought some confusion to this concept which may be due to the fact that the two year cycle in the behavior
of the midwinter warmings came out of phase with respect to the 26-month

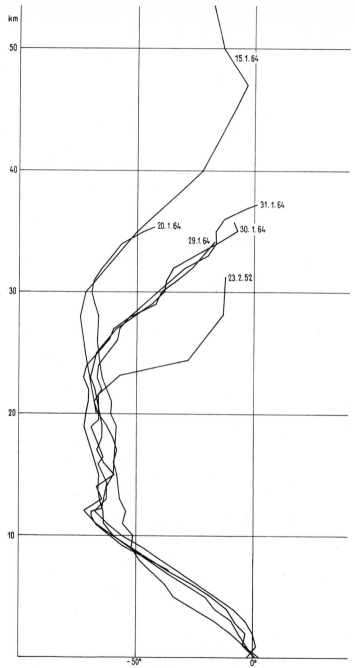

Fig. 21. Radiosonde measurements at Berlin and one rocket measurement at Loch
Boisdale, Scottland at the indicated dates (Madlow, 1964).

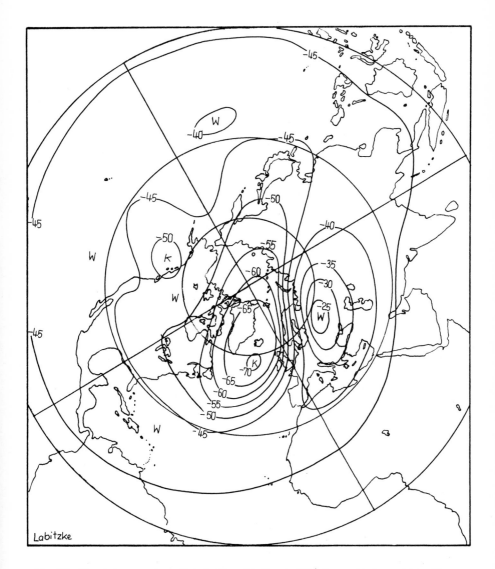

Fig. 22. 10 mb temperature distribution, 11 March 1965 (from: Daily and Monthly Northern Hemisphere 10-mb Synoptic Weather Maps of the Year 1965, 1965. Meteorologische Abhandlungen des Instituts für Meteorologie und Geophysik Berlin. LVIII (1)).

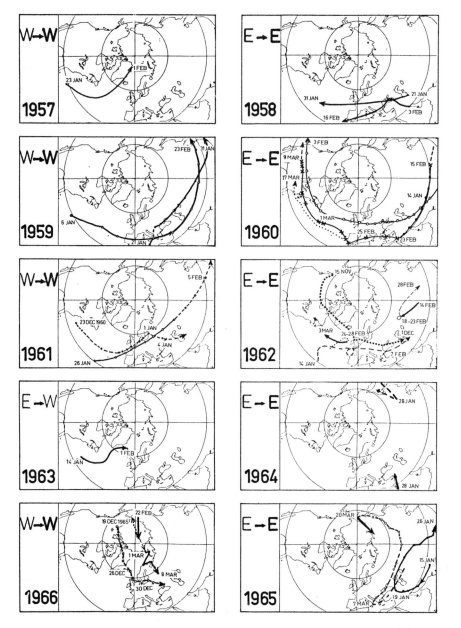

Fig. 23. Movements of the highs at the 10 mb level during periods of midwinter warmings (Labitzke, 1966).

cycle of the winds in the tropical stratosphere. This is another interesting
fact which was pointed out by Labitzke (1966) as a first synoptic evidence of
the existence of the 26-month cycle in higher latitudes. The American type
of warmings with anticyclones moving eastward seems to take place when
the wind oscillation in the tropics tends to westerlies in the middle and
higher stratosphere whereas the European type occurs when the tendency of
the oscillation is to easterlies. This is shown in fig. 23 by the letter which
indicate the phase within the 26-month oscillation between January and
March over Canton Island at the 10-mb level (heavy letters indicate wind
maxima). However, because the period of the wind oscillation is longer
than two years it must be expected that the cycle of the stratospheric warmings gets out of phase if there is any real connection.

It is a most interesting feature that the evolution of the final warmings
likewise showed such a two year periodicity. This may be seen by the
10-mb mean maps of March prepared by the Stratospheric Research Group
of the Free University Berlin (figs. 24-26). In March 1958 the circulation
of the stratosphere was still governed by a circumpolar vortex which indicates a late transition to the summer circulation. The next year, however,
showed a completely different pattern with a well developed anticyclone
over the western hemisphere and the polar vortex displaced to Siberia, thus
indicating an early final warming. The following years also showed this alternative behavior. There was, however, a break in the two year cycle in
March 1963 as the circulation was still governed by the polar vortex. In
1966 another break occurred and the 10-mb mean map of March again shows
a circumpolar vortex.

Looking for an explanation of this almost two year cycle Labitzke (1966)
again tried to link the type of final warmings with the stratospheric wind
regime in the tropics.

In table 1, prepared by Labitzke, the direction of the winds at the 20-mb
level over Canton Island for January and the following April is plotted, thus
indicating the phase within the 26-month oscillation. There are also included the early years; the classification remains a little doubtful, however, for those years before 1957 had a scarcity of high level data. From
this table it becomes obvious that the early type of final warmings took
place in the years when the tropical winds at the 20-mb level tended to westerlies between January and April, whereas late final warmings occurred
when the tendency of the oscillation was to easterlies. The break of the al-
ternation between early and late final warmings in 1954 and 1963 does well
coincide with a shifting of the easterlies, thus covering two consecutive
winters. The break in 1966 is the first exception within the years investigated, when a late final warming occurred although the tropical winds had
already shifted to westerlies in the 20-mb level.

It must be pointed out, however, that this classification is most tentative
because there is no security for the stratospheric events of the early years
and the others may represent perhaps not enough cases to be sure of a real
connection between the alternative behavior of the stratospheric warmings
and the 26-month oscillation. Only more years and further studies can help
to explain the complex nature of the stratospheric behavior.

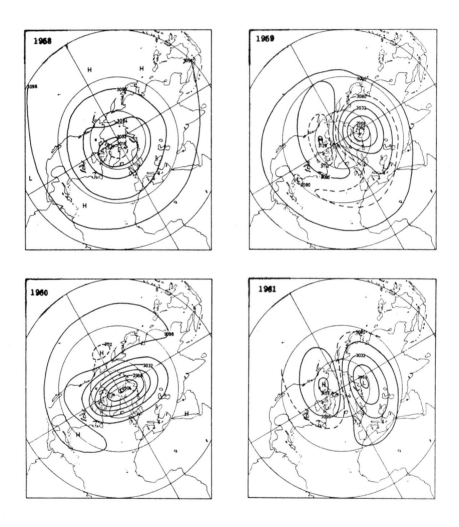

Fig. 24. 10 mb monthly mean maps of March, 1958 ... 1961 (Labitzke, 1966).

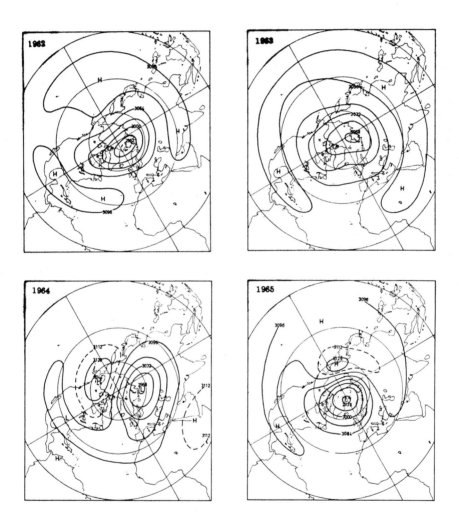

Fig. 25. 10 mb monthly mean maps of March, 1962 ... 1965 (Labitzke, 1966).

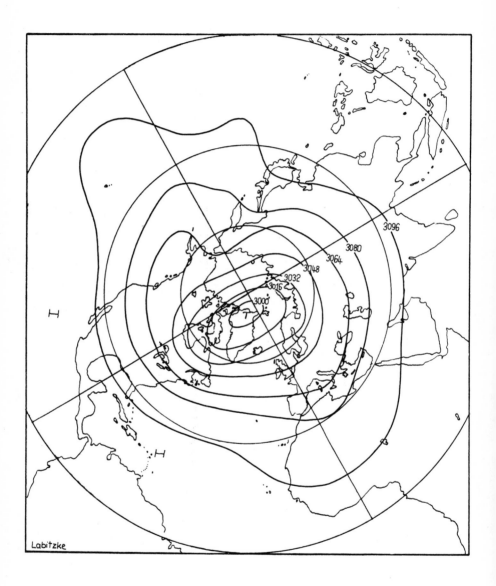

Fig. 26. 10 mb monthly mean map March 1966 (Labitzke, 1966).

Table 1
Winds at the 20 mb level over Canton Island for January and April and the type of the
final warmings (Labitzke, 1966).

Year	Winds at 20 mb		Type of final warming
	Jan.	April	
1952	?	W	early
1953	W	E	late
1954	E	E	late*
1955	W	W	early
1956	E	E	late
1957	W	W	early
1958	E	E	late
1959	E	W	early
1960	E	E	late
1961	W	W	early
1962	E	E	late
1963	E	E	late*
1964	CALM (W)		early
1965	E	E	late
1966	E	W	late**

3. CONNECTIONS TO THE TROPOSPHERIC BEHAVIOR

Another point of considerable interest is the possible linkage between
stratospheric warmings and tropospheric variations. Generally the stratospheric perturbations in winter are apparently independent of the disturbances in the troposphere. Only below roughly 25 km and equatorward from
the boundary of the polar regime is the stratosphere under tropospheric
control due to the Dine's compensation. It is certainly reasonable, however, to expect that such profound changes in the stratospheric circulation
as they occur during midwinter warmings would interact with the tropo-
speric circulation to some extent. As was pointed out by several authors
(Julian and Labitzke (1965), Finger and Teweles (1964), Labitzke (1965),
Craig and Hering (1959)) the stratospheric events have begun during strong
meridional circulation in the troposphere. The synoptic situations before
the warmings were all characterized by an exceptional strong jet stream
and the warmings took place above a region of intense tropospheric cyclonic
activity.

On the other hand, investigations by Julian (1960), Craig and Hering (1959),
Teweles (1958), Scherhag (1960), Labitzke (1965, 1966) have revealed that
there occurred an intense pressure rise in the troposphere in the area
of the greatest height increase in the stratosphere. By studying the European type of midwinter warmings Labitzke has shown that about 10 days after the beginning of the stratospheric warmings pressure rose over Europe
and a blocking pattern was formed. This pressure rise may be seen by the
time section for the heights at the 10-mb level and the sea level pressure
for Berlin 1960 (fig. 27). The sea level pressure rise occurred in cases of
weak stratospheric events slower but quicker in cases of major warmings
as may be seen by the time section for Thule 1957 (fig. 28).

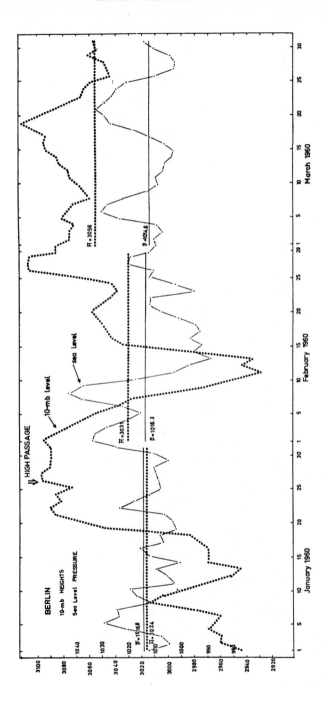

Fig. 27. Sea level pressure and 10 mb heights at Berlin (Labitzke, 1966).

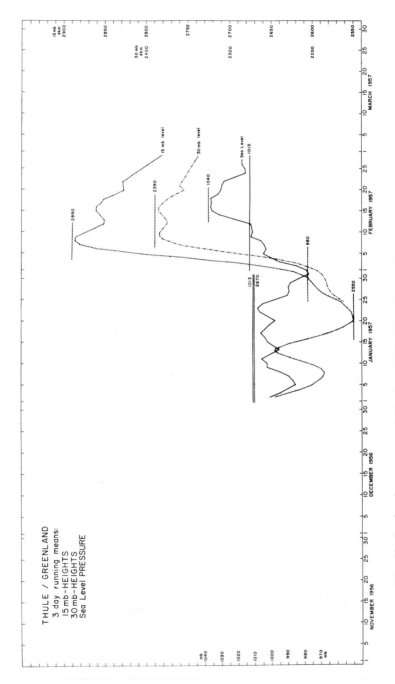

Fig. 28. Sea level pressure and 15 mb and 30 mb heights at Thule, Greenland (Labitzke, 1966).

Labitzke (1966) has pointed out that stratospheric warmings at least for the European area may give additional support for the forecast of blocking situations at sea level.

4. SOME THEORIES ABOUT CAUSES OF THE STRATOSPHERIC WARMINGS

There is no general agreement as to the causes of stratospheric warmings until today. The first explanations of the warming phenomenon were applied to direct heating from solar eruptions.

By most investigators nowadays the temperature increases during a period of stratospheric warming are ascribed to downward motion and adiabatic compression. This was attested by ozone observations which showed a close association between centers of marked total ozone excess and abrupt stratospheric temperature rises. By studying the stratospheric warming of 1958, London (1963) found that during the entire period the warming reached its most intense value at about the same place and time as the highest positive ozone anomaly occurred. He pointed out that a large scale vertical motion could explain both the observed warming and the ozone change patterns.

However, this is only the starting point of an explanation because these vertical motions in turn require explanation. There exists an agreement, however, that they presumably represent the growth of an unstable wave in the strong westerlies of the polar vortex. There has been discussion as to whether baroclinic or barotropic instability might be involved or a combination of the two. At first, the hypothesis of baroclinic instability seems to be reasonable. The decreasing intensity of sunlight during autumn creates a rapid cooling near the pole and a westerly vortex is established. The vortex expands and at the boundary of the polar regime a strong zonal jet stream is established. With the progression of the winter the vortex becomes increasingly baroclinic, finally transgressing the limit under which a stable zonal flow can persist. At this stage baroclinic waves or, in extreme cases, the explosive warming type of disturbances may develop.

There is one considerable objection to this hypothesis as a cause of the warming phenomenon. In the southern hemisphere there have never occurred comparable intense midwinter warmings although the southern hemisphere vortex shows stronger temperature gradients and a more pronounced jet stream.

By studying the atmospheric energetics during the stratospheric warming of 1957, Reed (1963) came to the conclusion that the polar night vortex of the northern hemisphere is stable to small perturbations. Large disturbances, however, impressed on the stratospheric flow through topographically influenced tropospheric disturbances may be amplified because of a mixed baroclinic-barotropic instability. The amplification of the disturbance begins in the upper stratosphere and propagates downward.

This result was confirmed by Julian (1965) who studied the atmospheric energetics during the stratospheric warming of 1963. Teweles (1957) earlier has drawn attention to the interesting phenomenon of a topographic feature influencing the circulation of the high stratosphere.

There still exists another hypothesis which is in favour of a connection between solar activity and the occurrence of stratospheric warmings although solar heating is no longer regarded as a possible direct cause of the warmings. It is assumed that the solar emission act as a trigger which releases a latent dynamic instability and thus leads to the breakdown of the polar vortex.

5. FINAL REMARKS

There are many open questions with regard to the nature and cause of the stratospheric warming phenomenon. What is the explanation for the different behavior pattern of the midwinter warmings with respect to their origin and direction of movement of the associated systems and what is the explanation for the alternative behavior of the final warmings? Why do the midwinter warmings sometimes develop to only moderate proportions while at other times they become so intense that the breakdown of the polar regime is attained? All studies concerning the causes of the stratospheric warmings do not show sufficient evidence as to present the real mechanism of this phenomenon.

We have to wait for more years to come, with hopefully major events, to go on with our investigations and to find the answer to all these problems.

REFERENCES

Arnold, A. and C. J. Brasefield, 1953, Atmospheric temperatures at 30 km, Proc. Toronto Met. Conference 1953.

Behr, K., 1960, Über markante Erwärmungen in der Stratosphäre, Met. Abh. IX, (2).

Craig, R. A., 1965, The upper atmosphere, meteorology and physics, New York.

Craig, R. A. and W. S. Hering, 1959, The stratospheric warming of January-February 1957, J. Meteorol. 16. (2).

Finger, F. G. and S. Teweles, 1964, The Mid-Winter 1963 stratospheric warming and circulation change, J. Appl. Meteor. 3, (1).

Godson, W. L. and R. Lee, 1958, High level fields of wind and temperature over the Canadian Arctic, Beitr. Physik d. Atmosphäre, 31, (1/2).

Julian, P. R., 1960, Tropospheric behavior associated with the arctic stratospheric warming phenomenon, Final Report, Contr. No. AF19(604)-2190, The Pennsylvania State University, University Park, Pa.

Julian, P. R. and K. Labitzke, 1965, A study of atmospheric energetics during the January-February 1963 stratospheric warming, J. Atmospheric Sci. 22, (6).

Labitzke, K., 1962. Beiträge zur Synoptik der Hochstratosphäre, Met. Abh., XXVIII, (1).

Labitzke, K., 1965, On the mutual relation between stratosphere and troposphere during periods of stratospheric warmings in winter, J. Appl. Meteor. 4, (1).

Labitzke, K., 1966, The nearly two year cycle of the midwinter warmings and the final warmings in the stratosphere, Symp. on Interaction Between Upper and Lower Layers of the Atmosphere, Wien 1966.

London, J., 1963, Ozone variations and their relations to stratospheric warmings,
    Symp. on Stratospheric and Mesospheric Circulation, Berlin 1962. Met. Abh.,
    XXXVI.
Lowenthal, M., 1957, Abnormal mid-stratospheric temperatures, J. Meteor. 14, (5).
Mädlow, E., 1964, Positive Temperaturen in der Stratosphäre, Met. Abh. des Insti-
    tuts für Meteorologie und Geophysik Berlin, XLIV, (2).
Reed, R. J., 1963, On the cause of the stratospheric sudden warming phenomenon,
    Symp. on Stratospheric and Mesospheric Circulation, Berlin 1962. Met. Abh.,
    XXXVI.
Scherhag, R., 1952, Die explosionsartige Stratosphärenerwärmung des Spätwinters
    1951/1952, Ber. d. DWD US-Zone 6, (38).
Scherhag, R., 1960, Stratospheric temperature changes and the associated changes
    in pressure distribution, J. Meteor. 17, (6).
Scherhag, R., 1963, The upper stratospheric circulation during the first quarter of
    1963 and the development of the sudden January warming, Met. Abh., XI, (1).
Scrase, F. J., 1953, Relatively high stratospheric temperatures of February 1951,
    Met. Mag. 82, 967.
Teweles, S., 1958, Anomalous warming of the stratosphere over North America
    in early 1957, Monthly Weather Rev. 86, (10).
Teweles, S. and F. G. Finger, 1958, An abrupt change in stratospheric circulation
    beginning in the mid-January 1958, Monthly Weather Rev. 86, (1).
Warnecke, G., 1956, Ein Beitrag zur Meteorologie der arktischen Stratosphäre,
    Met. Abh., III, (3).
Warnecke, G., 1962, Über die Zustandsänderungen der nordhemisphärischen Stra-
    tosphäre, Met. Abh., XXVIII, (3).
Wilson, C. V. and W. L. Godson, 1962, The stratospheric temperature field at high
    latitudes, Arctic Met. Research Group, Publication in Met. 46, Mc Gill University,
    Montreal.

DISCUSSION

Rawer:

Are the two classes of warmings only distinguished according to the
season when they appear, or is there also a distinction as to the type of the
phenomenon?

Kriester:

The two classes of stratospheric warmings are distinguished according
to their effect on the hemispheric circulation. The so-called midwinter
warmings are causing the breakdown of the cyclonic circulation of the winter season only for a short time (2-3 weeks), then a cyclonic flow is re-
established. The final warmings are changing the circulation to an anticyclonic for about half a year.

Rawer:

What is the order of the height change during a stratospheric warming
in the 10 mb surface?

Kriester:

The height change in the 10 mb surface may exceed 1/2 km at some locations per day. Considering the height of the 10 mb surface over the polar region where the lowest values are found before the warming starts you will find a change of about 3 km during the whole period of the warming.

Rawer:

Imagine the 10 mb surface was impermeable. Then a change below, for example a warming, would only lift the whole upper atmosphere by roughly 1 km. I cannot understant an "amplification" towards greater heights, except if some change goes up - for example an increase in temperature. On the other side, the stratospheric phenomena cannot be explained by mesospheric ones as far as the energy is concerned because the mass ratio is about $10^3 : 1$.

The conclusion is that neither the stratospheric warming is the reason for a mesospheric effect, nor the inverse is true. Both seem to be due to another common cause.

Misme:

Si on admet que la pression au sol ne varie pas pendant le réchauffement, la variation de l'altitude de la pression est explicable par un réchauffement de l'ordre de 10° si la surface isobare se déplace de 1 km environ en altitude.

Cela peut être expliqué de plusieurs façons dont une augmentation de l'absorption.

Les mouvements horizentaux seraient une conséquence et non une cause du réchauffement.

Bolganio:

In regard to the disturbance at D-region altitudes that might be expected to accompany midwinter stratospheric warmings, I believe one must recognize that the dynamical disturbance in the form of downward vertical motion, responsible for the "sudden" warming, extends throughout the atmosphere. Such a field of motion may be studied within the realm of the natural modes of the stratified atmosphere and it will then be apparent that a much greater vertical displacement will occur at 80 km than at 30 km. An elementary calculation indicates an amplification of order $\exp(\Delta Z / 2H) \approx 10$, so that a half kilometer displacement at 30 km would be expected to be accompanied by a 5 km displacement at 80 km.

Hoult:

A problem which arises in connection with these warmings is how such a warming is propagated to the ionosphere. Given the results of Shapley and those of Kriester, I wish to point out that there is no current theory available to explain the connection between upper and lower levels of the atmosphere.

Kriester says that, over several days, a warming consists of a downward movement of air of about 1 km at an altitude of 30 km. As the time scale is much longer than the longest available period of acoustic waves, if one Fourier decomposes this disturbance into normal modes, there remain only tides and gravity waves. But a tidal oscillation has an amplitude which does not increase markedly with altitude; and a displacement of a few km at an altitude of 100 km is completely negligible.

I have, from Kriester's data, estimated the properties of the gravity wave emitted, and found that the disturbance takes at least one order of magnitude longer than the characteristic time of the warming (~ 1 days) to reach 80 km.

RELATIONS BETWEEN STRATOSPHERE
AND MESOSPHERE

A. H. SHAPLEY

Environmental Science Services Administration.
Boulder. Colorado. USA

Abstract. Different methods for checking relationships between both atmospheric regions are discussed. The notion of a stratospheric event is defined and the method of studying associated stratospheric and ionospheric phenomena by comparison of events is presented in more detail and with examples. The conclusion is that stratosphere-ionosphere coupling exists under certain circumstances and in the higher geographic latitudes.

Résumé. On discute les différentes méthodes de contrôle des relations entre les deux régions de l'atmosphère. La notion de l'événément stratosphérique est définie et une méthode pour étudier les phénomènes associées stratosphériques et ionosphériques est présentée en détail. Des examples sont donnés. On arrive à la conclusion qu'un couplage existe entre la stratosphère et l'ionosphère dans certaines circonstances et en latitudes géographiques plus hautes.

1. INTRODUCTION

We will be considering here the evidence for the existence of interaction between the lower and the upper atmosphere. In effect we are inquiring into the relationships between levels accessible to meteorological balloons for which there is a huge amount of data and accompanying analysis and consequently fairly detailed theory, and those higher levels accessible to synoptic studies by radio techniques for which again there are many data, analyses and, again, fairly detailed theory. We ask: do these fit together and in what ways does one level affect the other? In addition to the synoptic body of data, the picture is filled out by numerous limited experiments - limited in time and space - and limited theory on special phenomena.

When radio data on the ionosphere began to become available in appreciable quantity, although in very crude form, about 1930, many correlations were attempted with all imaginable kinds of solar or geophysical phenomena. The correlations with sunspot numbers were quickly successful and with geomagnetic storms and aurorae. Later came the clear association of ionospheric changes with solar flares and magnetic bays. At these times, many comparisons were made with meteorological phenomena; many were published and undoubtedly many more - the more unsuccessful ones - were set aside in the cupboards.

The literature is pretty barren on this subject from about 1935 until a very few years ago, with some exceptions which I will mention. But now, in 1966, the subject is in fashion again and will doubtless remain so, as a result of more mature theoretical understanding of both the stratosphere and the mesosphere, but more importantly because of vast advances in techniques and the availability of more and better measurements at all levels in this part of the atmosphere. A measure of the current interest in this subject which brings together the fields of meteorology, ionosphere and aeronomy is the flurry of conferences and symposia. In the last eighteen months there have been at least six - at Mar del Plata, Brussels, Illinois, Ottawa, Vienna, Munich - and now one at Lindau.

Thus the question must be no longer 'is there a relation' between stratosphere and ionosphere or mesosphere, but what are the relations and how do they come about. In this introductory lecture, we will consider methods for finding relationships and treat some of the ones which have been found. From the title of the other lectures, it can be sure that the possible reasons for there being relationships will be fully covered, as well as the design of new experiments - with existing data or new data - for refining our understanding of the relationships.

2. TYPES OF RELEVANT DATA

Basically we are dealing with the fundamental properties of the atmosphere - composition, temperature, density, pressure, and movements. But it will be more meaningful to discuss briefly the main types of actual observations relevant to the problem.

For the stratosphere the main data are the pressures, temperatures, and winds from balloon radiosondes. Therefore there are height profiles daily or more often of each of these at some hundreds of stations over the world from ground level to about 25 km fairly dependably, to 30 km in considerable quantity and more rarely to about 35 km. More important, there are regional or hemispheric analyses of these data which provide interpolations to times and places and extrapolations to heights not covered by observation. The small but increasing number of meteorological rocket measurements to about 60 km are beginning to be treated in the same kinds of way. The main variable of interest and significance in the composition at stratospheric heights is ozone; the most common data are the total amount of ozone in a column of the atmosphere observed from ground by spectroscopic methods, but some height profiles from balloon ascents and a few from rockets are becoming available. Solar radiation data in optical wavelengths as observed under various meteorological conditions are also a potential tool for stratospheric-mesospheric studies.

As regards the mesosphere, our chief source of data is from radio methods. We must infer the properties and phenomena of the atmosphere as a whole from the behavior of a trace quantity of electrons and ions. There are few ways of indirectly observing the neutral atmosphere from ground: ordinary clouds occasionally are seen at heights as high as 14 km, noctilucent clouds give limited data, difficult to interpret, near 80 km, and the light scattering techniques and the uses of airglow below 100 km are still very experimental. In situ measurements by rockets are becoming more common; the meteorological rocket measurements which read into the lower mesosphere are now termed 'quasi-synoptic', but the true aeronomical rockets give only a few snapshots from a very few geographical locations. On the other hand there are radio data of the mesosphere in comparatively large quantity and variety. The principal methods include: a) ionospheric absorption A1 (pulse echo); b) ionospheric absorption A2 (cosmic noise); c) ionospheric absorption A3 (cw reflection); d) ionospheric absorption as indicated by ionosondes, f-minimum; e) low echoes at HF; f) partial reflections; g) cross modulation; h) LF and MF oblique propagation; i) VHF forward scatter; j) drifts by radiotechniques.

3. THE 'NORMAL' STRATOSPHERE

The atmosphere is typified by variability and disturbance, and the stratosphere certainly has these characteristics. The most recent 'Reference Atmosphere' tables can be taken as one point of departure. Over the height range of interest here, the tables give representative values of pressure, density, temperature, scale height, as a function of height and for different latitudes and seasons. Similarly the average amount of total ozone is described for latitude and season. In somewhat more useful form for our purposes are the derivations by Murgatroyd (fig. 1) of the height profiles of temperature and winds for a pole-pole cross section for summer and winter. These give a sort of reference against which to study variability, although the full annual variation ought also to be known.

The same sort of thing can be gained from the hemisphere maps of temperature and pressure compiled from actual daily observations, the longest series of which is the set beginning with IGY produced by the Freie University, Berlin. For example for 10 mb we can take a typical summer day and a typical winter one, selected from a consideration of the daily maps (fig. 2). One can also take monthly average data, but here I think that meteorologists can learn from their ionospheric colleagues. What is usually published are monthly mean contours; but to detect normal conditions among daily data with wide deviations more often in one direction than the other, the median is evidently the more suitable statistic. To my knowledge the problem has not been studied in this way. This technique may also be applicable to averages of total ozone.

In ionospheric studies we are very much accustomed to sort data into 'quiet' and 'disturbed'. For most studies our criteria are geomagnetic activity or solar activity. By now we would also exclude cases of intense polar cap absorption from our otherwise 'quiet' days. With what remains we can take suitable averages and introduce simple theory to construct what is, in effect, a reference ionosphere for different times and places. For the ionosphere below 100 km, the geomagnetic field distortions of the world maps for most phenomena (auroral absorption is an exception) are small though

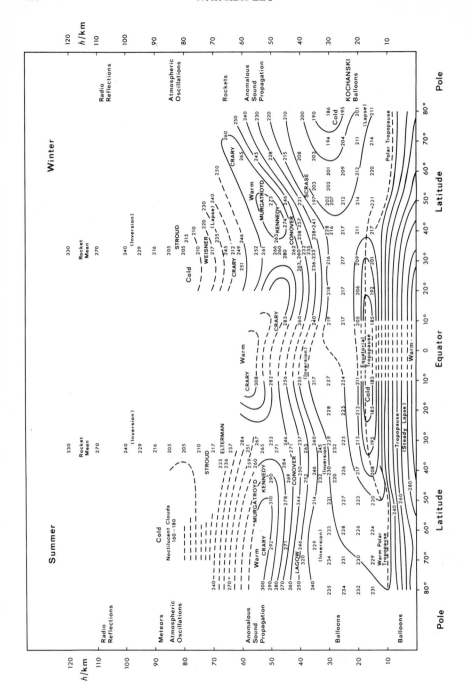

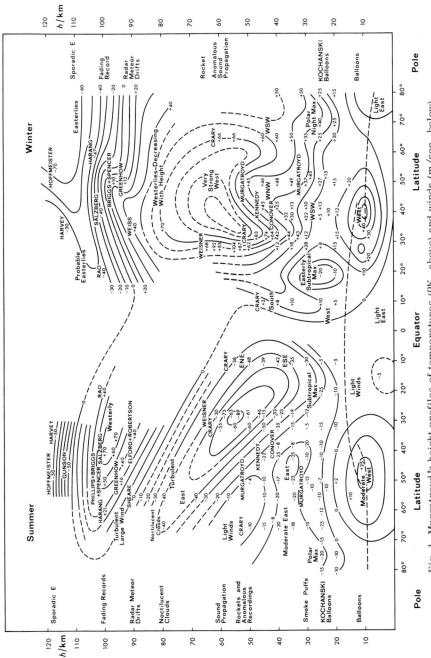

Fig. 1. Murgatroyd's height profiles of temperatures (OK. above) and winds (m/sec, below).

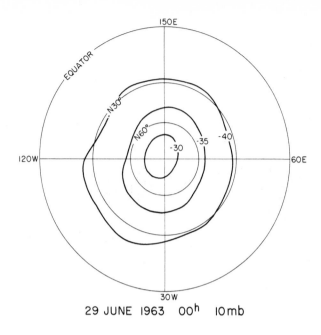

29 JUNE 1963 00ʰ 10 mb

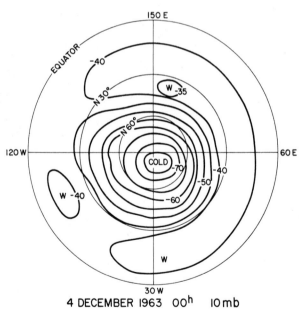

4 DECEMBER 1963 00ʰ 10 mb

Fig. 2. 10 mb-isotherms on typical summer and winter days. for northern hemisphere.

not negligible, although our observing networks are small compared to the meteorologists'. Thus detailed geographical interpolations are carried out in some ignorance. The deviations from 'quiet' data can be very large and are pushed under the carpet of the term 'anomalies', of which there are many, many types in ionospheric work. Some of the anomalies are disappearing as stratospheric-ionospheric studies progress.

4. APPROACHES TO STRATOSPHERIC-IONOSPHERIC STUDIES

There are many different ways of going about studies on the relationship between phenomena which on first glance appear to be quite different and separated. We will discuss some of these here and at the same time give examples of some of the work which has been done.

Beynon and Owen-Jones (1965) have studied seasonal characteristics of many parameters at ionospheric and stratospheric heights in a way which emphasizes any deviations from simple theory. They plot the means of the parameter against the cosine of the sun's zenith angle, χ, for the mid-month of each month in turn. If the parameter follows some $\cos^n\chi$ law without a time lag, the result is a straight line. Any solar cycle dependence will average out if several years' data are available. They systematically find a 'figure eight' pattern for most stations and phenomena, all the way from E region, down throughout the D, and at stratospheric heights. This technique does not give any more additional information than an ordinary time graph of monthly means but it does conveniently identify the time, the sense, and to a certain degree the magnitude of the anomalies. For instance the geographic areas of winter anomaly in absorption can be traced conveniently by this method. Further it is quite evident that most phenomena of the lower ionosphere lag the solstice by many weeks, as much as or more than stratospheric phenomena studied by the same technique. But this is only a suggestive method: one would expect geophysical phenomena under solar control to have seasonal variations and the time lags could be introduced through quite unconnected mechanisms at different levels. So the results could be obtained without there being any coupling between levels or phenomena. Beynon and Owen-Jones (1965) have attempted to trace the existence of similar seasonal patterns of any available ionospheric, mesospheric or stratospheric data throughout the height range of interest to see if there are steady and consistent changes, for example, as one descends in level from E-region heights to the stratosphere and troposphere; any such consistency would be evidence for the existence of coupling, but would not itself indicate the mechanisms. In this work they are hampered, of course, by the lack of quasi-synoptic data at the intermediate levels, but from what is available, a considerable amount of consistency has been found.

Geography can be used as a tool for identifying relationships. Thus one kind of ionospheric absorption phenomena is identified with the aurora since each is usually confined to a rather narrow belt roughly symmetrical around the geomagnetic pole. Similarly the fact that the winter anomaly in ionospheric absorption is weak or absent at latitudes below about 40⁰ was suggestive of a relation with the stratosphere which also is quite regular at low

latitudes. Further, the observation that each phenomena was regional in
occurrence was an indication in the same direction. The case for the stratospheric circulation patterns is now obvious from the daily 10-mb maps;
for ionospheric absorption, with only a handful of stations and with geomagnetic activity and other influences operating simultaneously, the regional
nature was first demonstrated clearly by Thomas (1962) in cross correlations among stations and even here he had to resort to monthly data.

A more significant clue to association of stratosphere and ionosphere
would be a correspondence in time between particular phenomena. Thus
Bossolasco and Elena (1963) plotted the smoothed time variations of 10-mb
temperatures and HF ionospheric absorption at the same geographic location for parts of two winter seasons; each showed deviations from seasonal
trends and the degree of parallelism of the two curves indicated a possible
association. One could additionally compute the correlation and evaluate its
significance, taking into account the conservatism of the data. This was not
done in their paper, but the curves presented are surely suggestive. Gregory (1965) has also used this approach, and many others. Jones et al. (1959)
in effect do this in comparing temperature from four successive IGY rockets with the data available from balloon measurements in the same time
period.

Of course if one had full and uniform coverage of an ionospheric parameter and a stratospheric parameter for the same place, a test of association would be full correlation, testing for time lags as appropriate. Most
data series are rather seriously incomplete, however. Also one must take
account of any seasonal effects common to the two series or the correlation
will be spuriously strong, and any extraneous major disturbing effects in
one parameter but not the other (such as geomagnetic activity) or the correlation will be spuriously weak. Such correlations have not yet been done
successfully with daily data.

Another statistical approach involves the study of events. Uniform criteria are established for identifying instances of unusual behavior in one
parameter and the behavior of the other parameter at the corresponding
time is analyzed. The method of superposed epochs was devised to demonstrate the association of geomagnetic disturbances with the occurrence of
major solar flares and has been widely used in solar-terrestrial and ionospheric studies. As concerns the present topic, the selections were on the
basis of distinc events in the daily course of stratospheric temperature
variations, and the correlation with ionospheric behavior demonstrated by
the corresponding variations in ionospheric absorption. These studies will
be described later. This technique is well adapted to identify relationships,
and any uniform time lags, even in the presence of many extraneous events
or 'noise', but only as long as the relationship is strong. The evaluation of
the significance of weak relationships or relationships exposed from a
small number of cases is a most difficult and unsatisfactory statistical ex-
ercise.

Finally there is the snapshot approach to identifying and studying relationships, as exemplified by the rocket experiment and certain others
which are not made repeatedly. Surely in the long run, these will explain

the relationships as they provide the physically most meaningful data. The problem is to be in a position to fit the data from the aeronomical or ionospheric or even the meteorological rocket into the perspective of the more nearly continuous data, in time and geography, from other sensors. And there is further the problem of arranging the time and place of the rocket launching to study the conditions of main interest. But these kinds of experiments will help provide new and more meaningful interpretations of the more nearly continuous data as well as provide an indication of what expanded measurement programs are desirable on a more nearly synoptic schedule with these more difficult or more expensive techniques.

5. STRATOSPHERIC EVENTS

The highest level for which there are systematic and synoptic observations on the stratosphere is the upper limit of the meteorological balloon flights. Recently these have been reaching rather dependably up toward 30 km, the 10-mb pressure level. This is usually safely above the tropopause, and it makes a great deal of difference whether the phenomena of interest are considerably above the tropopause or whether they are mixed with effects at that level. At lower latitudes, the temperature and wind profiles of the stratosphere change slowly with season and there are no great day-to-day changes. At higher latitudes and on the polar cap, the same is true in the summertime but definitely not in the winter. An extreme example of the variability in or the disruption of the stratosphere is the stratospheric warming phenomenon which was first identified by Scherhag (1952). Since about 1958 there have been consistent enough measurements so that daily maps of temperature fields at 30 km are now regularly produced.

Fig. 2 shows, at the 10-mb or 30-km level, what the normal temperature contours look like. This is looking down on top of the North Pole. The North Pole is at the center and the equator is the outer circle. Normally, there are very cold temperatures at the winter pole, and they are fairly systematic and regular.

Fig. 3 shows conditions near the very beginning of one of these stratospheric warming events. The one in the center will develop, grow and move. Otherwise, the very cold temperatures at the Pole exist. Fig. 4 shows the same stratospheric warming at approximately its fullest development. The temperature field and the pressure field will be similarly distorted and completely different. In the space of less than ten days, conditions have changed from a fairly normal situation to a completely different one. The temperatures at the 30-km level near the warm center have increased by some 60° in a few days. The distortion can affect the whole hemisphere for a matter of weeks or sometimes even a month after one of these intense warmings. Jones et al. (1959) launched a rocket before and during one of these stratospheric warmings and found that the mesosphere was affected by this phenomenon.

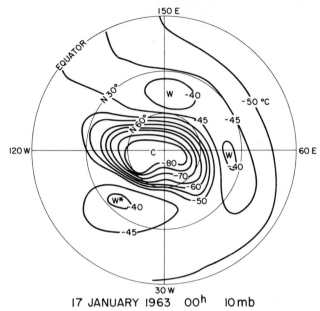

17 JANUARY 1963 00^h 10mb

Fig. 3. 10-mb isotherms at early stage of major stratospheric warming.

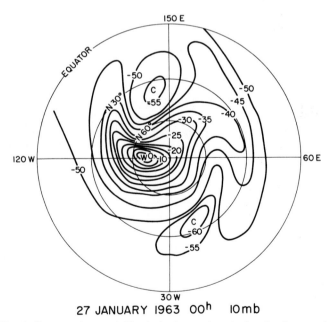

27 JANUARY 1963 00^h 10mb

Fig. 4. Temperatures at 10 mb during major stratospheric warming.

6. IONOSPHERIC EFFECTS

I believe it was Bibl of Rawer's group, who pointed out that the ionosphere underwent fluctuations in phase with the stratospheric warmings in
Europe in 1952. Little more was written on the subject until 1963. Fig. 5
shows the results in a short note by Bossolasco and Elena (1963). The lower curve describes 30-km temperatures which are greatly smoothed; the
upper curve is an ionospheric absorption index. Note the similarity of the
smooth variations in these two quantities. Fig. 6 shows a similar situation
for another winter. Correlations of this kind but somewhat more specific
will be discussed in this paper. Lauter in East Germany has worked on the
association of the ionized part of the atmosphere with these stratospheric
warmings, also. He has done a lot of work but has published very little; he
finds correlations of this kind, also.

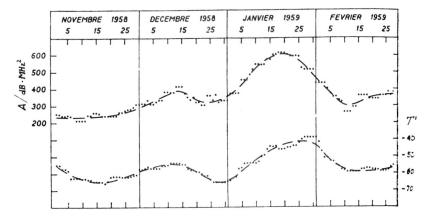

Fig. 5. Absorption during the period November 1958 to February 1959 (upper curve,
left ordinate). Compare with temperature (in °C) (lower curve, right ordinate).

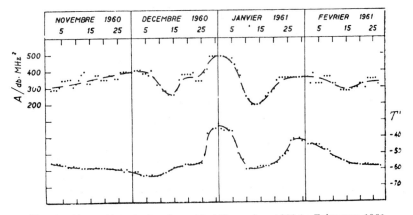

Fig. 6. Absorption during the period November 1960 to February 1961.

Gregory (1965) has done some of the most extensive work on this subject. Some of his results are presented in fig. 7. The top curve is the ionospheric parameter or electron density deduced from the partial reflection
experiment, and the lower curve is a time series of the stratospheric temperatures extending over a period of a couple of weeks; that is, the meteorological parameter is the temperature in the 20 to 25-km height region.
This is an example of the kind of simultaneous effect that has been observed; it is a Southern Hemisphere example and it has not been found at
such a low latitude in the Northern Hemisphere.

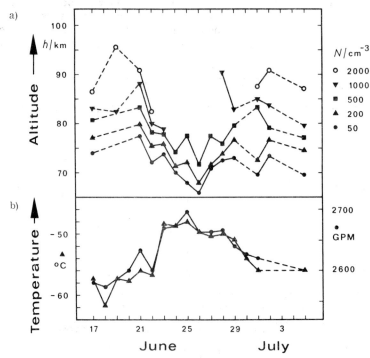

Fig. 7. a) Time series of electron density isopleths. June–July 1963. b) Time series
of stratospheric temperatures. 20-30-mb levels.

7. THE STUDY OF ASSOCIATED STRATOSPHERIC AND IONOSPHERIC
PHENOMENA BY COMPARISON OF 'EVENTS'

Our approach to the problem has been not to look at trends like this but
actually to identify relatively sudden events occurring in the stratosphere
and then to see whether or not the ionosphere is affected. The problem
here is to find an ionospheric parameter or index that is observed day after
day over a period of years in order to get enough data or examples of the
event to do the correlation. We are not at liberty to design the experiment;

we have to use what is available. The ionospheric absorption measurements are convenient and meaningful for this. The ionospheric absorption is the attenuation suffered by a radio wave upon vertical reflection and it is related to the integral of the electron density and the collisional frequency over the total path traversed by the wave. I will not explain the technique in any further detail except to say that the standard observatory-type measurements of type A1 and A3 seem largely to be sensitive * to N and ν in the 85 to 105-km range; but they can be affected by ionization at lower levels. There are a number of stations monitoring ionospheric absorption, particularly in Europe, and there exist fairly long time series. These absorption measurements have revealed the following: there are well-behaved seasonal and geographic variations in absorption except in winter in the middle and high latitudes. There may be major anomalies in winter; that is, absorption is greater than what would be expected for the rest of the year and extrapolations from lower latitudes. This winter anomaly in absorption has been fairly well known for some time (Shapley, 1965), and it is further true that not only is the absorption higher in winter but the day-to-day variability in winter is much greater than in other seasons. That is, some days are more anomalous than others.

Fig. 8 illustrates the preliminary work that has been carried out. This is a time history from August to April-May of the day-to-day variations of the absorption and the temperature at 30 km. This particular diagram is smooth, and the analyses were done with the raw data. There are some dramatic events, changes in the temperature at 30 km, and there are various sudden changes in absorption, also. It remains to determine whether these rather gross events correspond to one another. The technique of analysis is similar to that used in solar-terrestrial relationship for many years. The most outstanding events in one parameter are selected and then a superposed epoch analysis is done to see whether there is any systematic change in the other parameter in time relation with the one selected. Five years of winter measurements were selected and the very extreme events were examined. If the temperature at 30 km increased by at least 10° within a few days, then this was counted as an event.

The result is shown in fig. 9 as a superposed epoch diagram which includes only 16 cases; this is the selected epoch and the dashed curve is the 10-mb temperature curve. The full curve is what the ionospheric absorption at a nearby station did with relation to that. This suggests that they are associated and with a rather small time lag. Hence, this study is based on the 16 largest cases in the five-year period; the correlation does pass most of the qualitative tests of significance, however, fig. 10 shows two classes, the solid line corresponding to a temperature increase of 20° or more; and the dotted line corresponding to a temperature increase between 10° and 20°. The peak at the center, near the epoch day zero, is common to both.

The foregoing result is interesting and suggestive but some remarks and

---

* N is the electron density (number of electrons per m^3) while ν is the effective collision frequency per sec. It must be emphasized that this is not identic with the gas-kinetic collision frequency (but of the same order of magnitude).

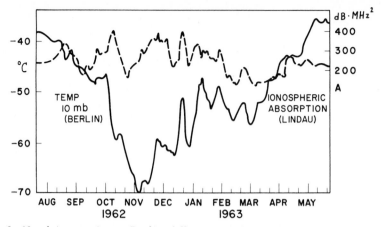

Fig. 8. 10-mb temperatures (Berlin. full curve) and ionospheric absorption A (Lindau. broken curve) during the period August 1962 to May 1963.

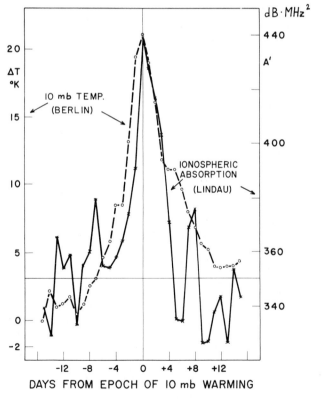

Fig. 9. 10-mb temperatures (Berlin) and ionospheric absorption (Lindau) versus days from epoch of 10-mb warming.

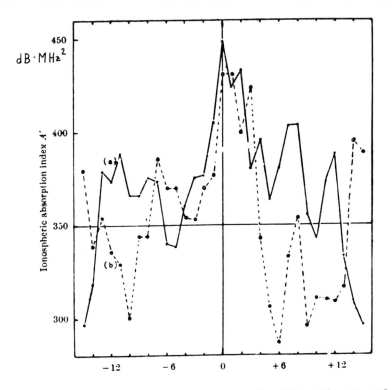

Fig. 10. Variation in ionospheric absorption a) $\Delta T > 20^\circ$; b) $10^\circ < \Delta T < 20^\circ$.

qualifications must be made. First, not all of the winter anomaly days are taken into account in this analysis. There are more days or more events in the absorption variation than there are in the stratospheric variation. This does hold if one considers smaller events, but it is getting down into the noise. Rather few of the events that go into this correlation are the major stratospheric warmings that are illustrated in the figures. Some of them are the effects of a major stratospheric warming seen at a distance. Even though the warming center was over Canada and Alaska, the effects of this were seen at the stations in Western Europe, Berlin, and the nearby iono-spheric station at Lindau. Some of them are more minor fluctuations in the temperature field which satisfied the criteria. Note that there was no large time lag in the correlation shown. This suggests that the atmosphere from 30 km up towards 90 km is coupled. There is no propagation time or time lag; if so, it is only a day or two.

We should mention another feature of the winter anomaly, illustrated in fig. 11, that stations at the same latitude but for apart do not show the same days of extreme anomaly. These are world maps showing observing stations, and the days of extreme winter anomaly are given. When the days of extreme winter anomaly were selected from the Washington data, Thomas

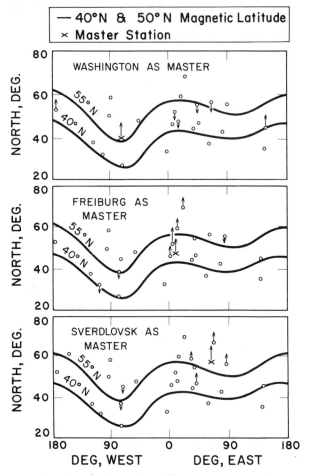

Fig. 11. Superposed epoch relations using different master stations (cross mark ×).

(1962) looked to see if other stations showed extreme absorption results. A dot indicates an average value and one can see that there is not a good correlation over a very wide area. When Freiburg in Europe was taken as the master, the stations in Europe behaved together; but farther apart they did not. And there is anti-correlation in the Americas. This is evidence that the winter anomaly is a regional phenomenon with characteristic dimensions of thousands of km. The characteristics of the winter anomaly in absorption are clearly of the same scale and are associated with the local characteristics of the winter stratosphere.

The correlations shown in this discussion have been applied to other data from other places. They are confirmed by other pairs of stations in Western Europe. The strength of the correlations seems to get poorer toward the auroral zone, Tromso and Oslo; the correlation is not as strong, the data are not equivalent and it is difficult to make comparisons. When widely separated regions are studied, one has to use a poorer measure of ionospheric absorption, namely the f-minimum characteristic obtained from ionograms. This kind of result is not confirmed in a partial study of the North American longitudes; here the data are poorer, but the correlation is not confirmed at those longitudes. It is confirmed in the Aleutian area and the result is only valid for certain specified places.

It should be noted that we are dealing here with D-region ionization created by solar radiation so that in the wintertime there is no D-region to be measured on the polar cap. The earlier figures showed that the disruptions in the stratospheric circulation are confined to latitudes from 40^0 or 45^0 and higher. This leaves just a narrow band in which with this technique, one might expect to find correlations of this kind. If we add the further restriction that comes out of these tests that the effect is obscured or absent in the auroral zone, or near the auroral zone, then this leaves rather restricted geography for which one might expect to find it. We have found it in Western Europe and in the Aleutians which are two of these. If there were only more plentiful data from the Russian sector, this would be a fruitful place to confirm or modify these results. In the Russian sector, the meteorological data are less available at present than the ionospheric data.

Referring to fig. 12, a comment on the time lag or lack of lag between the 30-km event and the ionospheric event is appropriate. For a major stratospheric warming there is indeed a time lag from the 10-mb to the 100-mb level (from 30 km down to about 16 km). We do not have good ways for checking whether or not this extrapolates up to higher levels. There have been some fragmentary rocket results which suggest that this lag of the event as seen at a single station does continue. The interpretation of this from observations is that the axis of the warm center is strongly tilted. But when doing single-station correlations this will appear to be a time lag. This is so on the large events, the major stratospheric warmings. Referring to fig. 13, if one takes smaller events, this does not seem to appear. On this diagram, which again covers about a month of daily values, the temperatures at these three levels have been plotted; notice that there is no consistent lag between an event at 30 km and one at lower heights. In fact, one can judge this that the height of the temperature minimum is fluctuating throughout this time. It is suggested that the 10-mb (30-km) level, by being surely and safely above the temperature minimum, is representative of the higher part of the atmosphere and that there, in fact, is no appreciable time lag between 30 km and the effects at higher levels.

8. CONCLUSIONS

There is compelling evidence for the existence of stratosphere-ionosphere coupling. At this time, it is not possible to explain why and how the coupling is accomplished. There is some evidence that large temperature

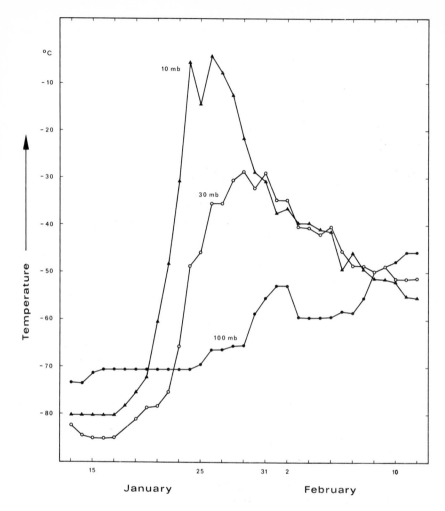

Fig. 12. Stratospheric temperatures near 75°N, 90°W. during January–February 1963.

deviations at as low as 30 km carry upwards into higher levels such that the pressure-heights at the ionospheric levels are markedly changed in the space of a few days. Applying simple principles, even if there was a great change of pressure-height, both the electron production and electron loss should give the same profile versus pressure, as both depend on pressure. There should be no change in the ionospheric absorption index which was studied. This implies strong motions and, therefore, certainly implies the possibility that there are changes in the mesospheric composition. The variability in composition should be examined in order to explain these coupling effects.

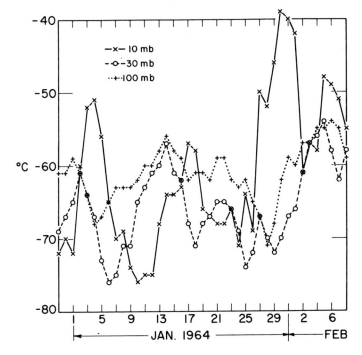

Fig. 13. Stratospheric temperature variations over Berlin.

REFERENCES

Beynon. W. J. G. and E. S. Owen-Jones. 1965. J. Atmosph. Terr. Phys. 27. 761.

Bossolasco. M. and A. Elena. 1963. Absorption de la couche D et température de la mesosphère. Comp. Rend. (Paris) 256. 4491.

Gregory. J. B., 1965. The influence of atmospheric circulation on mesospheric electron densities in winter. J. Atmos. Sci. 22. 18.

Jones. L. M., J. W. Peterson. E. J. Schaefer and H. F. Schulte. 1959. J. Geophys. Res. 64. 1331.

Scherhag. R.. 1952. Die explosionsartigen Stratosphären-Erwärmerungen des Spätwinters. Ber. Deut. Wetterdienst (US Zone) 6. 51.

Shapley. A. H. and W. J. G. Beynon. 1965. Winteranomaly in ionospheric absorption and stratospheric warmings. Nature 206. 1242.

Thomas. L.. 1962. J. Atmos. Terr. Phys. 23. 301.

DISCUSSION

Robert:

Quelles méthodes de mesure ont été utilisées pout déterminer la température à 30 km? Quelle est la précision des méthodes utilisées?

Maenhout:

In the upper air sounding network different types of radiosondes are in use. The sonde used at the Berlin Station is equipped with a thermistor as temperature sensor and an hypsometer as pressure element. Both sensors are very accurate, and the temperature measurement is not really influenced by radiation effects (radiation error less than $1^{\circ}K$).

D-REGION PHENOMENA ASSOCIATED WITH
METEOROLOGICAL INFLUENCES

W. DIEMINGER
Max-Planck-Institut für Aeronomie.
Lindau/Harz

Abstract. The propagation of radio waves through the lower ionosphere is discussed theoretically with special reference to the absorption phenomena. Observations of the absorption incurring to radio waves show that, besides the regular diurnal and seasonal variation with the solar zenith angle there is excessiv absorption on winter days in medium latitudes. This winteranomaly is to be ascribed to increased electron density in the lower ionosphere which is caused apparently by peculiarities of the general mesospheric circulation in winter.

Résumé. La propagation des ondes à travers la basse ionosphère est discutée en théorie tout en se référant particulièrement aux phénomènes de l'absorption ionosphérique. Les observations de l'absorption des ondes montrent qu'en dehors de la variation régulière journalière et avec la saison (dépendant de l'angle zénithal solaire). il y a aux latitudes moyennes une absorption excessive pendant des jours d'hiver. Cette anomalie d'hiver peut être attribuée à une densité accrue des électrons dans la basse ionosphère. dont la cause serait évidemment dûe a certaines particularités de la circulation générale mesosphérique en hiver.

1. INTRODUCTION

The title of this lecture is somewhat misleading. The listener may expect a lecture dealing with well established associations between meteorological factors and the behaviour of the lowest part of the ionosphere. As a matter of fact such associations have been suspected for quite a long time but progress in establishing them is slow because the region in question is accessible only with difficulty both for meteorological and aeronomical measurements. It is too high for balloons and too low for satellites. It is the domaine of the so-called meteorological rockets, and in spite of their extensive use data are collecting slowly because the measurements can be regarded only as pinpricks into the vast volume which needs to be investigated. Radio echo observations, however, are both scarce and difficult in interpretation.

2. THE AERONOMICAL STRUCTURE OF THE D-REGION

The D-region is the lowest part of the ionised part of the atmosphere,

extending from approximately 50-90 km. It merges into the E-region which
is at a height of approximately 90-140 km. A typical noontime electron density profile of the D- and E-region is shown in fig. 1a, and an expanded part
in fig. 1b.

The electron density in the D-region does not exhibit a distinct maximum but increases more or less monotonically with increasing height. Typical values of electron density at noon are a few 100 cm^{-3} between 60 and
70 km and a few 1000 cm^{-3} between 75 and 85 km.

The diurnal variation of electron density is characterized by a maximum
around noon (possible a few minutes later) and a depletion of electrons at
lower heights after sunset. At night only a few tens of electrons are left at
heights below 90 km. The seasonal variation is not a regular one. Apparently it follows roughly the cosine of the zenith angle of the sun in equatorial
and subequatorial regions all the year over. In middle latitudes the electron

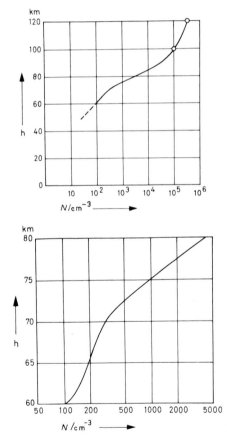

Fig. 1. a) Electron density profile between 60 and 120 km (noon).
        b) Electron density profile between 60 and 80 km (noon).

density, on a number of winter days, is abnormal high and even higher than in summer. This interesting feature will be discussed in more detail later on.

The electrons in the D-region are produced mainly by ultraviolet radiation of the sun. There are two major contributions: Nitric oxid is being ionised by solar Lyman-α radiation, which is a very prominent line in the solar spectrum and penetrates deeply into the atmosphere (down to 70-80 km) through a "window" in the absorption spectrum of molecular oxygen. On the other hand, X-ray radiation below 10 Å ionizes O_2 and N_2 mainly below 90 km.

These ionizing radiations vanish after sunset. There may be a contribution from cosmic rays maintaining an electron density of a few tens of electrons even at night down to very low levels. This contribution is thought to be constant because of the constancy and isotropy of the cosmic radiation[*].

The most important disturbance of the D-region is the increase of electron density during a Solar Flare Effect. The enhanced ionization has to be ascribed for the major part to an increase of the intensity, and an extension down to 1 Å, of the spectrum of solar X-rays. The total duration of the effect including the return to normal conditions ranges from a few to a few hundred minutes.

Another type of increase of electron density is being observed during aurorae. It appears to be caused by X-ray bremsstrahlung which in turn is created by particles of medium energy penetrating into the E-region, producing the visible aurora and the enhanced ionization which has been termed radio aurora. The duration of these effects may be as long as many hours. The occurrence is restricted to the same areas as the visible aurorae.

The third type of anomalous increase of electron density in the D-region occurs during the so-called Polar Cap Absorption (PCA) effects which are caused by solar protons travelling at a speed up to $\frac{1}{3}$ of the velocity of light and penetrating into the polar cap of the earth's atmosphere down to 40 km. It may last as long as 3 days. Frequently it is followed by an auroral effect which is caused by slower polar particles leaving the sun simultaneously but arriving later on the earth.

None of these effects seems to be associated with meteorological phenomena since almost all of the solar energy is absorbed at heights well above the troposphere and even in the stratosphere[**].

3. THE INFLUENCE OF THE D-REGION ON RADIO WAVE PROPAGATION

Before proceeding to the main topic of this lecture a discussion of the influence of the D-region on the propagation of radio waves seems approp-

---

[*] The influence of the very infrequent big increases of the intensity of cosmic rays has not been studied yet. Probably it will be veiled by simultaneous increases of X-ray intensity.

[**] For a more thorough discussion see Kellog (1966).

riate since radio waves are playing an important role in the investigation of the D-region.

Generally the propagation of radio waves in the ionosphere is controlled by the refractive index which is a function of the electron density and, to a minor degree, the collision frequency, the magnetic field of the earth, and the frequency and polarization of the radio wave (magnetoionic theory). The full theory may be found in Ratcliffe (1959), Gerson (1962), Bibl, Paul and Rawer (1962), Davies (1965). Here only the consequences will be summarized as far as they are relevant to the problem concerned.

Generally one has to distinguish between the frequency range where the geometric optical approximation (ray theory) is applicable, and the frequency range where a full wave solution must be used. The former is determined by the condition that the refractive index does not change appreciably over a distance of one wavelength, the latter deals with the cases where this condition is fulfilled no longer. The ray theory can be used for the propagation of decametric and hectometric waves (0.3 - 30 MHz). For myriametric waves (3 - 30 kHz) the waveguide theory is appropriate which, however, will not be dealt with here.

3.1. *Appleton-Lassen formula*

The refractive index in an ionized gas which is under the influence of a steady magnetic field is given by the Appleton-Lassen formula (Appleton, 1927; Försterling and Lassen, 1933; Hartree, 1931; Lassen, 1927):

$$n^2 = 1 - \cfrac{X}{1-jZ - \cfrac{Y_T^2}{2(1-X-jZ)} \pm \sqrt{\cfrac{Y_T^4}{4(1-X-jZ)^2} + Y_L^2}}$$

where

$$X = Ne^2/\epsilon_0 \, m\omega^2$$
$$Y_L = eB_L/m\omega$$
$$Y_T = eB_T/m\omega$$
$$Z = \nu/\omega$$

N = number of electrons/cm^3
c = charge of an electron
m = mass of an electron
v = collision frequency
$w = 2\pi f$; f wave frequency

The subscripts L and T refer to the longitudinal and transverse component of the imposed magnetic field with reference to the direction of the wave normal (i.e. phase propagation). The + sign refers to the ordinary, and the - sign to the extraordinary component of the radio wave in the ionosphere.

The refractive index is complex, that is to say the radio waves suffer both a refraction and an absorption. Putting $n^2 = (\mu-j\chi)^2$ the solution of the wave equation (wave progressing in x direction) is

$$E = E_0 \exp j\omega(t - \underbrace{\frac{\mu x}{c}}_{\text{undamped wave}}) \cdot \underbrace{\exp \frac{\omega}{c}\chi x}_{\text{absorption}}$$

where $\frac{\omega}{c}\chi = K$ is the absorption constant.

3.2. *No magnetic field*

Unfortunately the Appleton-Lassen formula is so complicated that a general discussion is practically impossible. We are interested here primarily in the absorption effects. Neglecting as a first order approximation the steady magnetic field we are getting

$$n^2 = 1 - \frac{X}{1+Z^2} - \frac{jXZ}{1+Z^2}$$

For the absorption constant K we are getting

$$K = \frac{\omega}{c} \frac{1}{2\mu} \frac{XZ}{1+Z^2} = \frac{e^2}{2\,\epsilon_0\,mc} \frac{1}{\mu} \frac{N}{\omega^2 + \nu^2}$$

(Here K is expressed in Nep/m.) We can distinguish between two extreme types of absorption, viz.,

a) Nondeviative absorption when μ is near unity and when the product $N\nu$ is large. This applies to the D-region.

For $\omega^2 \gg \nu^2$ we are getting:

$$K = \frac{e^2}{2\,\epsilon_0\,mc} \frac{N\nu}{\omega^2}$$

so that the absorption varies $\propto \dfrac{1}{\omega^2}$

For $\omega^2 \ll \nu^2$ the nondeviative absorption becomes

$$K = \frac{e}{2\,\epsilon_0\,mc} \frac{N}{\nu}$$

independent of frequency, and the absorption may decrease with increasing collisional frequency.

b) Deviative absorption when μ tends to zero. This occurs near the level of reflection, that is to say near the critical frequency. Then we have

$$K = \frac{\nu}{2\,c} \left(\frac{1}{\mu} - \mu\right)$$

which becomes very large for μ approaching zero.

3.3. *Magnetic field*

When the magnetic field is included the dispersion and absorption relationships are becoming very complicated with the exception of transverse propagation of the ordinary wave which is the same as the "no field" case.

To facilitate the discussion of the dispersion curves for any angle of propagation one introduces the so-called critical collision frequency which is given by

$$\nu_c = \frac{\omega}{2} \frac{Y_T^2}{Y_L} = \frac{\omega}{2} Y \frac{\sin^2 \theta}{\cos \theta} \,,$$

where θ is the angle between the direction of the magnetic field and the wave normal. Examples for $\theta = 20^\circ$ are given in fig. 2 (Davies, 1965).

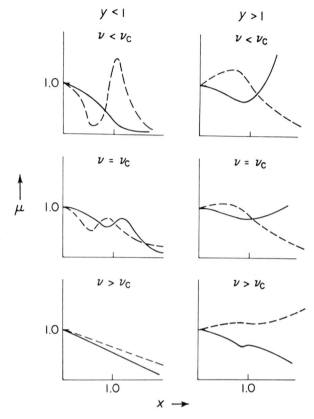

Fig. 2. Dispersion curves with magnetic field and collisions for a fixed angle $\theta = 20^{\circ}$ between the direction of the magnetic field and the wave normal.

For the case of quasilongitudinal propagation the nondeviative absorption is given, approximately, by

$$K = \frac{e^2}{2\,\epsilon_0\,mc}\,\frac{N\nu}{(\omega\pm\omega_B)^2+\nu^2}$$

ω_B being the gyropulsation of the electrons in the magnetic field. The + sign again applies to the ordinary, and the - sign to the extraordinary wave. It shall be mentioned only in passing that, in the Appleton-Lassen formula, it is assumed that all electron possess the same average velocity and that the collision frequency is independent of the electron velocity. A more realistic theory taking into account the Boltzmann distribution of the electron velocity was worked out by Sen and Wyller (1960). The Appleton-Lassen formula may be applied, however, by using an "effective" collisional frequency, which is between 1.5 and 2.5 times the actual one.

The physical reason for the absorption of radio waves in an ionized medium is the following: the energy imparted to the electrons by the electric field serves to enhance the motion of the electrons. The electrons do not move freely in the plasma. As soon as they collide with the ambient neutral particles they loose their excess energy. In this way the incident electric field is attenuated. The loss depends obviously on the ratio between the oscillation frequency and the collision frequency of the electrons.

Because the density of the gas and hence the collision frequency is rather high in the D-region, radiowaves are appreciably attenuated when penetrating the D-region on the way to the reflecting levels and back. The total absorption suffered by a plane wave is described by the absorption formula

$$ E = E_0 \exp \left(2 \int_0^{h_r} K \, dh \right) , $$

the integral taken from the lower boundary of the ionosphere to the height of reflection h_r. Since $\mu \sim 1$ in the D-region for decametric waves one has to deal with nondeviative absorption and since further $\omega^2 \gg \nu^2$

$$ K \propto N\nu . $$

Hence the attenuation suffered by the radio wave is a measure for

$$ \int_0^{h_r} N\nu \, dh . $$

Assuming that ν remains constant in time, the attenuation is proportional to the electron content below the reflecting level. We may proceed still a little further. Since the attenuation is controlled by the *product* $N\nu$ the largest contributions come from the region where both are high, and this is, since the collision frequency decreases exponentially with height, the region between 60 and 90 km. Hence the nondeviative absorption of radio waves is a useful indicator of the electron density in the D-region.

3.4. *Measurement of absorption of radio waves in the ionosphere*
The methods of measuring ionospheric absorption falls into the following main groups
   A1 Measurement of the amplitudes of pulses reflected from the ionosphere
   A2 Measurement of the absorption of extra-terrestrial radio noise
   A3 Measurement of the field strength of sky wave signals at short distances and oblique incidence on frequencies suitable for obtaining absorption data.
In addition, relative changes in absorption can be measured semi-quantitatively using ionogram parameters, in particular the lowest frequency f_{min} where echoes are recorded.
   It shall be mentioned that the data obtained by the different methods are not necessarily identical because different levels may contribute in a different manner to the total observed absorption (Piggott and Brown, 1963).

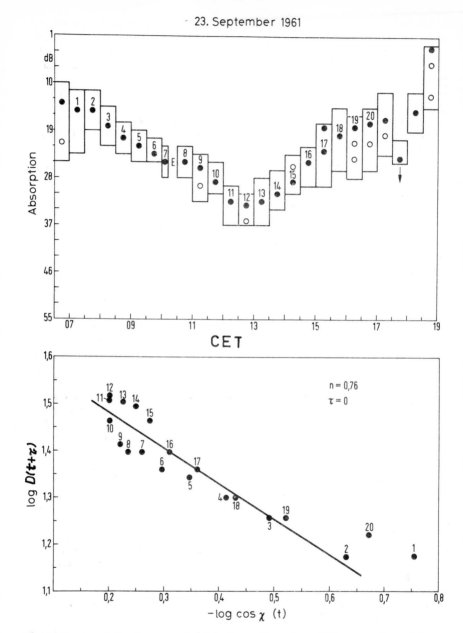

Fig. 3. Skywave intensity converted into absorption values (dB) versus time of day (upper part) and versus sun's zenith angle (lower part). The rectangles in the upper part indicate the quartile range, the full dots the most frequent values and the open circles the secundary maxima of half hourly observations.

It has been secured, however, that under proper precautions the methods
A1 and A 3 will give the same results.

Since most of the data shown in the following paragraph are based on A3
measurements the principle of this method will be shortly discussed in the
following.

The field strength of a cw radio transmitter is being recorded at a distance of a few 100 km. The distance, the antenna systems at the transmitter and the receiver, and the frequency are chosen in such a way that during
daylight only the one-hop E-reflection contributes appreciably to the field
strength recorded at the receiving site. Then the field strength is a
straightforward function of the absorption suffered on the way through the
D-region provided that the loss at the reflection point is negligible. This
can be secured by choosing a proper frequency.

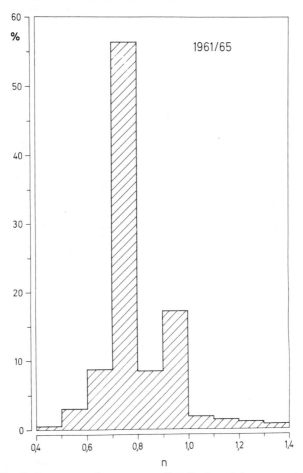

Fig. 4. Frequency of occurrence distribution of the exponent n.

4. OBSERVATIONAL RESULTS

4.1. *Diurnal variations*

A typical example of the diurnal variation of the field strength on a frequency of 2.6 MHz over a distance of approximately 300 km (Norddeich Radio, Lindau) is shown in the upper part of fig. 3. Since the field strength has been plotted in a logarithmic scale it may be converted easily into absorption values L in dB, increasing linearly downward (ordinate).

In the lower part log L has been plotted versus -log cos χ where χ is the zenith angle of the sun. Long series of such measurements (e.g. Schwentek, 1958, 1963) have shown, that the absorption loss L is given by

$$L \propto \cos^n \chi .$$

The subsolar absorption L_0 (or B in the literature) is obtained from the intercept of the (log L) versus (-log cos$_\chi$) curve with the ordinate, and the exponent n from the slope of the curve.

The value of n (fig. 4) varies between 0.4 and 1.4 with a very pronounced maximum at $n = 0.75$ and a secondary maximum at $n = 1.0$.

On many days the diurnal variation is quite regular and the hourly values are close to a straight line on the (log L) versus (-log cos$_\chi$) plot. Usually the morning and afternoon values are forming some sort of loop indicating that the absorption does not follow the sun's elevation immediately but with some delay. Thus a better fit of the individual points may be obtained by introducing a time shift τ which is of the order of 10-30 min.

$$L(t-\tau) \propto \cos^n \chi .$$

On days with solar flare effects (SFE) the smooth trend of the diurnal variation is interrupted in a characteristic manner (fig. 5a,b).

In summer and in the equinoctial months the day-to-day variation of the absorption is small on undisturbed days. In winter, however, the absorption may vary very considerably from day to day. This may be illustrated by fig. 6 where the noon values of absorption for all days of November 1962 and August 1962 have been plotted. The range of day-to-day variations is nearly twice as big in November as in August.

Another example is given in fig. 7 where the data obtained on four consecutive winter days are shown.

The first and the second day are characterized by very strong absorption which is much higher than the absorption would be in summer at comparable zenith angles of the sun. In addition the temporal variation on the first day is peculiar. Instead of a smooth variation, the absorption increases rapidly after sunrise and quickly attains a "saturation value" which is maintained for several hours. The afternoon decrease of absorption is also abnormally steep. Probably the saturation value which is rather low corresponds to the energy which is reflected partially at a height of 60-70 km during daylight conditions. Another example of the saturation effect is given in fig. 8. The excessive absorption on certain winter days is termed "winter anomaly of absorption" and will be dealt with further in the next paragraph.

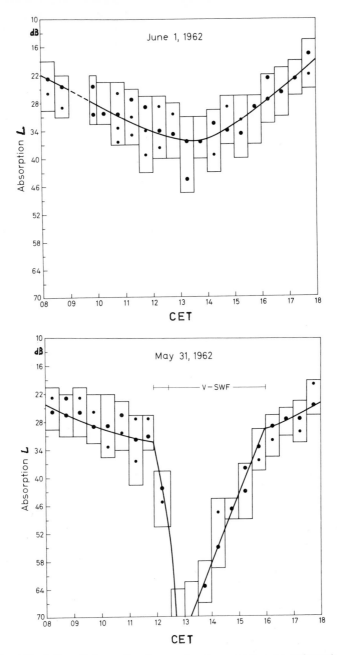

Fig. 5. a) Variation of absorption (increasing downward) on an undisturbed day.
b) Variation of absorption on a day with a "Short Wave Fadeout" (SWF) corresponding to a SFE.

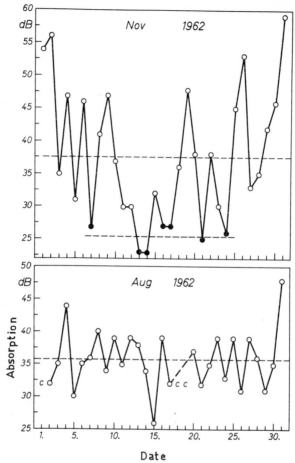

Fig. 6. Noon values of absorption (increasing upwards) in November and August 1962. About the meaning of full dots and open circles see fig. 12.

4.2. *Seasonal variation of absorption*

When plotting a full year's noon values of absorption versus the sun's zenith angle (fig. 9) one realizes that the regular trend which might be expected from the diurnal variations ($L \sim \cos^n \chi$) is disturbed in a twofold manner: the spring and fall data may be approximated by a straight line on the ($\log L$) versus ($-\log \cos_\chi$) plot corresponding to an exponent of $n = 0.75$, especially when taking into account the median values. The summer values are somewhat smaller ("summer anomaly") whereas the winter values exhibit very strong scatter and a median value which is much higher than expected from the $\cos^n \chi$ variation. Many winter values are even higher than the highest values in summer. The values shown in the diagram have been normalized to 1 MHz (A-values) assuming that the absorption varies pro-

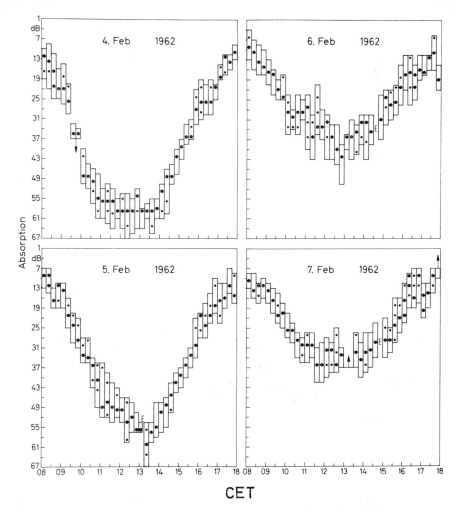

Fig. 7. Absorption loss (increasing downwards) versus time of day (UT + 1 h) on four consecutive days in winter (Symbols as in fig. 3) (CET = Central European Time).

portional to $1/(\omega \pm \omega_B)^2$ where ω_B is the pulsation of the electrons in the magnetic field of the earth. The justification of this conversion will not be discussed here.

It may be added that at least the noon values are practically free from the influence of deviative absorption since the measuring frequency was far enough from the critical frequency of the reflecting layer. The difference between the mean value of the winter months and the theoretical value corresponding to a $\cos^n \chi$ variation has been termed "amplitude of winter anomaly" ΔA (Schwentek, 1964).

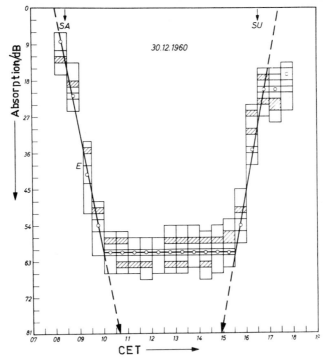

Fig. 8. Absorption loss (increasing downward) versus time of day (CET) on day with
"saturation effect". (SA = sunrise. SU = sunset).

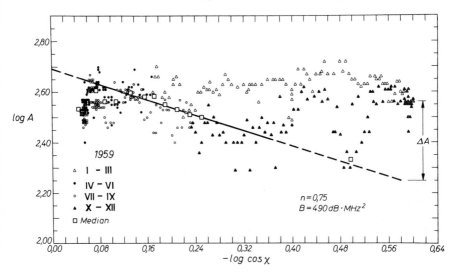

Fig. 9. Normalized absorption values A dB · MHz^2 at noon as observed during 1959
at Lindau. ΔA "amplitude of winteranomaly".

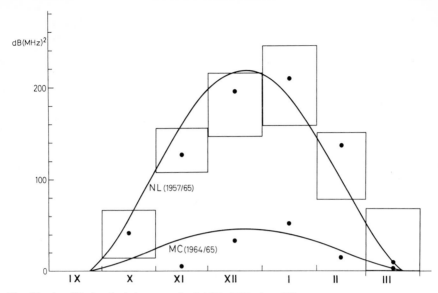

Fig. 10. Amplitude of winteranomaly ΔA dB · MHz for different months as observed at 53°N (NL) and 41°N (MC).

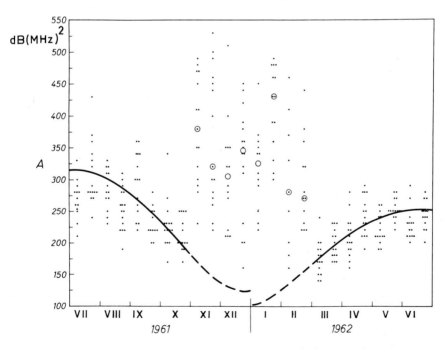

Fig. 11. Normalized noon values of absorption A for a full year (July 1961 to June 1962). The circles correspond to half monthly medians of Nov. - Febr., the discontinuity of the smooth (theoretical) curve allows for the change of solar activity.

Summing up all data from 1957 to 1965 and plotting them against an angle characterising the position of the earth on its way around the sun, one obtains a rather regular variation of the amplitude of the winter anomaly with a maximum in January (fig. 10). The winter anomaly occurs only between October and March and is absent during the rest of the year.

The winter anomaly shows up also very distinctly when plotting the individual noon values over a full year (fig. 11). The summer and equinox values are clustering quite nicely around the theoretical curve whereas the winter values are much higher, and exhibit very big scatter.

4.3. *Solar cycle variations*

The non-deviative absorption of radio waves depends very distinctly on the solar activity as shown in fig. 12. The absolute values of absorption both in summer and winter are much higher in sunspot maximum than in

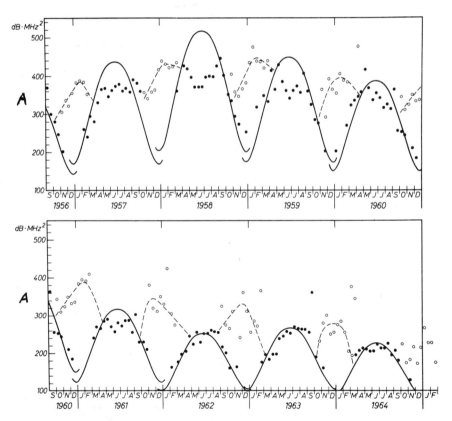

Fig. 12. Normalized monthly median values of absorption A as observed over half a sunspot cycle. The smooth curve corresponds to the theoretical variation. Full dots may be termed "normal values", open circles "anomalous values" (see also fig. 6).

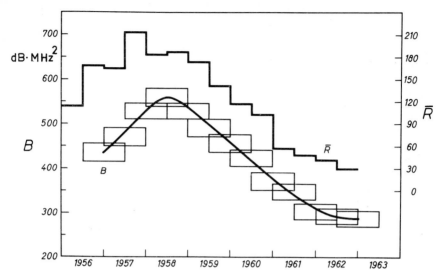

Fig. 13. Solar cycle variation of normalized subsolar absorption B and mean sunspot number R as observed over half a sunspot cycle.

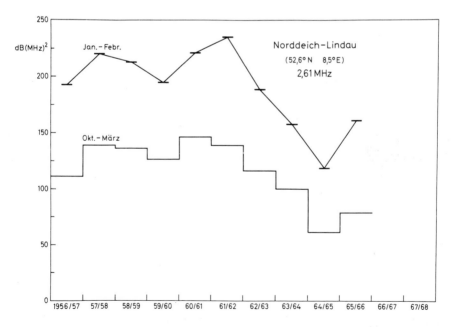

Fig. 14. Variation of the mean amplitude of winter anomaly ΔA during half a sunspot cycle. Upper curve: Jan. - Febr. values only, lower curve: all values (Oct. - March).

minimum. The difference is of the order of 200 dB·MHz² (fig. 13). For the
"amplitude of winter anomaly" ΔA the answer is a little more complicated.
As a matter of fact there was not much variation between 1956 and 1963. In
the subsequent winters, however, the intensity of the winter anomaly was
considerably smaller than in all previous winters (fig. 14). So we may say
that there is no straightforward correlation between the winter anomaly and
the solar cycle, and we have to wait for further observations before we can
decide which way it goes.

4.4. *Local variation*

Almost all values quoted in the previous paragraph pertain to observations at approximately 50ºN. A comparison with observations on the southern hemisphere shows that the winter anomaly is not an annual but a seasonal effect in the sense that it occurs in local winter with a maximum in
December/January on the northern hemisphere and a maximum in June/
July on the southern hemisphere. The winter anomaly does not show up in
the equatorial and subequatorial belt as shown by observations at Singapore
(1ºN) and Tsumeb (19ºS).

Attempts to delineate the boundary of the winter anomaly towards the
equator are in progress. A preliminary result obtained by Dieminger, Rose
and Widdel (1966) in Sardinia shows that the winter anomaly is still present

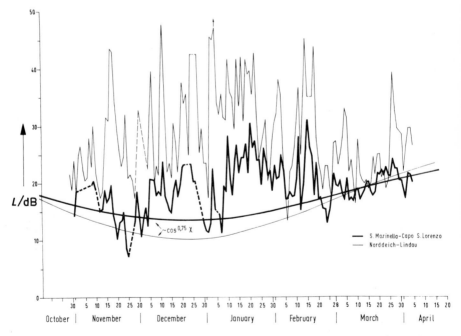

Fig. 15. Noon absorption values L/dB as observed simultaneously at 53ºN (light)
and 41ºN (heavy). The smooth curves correspond to the theoretical variation, and
are matched to the observed values on 15 March.

at 41°N but is less frequent and less intense than 53° (fig. 15). In Australia the winter anomaly has been observed even at latitudes as low as 35°S.

The boundary towards the pole may be obscured by auroral absorption effects. In addition there is no daylight in the polar region during winter.

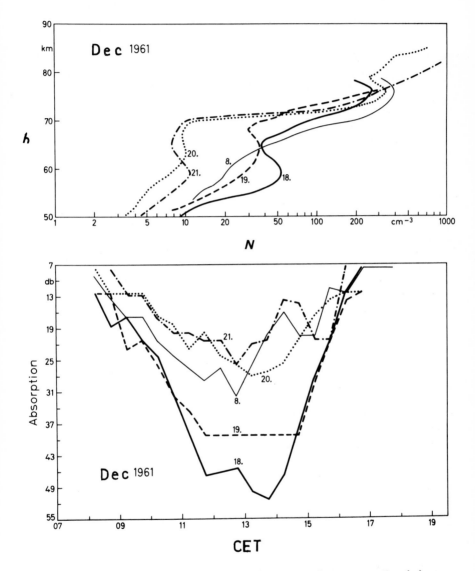

Fig. 16. Electron density profiles as observed over Canada (upper part) and absorption values as observed on the same days at Lindau, Germany (lower part). The numbers ascribed to the curves correspond to the individual days.

A rather big winter anomaly was found for a latitude of 59° by Rose (1965). The amplitude of the winter anomaly was still higher there than at 50° for certain months.

As for the worldwide distribution of the winter anomaly Thomas (1962) found an anticorrelation between the occurrence of days with winter anomaly over North America, Europe and Asia respectively. His findings are based on rather few observations and there are some doubts whether his statement, even though correct, tells the full story. Schwentek (1965) found to the contrary a very striking correlation between electron density profiles obtained by Belrose in Canada and the absorption as measured at Lindau on individual days (fig. 16). Much more coordinated measurements are indispensible for getting a worldwide picture.

Generally the situation in absorption measurements is much worse than in vertical soundings. As a result of IGY and IQSY there is a well planned network of vertical soundings stations covering all the world with only a few gaps. For absorption measurements no equivalent network exists in spite of the recommendations of the IGY and IQSY Working Groups for the Ionosphere. Obviously the reason is that the operation of the equipment and the reduction of the records is much more cumbersome than with vertical soundings.

Summing up this paragraph we may say: the winter anomaly is characterized by 3 features:

1) The absorption of radio waves is generally higher in winter than predicted by theory at middle and higher latitudes

2) The day-to-day variations are much more pronounced in winter than in summer

3) The winter anomaly is restricted to the latitude range between 35 and 60°.

5. RELATIONS BETWEEN IONOSPHERIC ABSORPTION AND METEORO-LOGICAL PHENOMENA

In a preceeding paragraph the increased absorption during Solar Flare Effects, Polar Cap Absorption and Auroral Absorption was attributed to extraterrestrial influences such as solar UV and X-ray radiation and solar particle influx. No similar correlation was found between the winter anomaly of absorption and any extraterrestrial phenomena investigated so far. Only a long term correlation between the mean values of absorption on winter days and the mean magnetic character figure has been established by Thomas (1962).

Since a control from outside can be excluded, it is very tempting to speculate on a terrestrial control of the winter anomaly by meteorological factors (Dieminger, 1952). The main reasons for this attempt are the following:

1) The winter anomaly is strictly a seasonal phenomena. It occurs only in local winter that is to say from November to February on the northern hemisphere and from May to August on the southern hemisphere. It is ab-

sent in the equatorial and subequatorial zones where is no winter, viz., where the sun's elevation at noon is higher than 45⁰ all the year over.

2) The winter anomaly occurs in groups of days just alike weather conditions in middle latitudes.

3) The winter anomaly occurs only within restricted areas which might change considerably in diameter.

4) There is no straightforward dependence of the winter anomaly on the solar cycle.

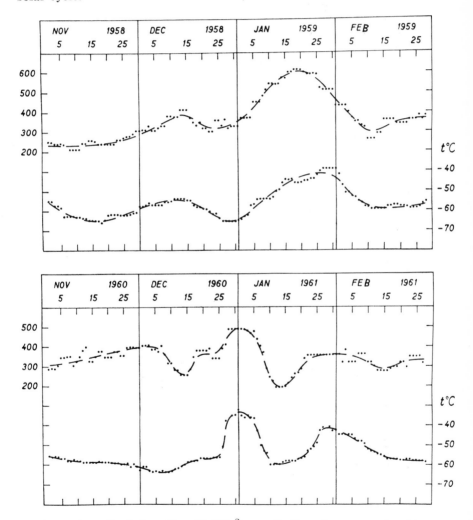

Fig. 17. a) Normalized absorption (dB·MHz²) over Freiburg (upper curve) and temperature at 10 mb over Middle Europe (lower curve) in winter 1958/1959.
b) The same for winter 1960/1961.

As to the mechanism of the winter anomaly of absorption there is little doubt that it is produced by increased electron density in the D-region. This has been proved by an inverse correlation between the intensity of E-echoes on the one hand and the strength of partial reflections from the D-region on the other hand, on days exhibiting excessive absorption (Dieminger and Hoffmann-Heyden, 1952; Dieminger, 1952; Gregory, 1965). It should be pointed out, however, that it is not the energy which is partially reflected on the way of the wave towards the E-region that accounts for the weakness of the E-echoes but the absorption which is suffered by the wave when penetrating the region of enhanced electron density. The height of the lowest echoes, however, seems to be a fair indicator of the increase of the electron density in the D-region.

A direct prove of a correlation between the winter anomaly and a mete-

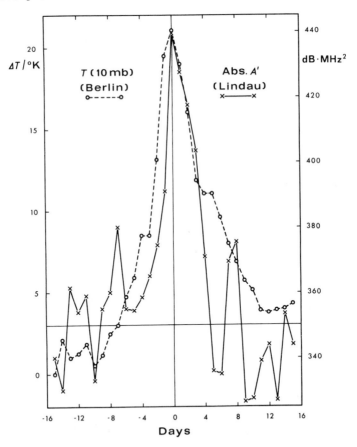

Fig. 18. Superimposed epoch diagram of excess temperature above normal at 10 mb over Berlin and normalized absorption $A'/dB \cdot MHz^2$ over Lindau for 14 selected periods.

orological parameter was given for the first time by Bossolasco and Elena
(1963) and still more convincingly by Shapley and Beynon (1965). The former correlated 7-day running means of ionospheric absorption, as observed
at Freiburg (48°N) and the corresponding values of temperature at the
10-mb level over Middle Europe (fig. 17a, b). They found correlation coefficients of +0.82 and +0.37 for winter 1958/1959 and 1960/1961 respectively. Whereas the value of +0.82 is significant the value of +0.37 is doubtful.
Gregory (1965) pointed out, however, that the low value may be caused by
extraterrestrial effects, viz. large solar flares and solar protons events
of 10 Nov. 1960 disturbing the otherwise good correlation.

Shapley and Beynon, using the method of superimposed epochs found a
very striking statistical correlation of the absorption values as observed
at Lindau (51°N) and stratospheric temperatures over Berlin. For the winter month of the years 1959-1964 they selected 14 periods each of a few
days during which the temperature at the 10-mb level exceeded the seasonal norm by 10°-30°K. Using the day of maximum temperature the "zero"
day they plotted deviations of the temperature at 10 mb and ionospheric absorption, normalized to 1 MHz and sunspot number $R = 100$, for the preceding and succeeding days (fig. 18). The peaks of both curves coincide
very well. In the average an increase of the temperature by 18°K corresponds to an 25% increase of the absorption on 1 MHz. Attempts to establish
phase relationships between both phenomena gave no unambiguous results.
Although the statistical correlation is very striking it should be pointed out
that there is no one-to-one correlation between both phenomena even when
introducing a time shift. Hence we may conclude that there is no causal in-
terdependence between stratospheric warmings and excessive absorption
but a common source of both phenomena. Most workers agree that this
source is the general mesospheric circulation.

Other cases of correlation have been reported by Gregory (1966). He
found that pressure ridges in the stratosphere over New Zealand and Australia were accompanied by the lowering of levels of radio reflection in the
D-region, and that this occurs only in winter.

Vassy (1966) investigated the lowering of the minimum height of the polar
night vortex from October to December 1964 and found a slowing down or
even a reversal of the downward movement during periods of enhanced total
electron content in the ionosphere. She attributes both phenomena to the
arrival of solar corpuscles which are less intense than those causing aurorae but powerful enough to produce heat in the upper atmosphere.

Belrose, Bourne and Hewitt (1966) investigated possible correlations between the D-region morphology and ozon concentration in the mesosphere.
Although the investigations were not conclusively they reveiled additional
complications in the behaviour of the D-region caused by the presence of
the variable ozon and atomic oxygen concentration in the mesosphere.

5.1. *General mesospheric circulation in winter*

Information on the structure of the atmosphere above 30 km was very
scarce before the introduction of rocket technique. Since 1950 data are ac-
cumulating at an increasing rate so that the values for W-to-E winds, tem-

peratures, pressures, and densities are known with some precision for the range between 30 and 80 km. Less information is available on meridional winds, and very little on vertical movements (Cira, 1965).

a) Temperature. Average temperature data as obtained at Fort Church-ill are given in fig. 19. The most important feature is a reversal of temperature variation between summer and winter at a height of 60 km. Below 60 km the air is warmer in summer, beyond 60 km it is warmer in winter. The amplitude of the temperature variation attains a maximum of 50°K at 80 km.

Models of temperature as function of height and latitude have been constructed. Two examples are given in figs. 20 and 21. They again show warm air over the winter pole and cold air over the summer pole, and a rather uniform distribution at equinox, for the height range 60-80 km.

b) Winds. Data of the zonal and meridional flow as observed over White Sands at a height of 50 km are shown in fig. 22. The zonal flow is predominantly from the east in summer and from the west in winter. The meridional flow is almost all the year over towards the pole with the exception of some winter days when it is in the opposite direction. Warm air from the pole is flowing towards the equator on those days apparently.

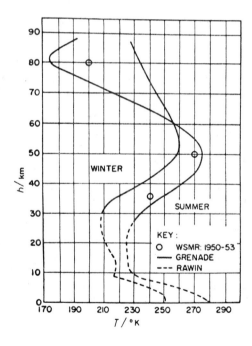

Fig. 19. Fort Churchill rocket-grenade data. The curves are the rough averages of the summer and winter firings and coincident Ravin data. Some White Sands Missile Range data obtained by this experiment in 1950-1953 are shown by circles.

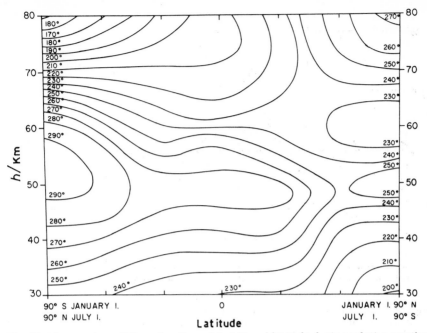

Fig. 20. Temperature (°K) as function of height and latitude during solstice months.

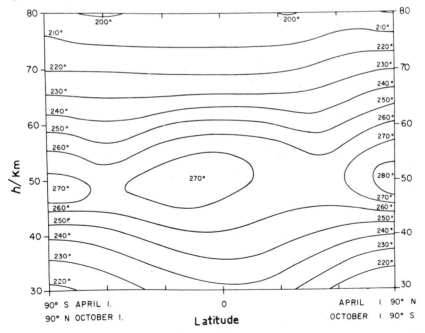

Fig. 21. Temperature (°K) as function of height and latitude during spring and fall.

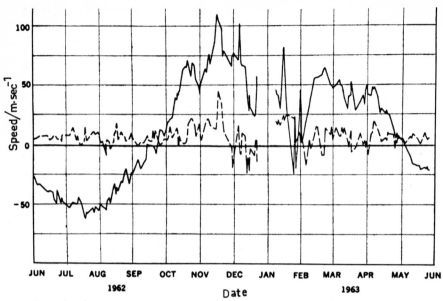

Fig. 22. The zonal (solid curve) and meridional (dashed curve) flow (m/sec) obtained by averaging the individual White Sands Missile Range soundings over a 10-km layer centered at 50 km. Positive values refer to components to the north and to the east.

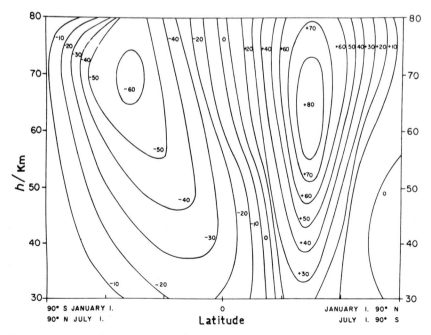

Fig. 23. Zonal wind components (m/sec) as function of height and latitude during solstice months.

Although the number of locations where such measurements have been carried out with some regularly is small it was possible to draw meridional cross sections of average conditions. An example is given in figs. 23 and 24. It illustrates very well the principal difference between mesospheric circulation in summer and winter and the gradual transition during equinoctial months.

Still more interesting for our problem are the day-to-day variations of the W-to-E flow as observed at an individual location. As shown in fig. 25 the variability is much larger during winter than during summer for all heights between 30 and 60 km. It is very striking that the scatter of the individual values is approximately 4 times as large from November to March as for the rest of the year.

This variability has to be attributed to the breakdown of the polar-night vortex which is a characteristic feature of the circulation in the northern hemisphere in winter (Murgatroyd et al., 1965). The polar night vortex consists of a strong westerly wind system in the stratosphere which is centred on the Eurasian side of the pole and extends down to the 100-mb level. A similar system which is less excentric exists over the south-pole.

The breakdown of the polar night westerlies takes the form of sudden or even explosive warmings (of 30-60°) which begin in the upper stratosphere, and spread laterally and downward until the entire stratosphere's tempera-

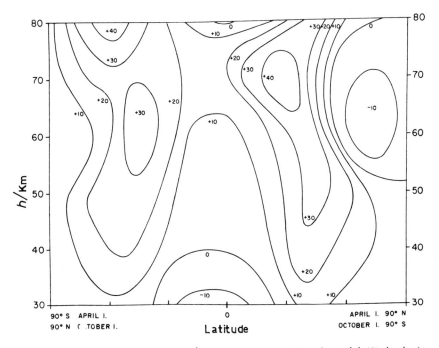

Fig. 24. Zonal wind components (m/sec) as function of height and latitude during spring and fall.

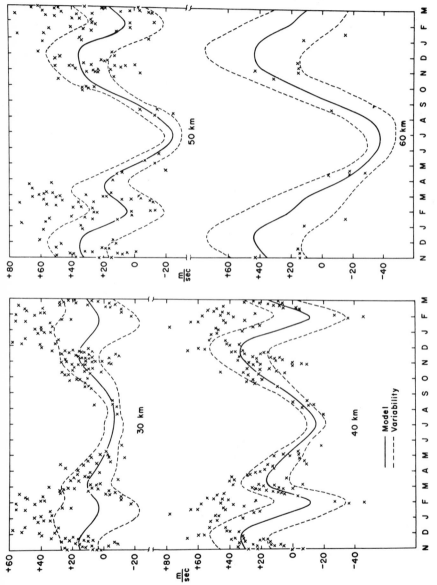

Fig. 25. Comparison between model and measurements of W-to-E winds at Fort Greely (64°N) for different heights.

ture is raised to levels above those of high summer. Simultaneously the direction of the wind is reversed. After a few days the original state is restored, apparently by cooling. This is repeated several times until the final warming takes place in spring where the polar night vortex is driven out of the polar regions. Its place is taken by irregular anticyclones that slowly settle down into the symmetrical westerlies of summer.

Pressure and density data show higher values in summer than in winter for all heights and all latitudes. Excluding stratospheric warmings the quartile range of the variability of pressure is approximately 10 (5)% at a height of 50 km and 19 (8)% at a height of 70 km at 30 (60)⁰ latitude. Increases of pressure by 50% at the 10-mb level have been observed during stratospheric warmings of 30⁰K.

5.2. *Production of enhanced electron density*

Although there is a striking resemblance between these features of the general mesospheric circulation and the occurrence of the winter anomaly we do not fully understand yet the processes leading to an increased electron density in the D-region and, as a consequence, the excessive absorption of radio waves. Only a few systematic investigations have been made so far, aimed at explaining the production mechanism. Even these were not based on measurements at the same height since no temperature measurements were available for the 60-80 km range.

Instead Gregory (1965) used temperature measurements at 20-30-mb levels (or equivalent layer thicknesses) over Australia and compared them to the isopleths of electron density for a period of 19 days (fig. 26). Clearly

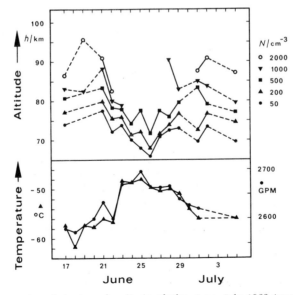

Fig. 26. Time series of electron density isopleths. June-July 1963 (upper part): time series of stratospheric temperatures 20-30 mb levels (lower curve).

enough the increase of temperature at the 20-30-mb level is accompanied by a downward movement of the isopleths leading to an increase of total electron density and hence of absorption.

Gregory attempted to determine the process responsible for the temperature increase. Data for winds above the 70-mb level were not available for the period 21-25 June. For 23 June, the amount of horizontal advection of temperature in the layer 100-70-mb was estimated from vertical shear of measured winds which were assumed to be geostrophic. The advection proved to be small and cold. The contribution from local pressure changes in the same altitudes was negligible. A probable origin of the warmings, however, appears to be a downward motion, which, for the period 22-23 June, would have a magnitude of 1 cm sec^{-1} around the 20-mb level. Consequently a possible interpretation of the events between 22-25 June is that downward motion occurred in both the mesosphere and the stratosphere increasing the electron density in the former and the temperature in the latter. From 25-29 June, the vertical motion appears to have decreased or even reversed its direction.

Pending further studies this reasoning may be regarded a working hypothesis which must be proved or disproved by systematic investigations. Accepting it for a moment the question remains open how the electron density is increased. The simplest way is direct downward transport from the E-region which may be regarded an inexhaustible reservoir of electrons. It has been inferred that the lifetime of the electrons at the respective heights is much too short to allow a detectable increase of electron density at levels some 10 km below the E-region. A calculation by Kohl (1966) based on rather simplified assumptions (no electron production below 100 km, constant electron production above 100 km) shows that electron density increases of the observed order of magnitude do occur for vertical motions of the neutral gas with a speed of a few m sec^{-1} (fig. 27). Vertical speeds of that magnitude should be easily detectable in the mesosphere, and have been observed in some cases. But even if this assumption is disproved a redistribution of the ionisable constituents by vertical motion may also lead to the observed effects. The electrons may be produced then by the solar radiation in situ. The question arises, however, why this radiation is not being absorbed already at greater heights. Also negative ions which are rather frequent in the lower ionosphere (10^3 cm^{-3} at 65 km and 3×10^3 cm^{-3} at 50 km during night time (Hale, 1966) may be a source of electrons produced by photodetachment during daylight. Here the difficulty of absorption at greater heights does not exist, because even visible light is energetic enough for detachment. Hence an enhanced vertical transport of negative ions may also lead to an increase of electron density. Also an increase of the collisional frequency cannot be excluded a priori.

5.3. *Irregularities in the D-layer*

Finally we may discuss very briefly the question of inhomogeneities in the D-region. The increased absorption does not necessarily presuppose the existence of irregularities in the D-layer. Even a perfectly smooth distribution of the electron density would create absorption of radio waves.

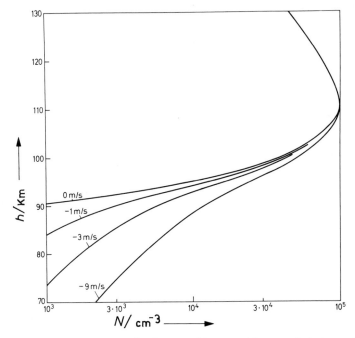

Fig. 27. Redistribution of electrons by downward transport for speeds between 1 and 9 m sec^{-1}.

The existence of partial reflections, however, is bound to the existence of, although small, irregularities in the distribution of electrons. Even a variation of a few percent of the electron density over a distance of one wavelength is sufficient to explain a reflection coefficient of 10^{-5}. The rapid variations of the amplitude of partially reflected wave point also to (moving) irregularities. Whether the irregularities are concentrated at certain heights spaced by 6-10 km (Gregory, 1961) is still controversial. Generally these results are in accordance with meteorological observations which have revealed strong winds and very pronounced vertical wind shear in the mesosphere.

6. CONCLUDING REMARKS

It results from our discussion that the problem of the control of the D-region by meteorological phenomena is far from being solved. Much more coordinated experiments are necessary in order to test the various hypothesis. Emphasis should be laid on a proper coordination of the observations. Only a combination of simultaneous aeronomical and meteorological measurements will expedite the understanding of the interrelations at the present stage. The goal of these efforts is very attractive indeed. It would establish a link between the lower and the upper atmosphere for the first time.

REFERENCES

Appleton. E.V., 1927, URSI Proc. Washington.
Belrose. J.S., I.A.Bourne and L.W.Hewitt, 1966, The winter anomaly of electron
   number density in the lower ionosphere over Ottawa. A discussion of results and
   possible cause, in: Electron density profiles in ionosphere and exosphere, J. Fri-
   hagen, ed. (Amsterdam).
Bibl. K., A.Paul and R.Rawer, 1962. Absorption in the D- and E-regions and its
   time variation, in: Radio wave absorption in the ionosphere, N.C.Gerson, ed.
   (Oxford) (AGARDograph 53).
Bossolasco, M. and A.Elena. 1963. Absorption de la couche D et temperature de la
   mésosphère. Compt. Rend. 256, 4491.
Davies. K., 1965. Ionospheric radio propagation. National Bureau of Standards
   Monograph 80 (Washington D.C.).
Dieminger. W., 1952. Über die Ursachen der excessiven Absorption in der Iono-
   sphäre an Wintertagen. J. Atmos. Terr. Phys. 2, 340.
Dieminger. W. and A.E. Hoffmann-Heyden. 1952. Reflexionen von Kurzwellen aus
   Höhen unter 100 km. Naturwiss. 39, 84.
Dieminger. W., G.Rose and H.U.Widdel. 1966. On the existence of anomalous radio
   wave absorption during winter in 40^0 northern latitude. J.Atmos.Terr.Phys.28,317.
Dieminger. W., G.Rose and H.U.Widdel. 1966. The morphology of winter anomaly
   of absorption. COSPAR Meeting Vienna.
Försterling. K. and H.Lassen. 1933. Kurzwellenausbreitung in der Atmosphäre,
   Jahrb. drahtl. Telegr. Teleph. 42, 158.
Gerson. N.C., ed., 1962. Radio wave absorption in the ionosphere (Oxford) (AGARD-
   ograph 53).
Gossard. Earl E., 1967, in: Space Research VII. R.L.Smith-Rose, ed. (North-Hol-
   land, Amsterdam) 76.
Gregory. J.B., 1965, The influence of atmospheric circulation on mesospheric
   electron densities in winter, J. Atmos. Sci. 22, 18.
Gregory. J.B., 1967, Evidence for propagation of mobile waves from the troposphere
   to the mesosphere. Symposium on interactions between upper and lower layers of
   the atmosphere (Vienna, 1966).
Hale. L.C., 1967, in: Space Research VII. R.L.Smith-Rose, ed. (North-Holland,
   Amsterdam) 140.
Hartree. D.R., 1931. The propagation of electromagnetic waves in a refracting me-
   dium in a magnetic field. Proc. Cambridge Phil. Soc. 27, 143.
Kellog. W.W., 1967. Report on the symposium on interactions between the upper and
   lower layers of the atmosphere (Vienna, 1966).
Lassen. H., 1927. Über den Einfluss des Erdmagnetfeldes auf die Fortpflanzung der
   elektrischen Wellen der drahtlosen Telegraphie in der Atmosphäre. Elektr.
   Nachr. Techn. 4, 324.
Murgatroyd. R.J., F.K.Hare, B.W.Boville, S.Toweless and A.Kochansky, 1965.
   The circulation in the stratosphere. mesosphere and lower termosphere. WMO
   Technical Note 70 (Geneva).
Narcisi. R.S., 1967, in: Space Research VII. R.L.Smith-Rose, ed. (North-Holland,
   Amsterdam) 186.
Piggott. W.R. and G.M.Brown (eds.). 1963. Absorption measurements. IQSY In-
   struction Manual No. 4 Ionosphere. CIG-IQSY Committee (London).
Ratcliffe. J.A., 1959. The magnetoionic theory (Cambridge).
Rose. G., Über die Bestimmung der D-Schichtabsorption für eine 2000 km lange
   Strecke und ihre Endpunkte. A.E.Ü. 19, 103.
Schwentek. H., 1958. Bestimmung eines Kennwertes für die Absorption der Iono-
   sphäre aus einer automatisch-statistischen Analyse von Feldstärkeregistrierun-
   gen. A.E.Ü.12, 301.
Schwentek. H., 1964. Der Verlauf der mittäglichen Dämpfungskennwerte der Iono-
   sphäre von 1956-1963 (Jahresgänge und Winteranomalie). A.E.Ü. 15, 200.

Schwentek. H.. 1965, Zur Absorption von Grenzwellen in der Ionosphäre. Kleinheu-
bacher Berichte 11. 191.
Sen. H.K. and A.A.Wyller. 1960, On the generalisations of the Appleton-Hartree
magnetoionic formulas. J. Geophys. Res. 65, 3931.
Shapley. A.H. and W.J.G.Beynon. 1965. "Winteranomaly" in ionospheric absorption
and stratospheric warmings. Nature 206. 1242.
Thomas. L.. 1962. The winter anomaly in ionospheric absorption. Radiowave absorption in the ionosphere. G.Gerson (ed.). Pergamon Press (Oxford) (AGARD-
ograph 53).
Tříska. P.. 1967. in: Space Research VII. R.L.Smith-Rose. ed. (North-Holland,
Amsterdam) 247.
Vassy. A.. 1967. Relations between total electron content of the ionospheric absorption in winter. Symposium on interactions between upper and lower layers of
the atmosphere (Vienna. 1966).

DISCUSSION

Rawer:

To my knowledge no geomagnetic control is known to exist in meteorology. As the phenomena of winter anomaly seem to depend mainly on meteorological effects I cannot see how a geomagnetic control could be produced
except for an influence on the electron density. However, there seems also
to be no relation between magnetic perturbations and winter anomaly so that
I cannot see how a geomagnetic influence would be produced.

Triska had also the idea that ions with rather low ionization potential
could be important at a downward transport of ionization. It is known now
that the Es-layers contain mainly metallic ions of low ionization potential.
This is a trap situation as the usual dissociative recombination is excluded
for these ions which cannot transfer their charge to a neutral gas molecule
(because the energy difference is too large). Therefore for ions from certain minor constituents only very slow recombination processes are possible, so that the effective recombination coefficient may be smaller than
usual by at least one order of magnitude, so that a slow downward motion
could transport enough ionization from the E-region downwards.

Houll:

Dr. Hale plans to make measurements in Alaska of negative night time
ion densities. I think these data may be significant for your hypothesis of
electron production.

Dieminger:

Any measurement of negative ion densities would be very welcome in
order to elucidate the phenomena.

Nguyen:

Remarque concernant l'éventuel transport d'ionisation de la région E à
la région D, mentionné par le Prof. Dieminger (p. 172):

Le principal obstacle de l'efficacité du mouvement de transport d'ionisation créé par le gaz neutre est la faible durée de vie des ions de struc-

ture (O_2^+, NO^+ etc.), ce qui n'est pas le cas si l'on considère les ions mé-
talliques tels les ions d'origine météorique dont la durée de vie est très
grande (comme a mentionné le Prof. Rawer dans la discussion d'hier). A
ce sujet, il serait peut-être intéressant de remarquer que la phénomène
mentionnée par le Prof. Dieminger à lieu vers la fin du mois de juin, période qui correspond en général à une forte activité météorique. (Pour le
mois de juin on peut citer des forts courants météoriques comme Arietids
D, Perseids D, Ophuichids S).

En ce qui concerne les mouvements de gaz neutre susceptibles de créer
un transport vertical d'ionisation vers le bas, on peut en citer deux:

1) Le mouvement vertical de gaz neutre qui entraîne l'ionisation avec
lui.
2) Les cisaillements verticaux de vent horizontal qui, en présence du
champ magnétique, ont pour effet d'entasser l'ionisation à des niveaux déterminés, solidaires du système de vents (force de Lorentz).
Or, les observations de vents par les trainées de Sodiom et par les
échos météoriques montrent que les systèmes de vent horizontal à
faibles échelles (verticales) effectuent un mouvement vertical de descente de l'ordre = 1 km/h. De là on peut s'attendre à que l'ionisation
soit entraînée vers le bas avec le système de vent.

Dieminger:

The existence of rather large numbers of long-lived ions in the D- and
E-region which may be brought in by meteors has been shown by Narcisi
(1966) recently. During rocket ascends on 16 and 17 November 1965 he
found unexpectedly large number densities of positive ions other than N_2^+,
O_2^+ and NO^+. These ions are supposed to be natrium, magnesium, aluminium, calium, iron and nickel and their oxides. The observations, however,
coincided with the shower of the Leonid meteors which was unusually strong
in 1965. Therefore, it is doubtful whether these ions or part of them are
present in great numbers all the time over, or only temporarily as a result of the exceptional meteor shower on 16 November 1965. With these
long-living ions a much slower vertical transport would be sufficient to explain the enhanced electron density in the D-region. For the winter anomaly, however, only movements are relevant which are typical for winter
conditions, and which are present only on days exhibiting anomalous absorption.

Ranzi:

It is important to observe that the large-scale travelling disturbances in
the F2-layer present a behaviour which is very similar to the one of the
winter anomaly. Such moving irregularities occur especially during winter,
in group of days, and appear to originate at about 60° of latitude; they proceed towards the equator with a vanishing amplitude, so that at about 30° of
latitude they are scarcely visible. Furthermore, they are not correlated
with the magnetic activity.

Dieminger:

Prof. Ranzi's comment adds a further phenomenon which should be taken into account when studying the winter anomaly.

Stilke:

For the explanation of the anomal winter effects (absorption in the D-layer, stratospheric warming in 20-10 mb levels) *by subsidence*, a downward motion of some 100 cm sec^{-1} in 70 km height and of about 1 cm sec^{-1} in 30 km height has been calculated. The difference might be explained by the density change with height, assuming nearly *constant* downward *mass transport*. If between these layers no divergence occurs, a downward motion of 1 cm sec $^{-1}$ at 30 km height (air density $\sim 1.8 \times 10^{-2}$ kg m^{-3}) would correspond to a downward motion of about 60 cm sec^{-1} in 60 km height ($\rho \sim 3.06 \times 10^{-4}$), 210 cm sec^{-1} in 70 km height ($\rho \sim 8.75 \times 10^{-5}$) and 900 cm sec^{-1} in 80 km height ($\rho \sim 2.0 \times 10^{-5}$).
The values for air density have been taken from Dr. Fedele's paper: Atmospheric structure between 30 and 120 km, table 1.

Dieminger:

The comment of Dr. Stilke shows that the velocities necessary for explaining the enhanced electron density by transport of electrons are not a priori incompatible with well established meteorological observations. For a final decision, in situ measurements are highly desirable.

Shapley:

I would inquire whether all days in winter are anomalous, and some more anomalous than others. (The reply from the discussion was that perhaps 80% of winter days at Lindau deviate greatly from the cosχ law, while the remainder are "normal"; Sardinia has about $\frac{2}{3}$ as many anomalous days.)

Comment: I would point out that effectively all the ionospheric and aeronomic rocket results and most of the meteorological rocket results refer to the North American hemisphere, which is just the area where data are few on the Winter Anomaly in ionospheric absorption and where the indications which do exist hint that the Winter Anomaly is much weaker than in the European zone. Thus even though the geographic latitudes are similar, the phenomena may or may not be comparable. For example, the very intense stratospheric warming of 1963 passed close to St. Johns and to Ottawa in Canada, but the *fmin* data from the windsondes there, admittably not a very sensitive indication of absorption, showed no detectable effect.

However, it can be said that the stratospheric-ionospheric relation as studied by the superposed epoch method, is successful in the Aleutian area, where the geographic and geomagnetic latitudes are similar to Europe.

In future one should try to arrange full radio observations in the American, or more rocket observation in Europe, or both.

STRUCTURE OF THE D-REGION FROM PARTIAL
RADIO REFLECTION OBSERVATIONS

W. DIEMINGER
Max-Planck-Institut für Aeronomie
Lindau/Harz

Abstract. The partial reflection method is based on the simultaneous measurement of the amplitude of the o- and x-component of partially reflected radio waves. Both the collision frequency at the lower boundary of the ionosphere and the electron density versus height can be calculated from the measurements for the region between 60 and 90 km. Approximately 80 profiles have been derived in different latitudes for undisturbed conditions, and during SID's and PCA's. Generally the results agree with those obtained by other methods.

Résumé. La méthode de la réflection partielle dépend de la mésure simultanée de l'amplitude des componentes d'ondes o et x après réflexion partielle. Des mésures effectuées on peut déduire d'une part la fréquence des collisions à la limite inférieure de l'ionosphère, d'autre part le profile de la densité électronique en fonction de l'altitude entre 60 et 90 km. Presque 80 profiles ont été dérivées à différentes latitudes pour des conditions non-perturbées, mais aussi durant des perturbations brusques (SID) et des évènements d'absorption polaire (PCA). En général les résultats sont conformes à ceux obtenus par d'autres méthodes.

1. INTRODUCTION

The conventional method of measuring the electron density in the ionosphere, viz. vertical echo sounding, fails for the lowest part of the ionosphere for several reasons. First the electron density in the D-region is so small that the corresponding plasma frequency is in a frequency range where echo soundings are hardly possible for organisational (other services) or technical (expensive antenna systems) reasons. Second the collision frequency is so high that absorption is very pronounced especially for low frequencies. Third the interpretation of the observations becomes difficult because of the complex influence of the collisions and the geomagnetic field on the refractive index. Fourth the ray theory breaks down for frequencies low enough to be totally reflected in the lower part of the D-region. Other radio methods, therefore, must be applied for exploring the D-region. One of them, notably the partial reflection method, will be discussed in detail in the following chapters.

2. DETERMINATION OF THE ELECTRON DENSITY PROFILE BY THE PARTIAL REFLECTION TECHNIQUE

There are three main experiments for measuring the electron density distribution in the D-region: partial reflections, pulse cross-modulation, and VLF propagation. Although all of them have contributed considerably to the knowledge of the D-region it seems fair to say that up to now the partial reflection technique has given the most accurate and most numerous information. It has been introduced by Gardner and Pawsey (1953), and its experimental and theoretical background will be discussed in the following paragraph.

2.1. *Experimental system*

Using conventional ionospheric sounders the lowest echoes are being recorded at a height of 100 km. These echoes are attributed to total reflections at levels where the refractive index approaches zero. Increasing the overall sensitivity of the equipment (by increasing the power of the sender, the efficiency of the receiver, or by selecting locations with very low noise level) more and more echoes become visible at heights down to 60 km (fig. 1) (Dieminger and Hoffmann-Heyden, 1952). The simultaneous occurrence of these low echoes, and of echoes from the E-region proves that the low height reflections are partial ones. The echoes are most distinct on frequencies below 3 MHz. For most locations the use of frequencies below 1.6 MHz is excluded by the extensive and continuous use of these frequencies by broadcast and other services. Therefore most observations have been carried out between 2 and 3 MHz. In principle they are possible also on higher frequencies.

The experimental system has been improved considerably since the early experiments of Gardner and Pawsey (1953). This may be illustrated by comparing the original equipment of Gardner and Pawsey with a more modern one employed by Belrose, Bodé, Hewitt and Griffin (1964) in Canada. The great expenditure in equipment such as Belrose's unfortunately prevents a worldwide application of this powerful technique.

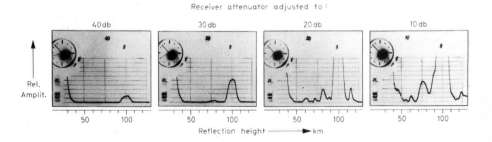

Fig. 1. A 2-second sequence of amplitude-reflection height snapshots for different gains of the receiver (Tsumeb 21 April 1965, 15.52 h, 15° EMT, frequency 750 kHz).

Table 1

	Gardner and Pawsey (1953)	Belrose et al. (1964)
Frequency	2.28 MHz	2.66 MHz
Peak power	1 kW	1000 kW
Transmitting aerial	$\frac{1}{2}\lambda$ dipole	4 dipoles circularly pol.
Receiving aerial	2 dipoles circularly pol.	4 dipoles circularly pol.
Rejection ratio	22 dB	40–60 dB

Since the partial reflection method is based on a simultaneous measurement of the amplitude of both magnetoionic components of the downcoming wave the separation of the ordinary (o) and extraordinary (x) mode is essential for the purpose of the experiment.

The separation into the ordinary and extraordinary component may be achieved either at the receiving or the transmitting site by using a pair of crossed dipoles, and a network shifting the phase of the emf of one dipole by + or -90°. Since for a circular polarized wave and vertical incidence the two rectangular components are out of phase by + or -90°, according to the direction of rotation, the phase difference of both emf's after the phase shifting network will be 0 for the one component and 180° for the other, and the latter will be cancelled when superposing both emf's. Since the polarization is not exactly circular for dip angles < 90° some rest of the unwanted polarization will remain. For dip angles > 45°, however, a suppression of 20 dB is possible without difficulty. Near the magnetic equator the system does not work any longer since the polarization becomes linear there. A separation of the o and x component at the magnetic equator may be achieved by using linear dipoles parallel to the magnetic meridian for the o, and perpendicular to the magnetic meridian for the x component (Dieminger, Rose and Widdel, 1966).

The most convenient method of displaying the amplitude of both components simultaneously is by an A-scope indicating the amplitude of the one component in the positive x-direction and of the other component inversely in the negative x-direction. If the position of the phase shifter and the direction of the deflection on the A-scope is changed synchronously in quick succession a standing pattern is obtained on the A-scope showing the amplitudes of both components simultaneously (fig. 2).

2.2. *Theory of partial reflections*

The theory used by Gardner and Pawsey is based on the assumption that the reflections are caused by irregularities in the electron density distribution. The partial reflection coefficient at a plane interface at which the refractive index changes from n_1 to n_2 is given by

$$A = \frac{n_1 - n_2}{n_1 + n_2}$$

The (complex) refractive indexes for the ordinary and extraordinary waves are given by

$$(n_{o,x})^2 = 1 - \cfrac{X}{(1-jZ) - \cfrac{Y_T^2}{2(1-jZ-X)} \pm \sqrt{\cfrac{Y_T^4}{4(1-jZ-X)^2} + Y_L^2}},$$

where N = electron density, e = charge, m = mass of electron, $w = 2\pi f$, f = wavefrequency, $B_{L,T}$ = strength of the longitudinal (transversal) component of the earth's magnetic field,

$$X = \frac{Ne^2}{\epsilon_o\, m\omega^2}; \qquad\qquad Y_{L,T} = \frac{eB_{L,T}}{m\omega}; \qquad\qquad Z = \frac{\nu}{\omega}$$

or for brevity
$$(n_{o,x})^2 = 1 - \frac{X}{W_{o,x}}.$$

For the frequency and the height range concerned

$$X \simeq 10^{-7} \text{ and } W \simeq 1\ ,\qquad\qquad \frac{X}{W} = \ll 1;\ n \simeq 1 - \frac{X}{2\ W_{o,x}}.$$

Taking into account that $n_1 \simeq 1$; $n_2 \simeq 1$, $A_{o,x} = \dfrac{X_1 - X_2}{4\ W_{o,x}}$,

where $A_{o,x}$ are the reflection coefficients of the o, x waves.
The ratio A_x/A_o is then given by

$$\frac{A_x}{A_o} = \frac{W_o}{W_x}.$$

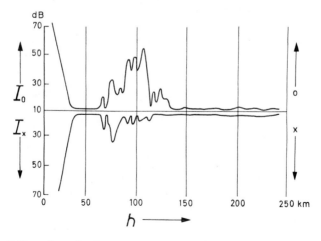

Fig. 2. Partially reflected echoes from D-region. Upper trace: ordinary component I_o, lower trace extraordinary component I_x.

Furthermore $W_{0,X}$ are practically independent of X.

The absorption coefficients $K_{0,X}$ for small values of X are given by

$$K_{0,X} = \frac{\omega}{c} \operatorname{Im}\{n_{0,X}\} = \frac{\omega}{c} \operatorname{Im}\left\{\frac{X}{2W_{0,X}}\right\} .$$

We now turn to the reflection coefficient R of the radio waves on the ground. It will be given by

$$R = A\, e^{-\rho} .$$

$\rho = \int K ds$ is the integrated absorption, up and down in nepers. The observed ratio of the ordinary and extraordinary component is given by

$$\frac{R_X}{R_0} = \frac{A_X \exp(-\rho_X)}{A_0 \exp(-\rho_0)}$$

For the lower boundary of the ionosphere where the electron density starts to raise, ρ is negligible. Hence

$$\frac{R_X}{R_0} = \frac{A_X}{A_0} = \frac{W_0}{W_X}$$

and since W is independent of X

$$\frac{R_X}{R_0} = f(Y_T, Y_L, Z)$$

and for $Y_T = \text{const}$, $Y_L = \text{const}$, $Z = \text{const}$

$$\frac{R_X}{R_0} = f(\nu) \text{ only },$$

that is to say the ratio of amplitudes for a given magnetic dip and a given frequency depends only on the collision frequency at the reflection level, for echoes coming from the lower boundary of the ionosphere. Hence the collisional frequency may be derived from that ratio inserting proper values for the dip angle and the frequency of the sounding wave.

As soon as the waves penetrate into the ionosphere absorption becomes appreciable, and differs for the **O** and **X** component. The ratio of the observed amplitudes is given by

$$\frac{R_X}{R_0} = \frac{A_X \exp(-\int 2K_X dh)}{A_0 \exp(-\int 2K_0 dh)} = \frac{A_X}{A_0} \exp(-\int 2(K_X - K_0)dh) = \frac{A_X}{A_0} \exp(-\rho_d)$$

$A_X/A_0 (h)$ may be calculated from the profile $\nu(h)$ under the assumption that ν varies exponentially with height:

$$\nu = \nu_0 \exp\{-(h - h_0)/H\} ,$$

where H is the scale height and ν_0 the collisional frequency at height h_0; the collisional frequency ν_0 in turn may be derived from $R_X/R_0 = A_X/A_0$ of the echoes coming from the lower boundary of the ionosphere.

The electron density can be derived by using the equation

$$K_{0,X} = \operatorname{Im}\left\{\frac{X}{2W_{0,X}}\right\}, \quad \text{where} \quad X = \frac{Ne^2}{\epsilon_0\, m\omega^2} .$$

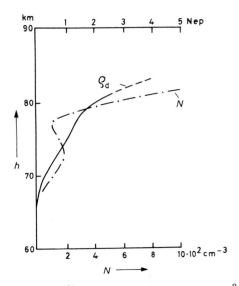

Fig. 3. Differential absorption ρ_d/Nep and electron density N cm^{-3} versus height derived from the amplitude ratio R_x/R_o.

Since the differential absorption ρ_d is given by an integral, the total electron density $\int N dh$ up to the height h must be derived first and then N from the slope of the $\int N dh$ curve.

An example is given in fig. 3, where ρ_d and N have been plotted versus h.

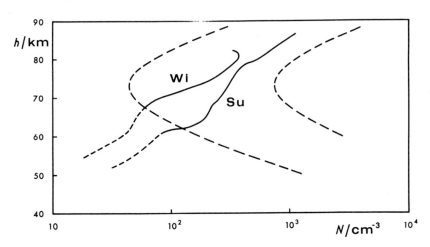

Fig. 4. Representative summer (Su) and winter (Wi) electron density profile and estimated upper and lower limits of measurable electron density (broken lines). (equipment of Gardner and Pawsey.)

The original theory of Gardner and Pawsey has been criticized for three reasons: First it is assumed that the partial reflections are caused only by irregularities of the electron density. It might be, however, some contribution of irregularities of the collisional frequency. This is the most serious deficiency of the theory. Second the ratio A_x/A_O depends to some extent on the polarisation of the transmitting antenna when frequencies near the gyrofrequency are used. This may be eliminated by using circularly polarized transmitting antennas. Third the Appleton-Lassen formula has been used for calculating the collisional frequency. In more recent work, however, the generalized magnetoionic theory of Sen and Wyller (1960) has been used giving significantly different values of ν and consequently of N.

Generally the applicability of the method is limited by experimental accuracy to the height range between 60 and 80 km with a maximum of accuracy between 65 and 75 km. The range of measurable electron density also depends on the height as shown in fig. 4.

3. OBSERVATIONAL RESULTS

A summary of the partial reflection experiments is given in table 2. Typical records on 2.66 and 6.275 MHz made at about the same time, are shown in fig. 5a (Belrose and Burke, 1964). The center of the ground pulse is taken as zero height, and the o component is shown by the upper trace. Transmitter powers of 80-100 kW and four dipole arrays were employed at both frequencies. The following features should be noted.

At 2.66 MHz echoes are observed for heights above about 55 km. The o component amplitude (upper trace) increases with height up to the E-region, whereas the x mode amplitude (lower inverted trace) which was at first the stronger, is rapidly absorbed at heights above about 80 km. The echo marked A is a leak-through due to incomplete suppression of the O component reflected at the E-layer.

The signal strength of the 6.275-MHz partial echoes is generally some 20 dB weaker than that of the 2.66-MHz echoes. The 6.275-MHz waves are reflected from heights above 100 km. Scatter echoes are observed for heights above about 75 km, and the strongest returns are from heights between 90 and 100 km. The echoes above about 100 km are believed to be oblique echoes from lower strata, although there are other complications, since the echo peaks for the o and x component do not always appear at corresponding heights (e.g. the echo marked B). The echoes in the 100-km range may be due also to the ionised trails of micrometeorites. These complications point to the fact that much care must be exercised in analysing the records.

Fig. 5b shows records taken on a day with excessive absorption. On both frequencies the signal strengths are much weaker than those in fig. 5a. On 2.66 MHz the echoes are 70 to 80 dB weaker than normal.

We shall not go into details of the reduction of the records. An example of the spread of the values of A_x/A_O as observed for different heights on the same day is given in fig. 6. The spread is considerable, and it is

Table 2
A summary of partial reflection experiments.

Date	Group	Location	TX antenna polarization	Display	ν_m	N(h)	Theory
May 1952	Gardner and Pawsey	Bimlow Australia 33°S, 151°E	linear	Intensity recording o, x, o sequence in 1 min	1 value	2 profiles	Appleton–Hartree
Jan–June 1958	Fejer and Vice	Frankenwald South Africa 26°S, 28°E	circular	Double trace A–scan o and x separated by $\frac{1}{4}$ sec	1 value	1 profile	Appleton–Hartree
1958 to 1964	Holt, Landmark and Lied Holt Haug	Lavangsdalen Norway 69°N, 19°E	linear	Double trace A–scan o and x separated by $\frac{1}{50}$ sec		22 profiles	Sen and Wyller
1961 to 1965	Belrose Belrose and Burke Belrose and Cetiner Belrose and Hewitt Belrose, Bourne and Hewitt	Ottawa Canada 45°N, 76°W	circular	Double trace A–scan o and x separated by $\frac{1}{15}$ sec	17 values	33 profiles	Sen and Wyller
1963 to 1965	Belrose, Bode and Hewitt	Resolute bay Canada 75°N, 95°W	circular	Double trace A–scan o and x separated by $\frac{1}{15}$ sec	3 values	1 profile	Sen and Wyller
1965	Belrose, Matthews and McNamara	Churchill Canada 58°N, 94°W	circular	Double trace A–scan o and x separated by $\frac{1}{15}$ sec		1 profile	Sen and Wyller
1963 to 1965	Gregory	Christchurch New Zealand 43°S, 172°E	linear	Double trace A–scan o and x separated by $\frac{1}{50}$ sec		14 profiles	Appleton–Hartree

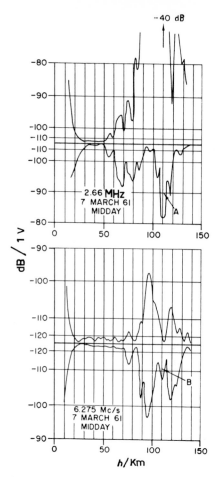

Fig. 5a. A-scan records for a quiet day. The upper trace on each frame is the ordinary component. the lower trace the extraordinary. The center of the ground pulse
is taken as zero height.

questionable whether mean or median values should be used for the calculations.

4. THE DETERMINATION OF THE COLLISION FREQUENCY

It has already been pointed out that $A_x/A_0 = R_x/R_0$ for negligible differential absorption. Collision frequencies obtained in such a way are shown
in fig. 7. They fit well to the values calculated from Interim Supplementary
Atmospheres (ISA) published by Cole and Kantor (1963). The winter values

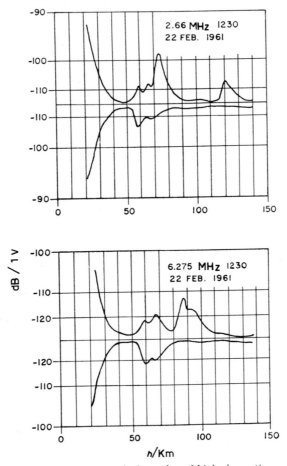

Fig. 5b. A-scan records for a day of high absorption.

are generally lower than the summer values. Typical mean values of the collisional frequency are given in table 3. It should be pointed out, however, that the general agreement between measured and calculated values of the collisional frequency disappears at heights above 90 km for still unknown reasons (Thrane and Pigott, 1966).

5. ELECTRON DENSITY PROFILES FOR THE D-REGION

We are now in a position to calculate a particular $N(h)$ curve and to discuss the possible errors in its determination. An example is given in figs. 8 and 9.

In fig. 8 the mean observed values of A_x/A_o are plotted versus height,

Table 3.

Height (km)	$\nu(\text{sec}^{-1})$
30	$9,7 \times 10^8$
40	$2,3 \times 10^8$
50	$6,3 \times 10^7$
60	$1,8 \times 10^7$
70	$4,5 \times 10^6$
80	$8,4 \times 10^5$
90	$1,3 \times 10^5$

the bars indicating the standard error of the individual readings. The continuous line (a) is a 3-point running average, the dashed line (b) has been drawn through the data points disregarding the value at 78 km, and for the dotted line (c) a correction has been applied taking into account the inaccuracy of the measurements below 65 km. The variation of R_x/R_0 as a function of height has been calculated from two different models (dashed curves 1 and 2). The corresponding electron density profile $N(h)$ is shown in fig. 9.

On realizes that rather minor changes of the A_x/A_0 curve produce significant differences of the $N(h)$ curve. Nevertheless the minimum occurring near the mesopause at 80 km seems to be real.

Further examples of $N(h)$ curves are given in fig. 10 for December 1961, March 1962 and June 1962.

The general trend is similar on the individual days in spring and summer, although there are particularities changing from day to day. In winter big differences occur between groups of subsequent days especially below 70 km. This variations are likely to account for the large interdiurnal variation of absorption during winter months (winter anomaly) which has been dealt with in the preceding lecture.

A comparison of electron density profiles as obtained by different methods (for details see legend of the fig.) are shown in fig. 11. The general agreement between the results of the different methods is rather good taking into account that the measurements have been made at different times at different locations. The electron depletion of the region below 80 km at night is evident. A comparison with fig. 4 shows that because of the applicability limits of the partial reflection method, other methods are preferable at night.

The variations of the electron density profile with the zenith angle of the sun have been measured at Crete (35.4ºN) by Haug and Thrane (1966). Average values obtained between 30 Aug. and 11 Sept. 1965 are shown in fig. 12, and individual values of 11 Sept. in fig. 13. Data of a series of measurements at Tsumeb (19ºS) are not available yet. Generally there are too few systematic measurements to derive the variations of the $N(h)$ profile with latitude so far.

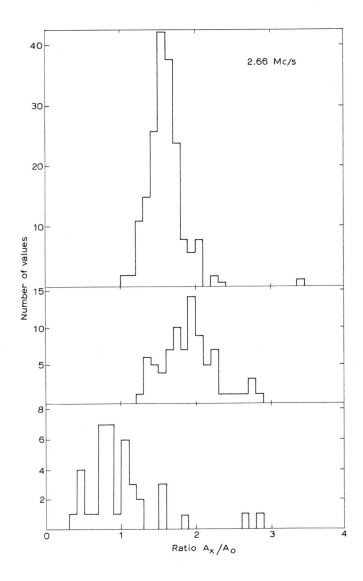

Fig. 6. Distribution of amplitude ratio A_X/A_O for 58, 68 and 78 km height (7 Nov. 1962).

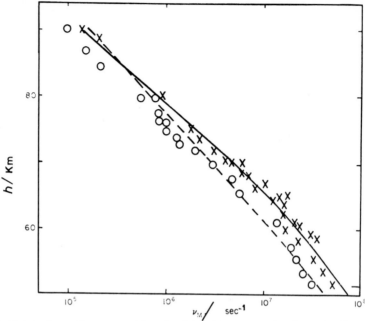

Fig. 7. Comparison of summer (x) and winter (o) measured values of collission frequency ν with values computed from the summer (———) and winter (-----) interim atmosphere for 60°N. The absolute value is adjusted to fit the summer data.

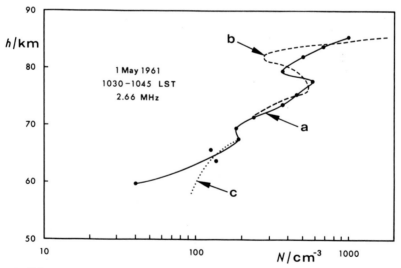

Fig. 9. $N(h)$ profile for 1 May 1961, as derived from the observational data of the preceding fig. Notation as in fig. 8.

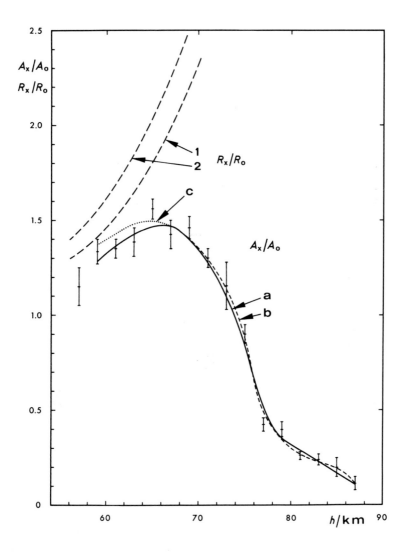

Fig. 8. Amplitude ratio R_X/R_O and A_X/A_O as function of height for 2.66 MHz for a quiet day, 1 May 1961, 10.30 - 10.45 LST. Standard deviation as derived from least squares is shown by bars. Curves 1 and 2 refer to different collission frequency curves. The smooth curves through the A_X/A_O data are: a) (solid curve) 3-point running average, b) (dashed curve) drawn through all points except for the bite out at 78 km, c) (dotted curve) on the assumption that $N(h)$ is proportional to the amplitude $A_O(h)$ for low heights, the electron density has been separately estimated and A_X/A_O calculated.

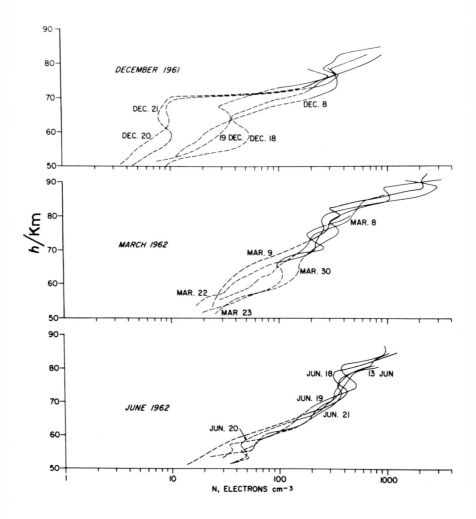

Fig. 10. Electron density profiles over Ottawa for average midday data on 5 magnet-
ically quiet days during winter (December 1961), equinox (March 1962) and summer
(June 1962).

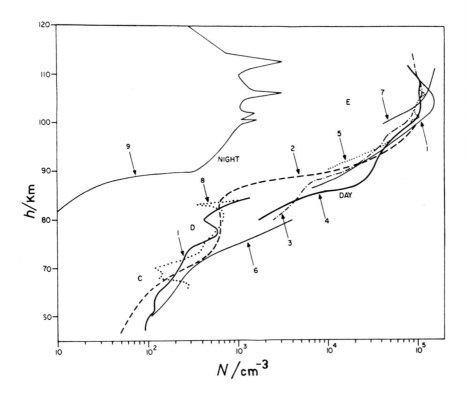

Fig. 11. Electron density profiles for the D- and E-regions obtained by different techniques. Curve 1 (two parts): partial reflection experiment, 1 May 1961, 10.30 - 11.30 LST, Ottawa, Canada; curve 2: theoretical, after Aikin et al. (1963), middle latitude, midday; curve 3: rocket Langmuir probe, after Yonezawa (1961), 22 September 1960, 15.32 LST, Michikawa, Japan; curve 4: rocket propagation experiment, after Adey and Heikkila (1960), 17 September 1959, 12.37 LST, Churchill, Canada; curve 5: rocket propagation experiment, reported by Friedman (1959), 26 June 1954, 17.30 LST, USSR, middle latitude; curve 6: pulse cross-modulation experiment, after Barrington et al. (1963), March–April 1960, 10.00 - 14.00 LST, Kjeller, Norway; curve 7: ionosonde experiment, after Robinson (1960), 27 March 1957, midday, Cambridge, England; curve 8: rocket Faraday rotation experiment, after Aikin et al. (1963), 8 March 1963, 14.30 LST, Wallops Island, USA; curve 9: rocket Langmuir probe, after Smith (1962), 27 October 1961, 04.35 LST, Wallops Island, USA.

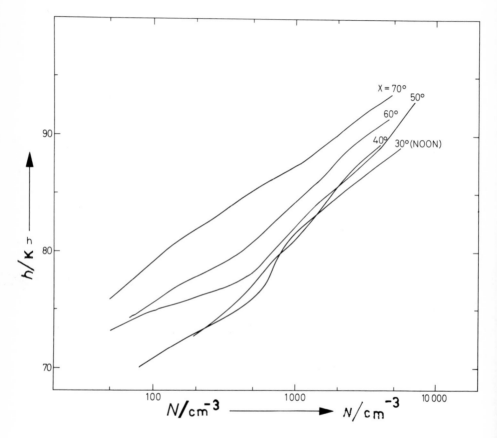

Fig. 12. Average electron density profiles derived for different zenith angles of the sun.

Measurements carried out at Ottawa (magnetic shell latitude 58.2⁰), Churchill (70.5⁰) and Resolute Bay (84.2⁰) (Belrose, Bourne and Hewitt, 1966) show that, during daylight, the electron density profile at Ottawa and Churchill are very similar for the same solar zenith angle, whereas the electron densities at Resolute Bay as a typical polar station, for heights below 75 km, are much smaller than would be expected from the results obtained at lower latitudes.

A few measurements made at Resolute Bay during nighttime seem to indicate that also at night the electron density is much smaller than for comparable conditions at lower latitudes.

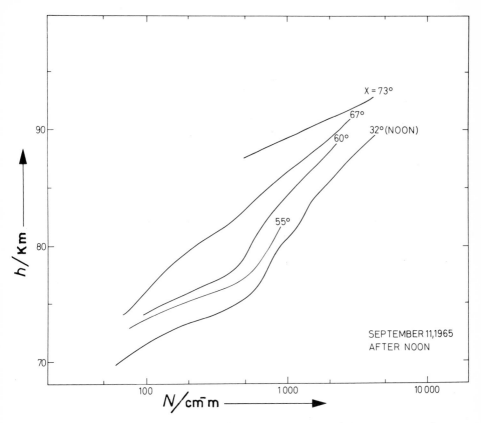

Fig. 13. Electron density profiles for different zenith angles of the sun measured on 11 Sept. 1965.

6. ELECTRON DENSITY DISTRIBUTION AT TIMES OF IONOSPHERIC DISTURBANCES

Electron density changes at low heights by several orders of magnitude occur at times of ionospheric disturbances, viz., Solar Flare Effects (SID) and Polar Cap Absorption (PCA) (Belrose and Bourne, 1966). During an SID of class 2+ an increase of the electron density by a factor of 10 at a height of 70 km and a downward shift of all the profile by about 13 km has been observed (fig. 14).

An increase of the electron density by a factor of 10 and 13 in all the height range between 60 and 80 km has been observed for Polar Cap Absorption with a maximum absorption of 0.9 and 3 dB respectively, as observed on 30 MHz by riometer (fig. 15). Since the absorption during PCA's can amount to 20-30 dB occasionally very large increases of electron density are to be expected simultaneously.

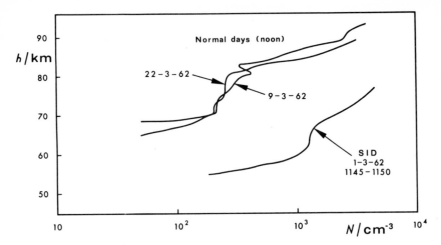

Fig. 14. Electron density profiles for a "Class 2" Solar Flare (SID) and for normal days in March 1962, measured by the partial reflection technique over Ottawa.

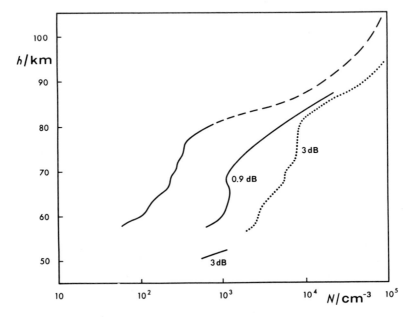

Fig. 15. Electron density profiles during PCA and during normal conditions (uppermost curve) in summer (June, July and August 1962, Ottawa). The numbers marked on the curves give the absorption measured simultaneously by a riometer on 30 MHz. Dotted curve: profile obtained during SID with rocket ascent at Fort Churchill by Kane.

No partial reflection measurements have been made during Auroral Absorption Effects so far. From other observations increases of the electron density by a factor of 100 in the height range between 60 and 80 km have been derived.

7. CONCLUDING REMARKS

Considering the observational results as obtained by the partial reflection technique and by other methods, one may ask whether the observed features do support the current theory of electron production in the D-region. The answer seems to be "Yes" as far as the three major sources of ionisation during undisturbed conditions are concerned, viz. background cosmic radiation, solar X-rays 2-8 Å, and photoionization of nitric oxide by solar Lyman alpha radiation at 1215.6 Å. In addition large changes in the flux and spectrum of solar X-rays are causing the disturbances. For the details of the processes, however, we are far from a full understanding. May I quote Aikin (1966) in that context: "Clearly, more measurements of the positive ion composition in the D-region must be carried out. The species of negative ions and their altitude distribution must be known. More laboratory measurements of pertinent reaction rates are also needed. Only then it will be possible to give an adequate theoretical description of the lower ionosphere".

REFERENCES

Aikin, A. C., 1966. Theoretical models of the lower ionosphere, Conference of ground-based radio wave propagation studies of the lower ionosphere, Ottowa 1966.

Belrose, J.S., L. R. Bodé, L. W. Hewitt and J. M. Griffin, 1964, An experimental system for studying partial reflections from the lower ionosphere, Defence Res. Board DRTE Rapt. 1136.

Belrose, J.S. and I. A. Bourne, 1966, The electron distribution and collisional frequency height profile for the lower part of the ionosphere (the D- and E-regions), Conference on ground-based radio wave propagation studies of the lower ionosphere, Ottawa 1966.

Belrose, J.S., I. A. Bourne and L. W. Hewitt, 1966, A preliminary investigation of diurnal and seasonal changes in electron distribution over Ottawa, Churchill and Resolute Bay as observed by partial reflections, Conference on ground-based radio wave propagation studies of the lower ionosphere, Ottawa 1966.

Belrose, J.S. and M. J. Burke, 1964, Study of lower ionosphere using partial reflections, I. Experimental technique and method of analysis, J. Geophys. Res. 69, 2799.

Dieminger W. and A. E. Hoffmann-Heyden, 1952, Reflexionen von Kurzwellen aus Höhen unter 100 km, Naturwiss. 39, 1.

Dieminger, W., G. Rose and H. U. Widdel, 1966, Ionosondenmessungen am Kreuzungspunkt des geographischen und magnetischen Äquators, Atlantische Expedition (IQSY) des Forschungsschiffes Meteor, Naturwiss. 53, 393.

Gardner, F. F. and J. L. Pawsey, 1953, Study of the ionospheric D-region using partial reflections, J. Atm. Terr. Phys. 3, 321.

Haug, A. and E. V. Thrane, 1966, D-region electron densities deduced from measurements of partial reflections at a middle latitude station, Conference on ground-based radio wave propagation studies of the lower ionosphere, Ottawa 1966.

Sen, H. K. and A. A. Wyller, 1960, On the generalisation of the Appleton-Hartree magnetoionic formula, J. Geophys. Res. 65, 3931.

Thrane, E. V. and W. R. Pigott, 1966, The collision frequency in the E- and D-regions of the ionosphere, J. Atmos. Terr. Phys. 28, 721.

DISCUSSION

Rawer:

The very first formula is that of Fresnel for normal incidence. It is valid for steep gradients only; the thickness of the transition region must be inferior to the wavelength, something like 0.2 vacuum wavelength or less. There exist probably rather often in the lower ionosphere a few such discontinuities. But I cannot see how the method could be applied in a continuous manner for any height.

Dieminger:

This is true and corresponds to the statement on page 173 that the existence of partial reflection presupposes the existence of, although small, irregularities whereas absorption occurs also in a perfectly smooth distribution of electrons. As a matter of fact one has normally quite distinct echoes from individual heights, and the production of irregularities by turbulence is very likely.

Rawer:

With respect to the large spread of the A_x/A_0 values one should know what is the reason of the fluctuations. For other absorption measuring methods, too, fadings are important. If one knew the reason for the fluctuations, i.e. the mechanism of the fadings one could better state whether the average or the median or another procedure should be used in order to obtain a representative value.

Dieminger:

This question has been treated to some extent in the paper of Belrose and Burke (1964), but not resolved completely. It becomes rather complicated because of the possibility of oblique echoes from lower heights interfering with the vertical ones. In practice only clean echoes are selected for determining the amplitude ratio A_x/A_0. Nevertheless the spread is considerable.

Lalonde:

Fig. 4 shows a range of measurable limits of electron density by this method. Fig. 10 shows profiles which indicate densities one or two orders of magnitude lower than the lowest detectable limit, in considerable detail. Are these densities real?

Dieminger:

Fig. 4 was prepared for the Gardner-Pawsey equipment. Fig. 10 is from work by Belrose with much higher power, therefore of increased accuracy.

Spizzichino:

La méthode utilisant les réflexions partielles pour déterminer les densités électroniques dans la région D repose sur la comparaison des coefficients de réflexion d'une même couche réfléchissante pour les ondes ordinaire et extraordinaire.

Pour cela, on néglige la dépolarisation de l'onde après réflexion par de telles couches dans le cas où elles ont une forme irrégulière. Des travaux théorique (Becjmann) et expérimentaux (Spizzichino) ont en effet montré que l'onde réfléchie par une surface irrégulière est fortement dépolarisée. S'il en est ainsi pour les réflexions partielles pour la région D, le rapport des coefficient de réflexion de l'onde ordinaire et de l'onde extraordinaire n'a aucune signification physique évidente.

Dieminger:

The comment of Spizzichino challenges the applicability of the partial reflection method. The fact, however, that the results correspond rather well to the results of other methods seems to demonstrate that the irregularities in the ionosphere are predominantly one-dimensional (in h) so that no serious depolarisation occurs at the reflection level.

Spizzichino:

(Après la réponse de Dieminger, me renvoyant au texte de Fejer et Lansey, et après avoir examiné ce texte, celui-ci me semble éluder beaucoup trop sommairement la question.)

Ranzi:

I would like to point out that the observation of weak echoes from partial reflections may de disturbed by horizontal backscattering from ground reliefs and from sea waves (especially from coastal stationary sea waves systems). It is practically impossible to avoid the emission of vertically polarized energy from the antenna systems used in the vertical soundings. As the backscatter from the sea waves changes with the sea conditions, it is impossible to distinguish the ionospheric echoes on the ground of a statistical study, which may eliminate only the systematic and stable component of the echoes (during calm periods, a diurnal change of intensity of the sea backscatter may be observed, with a maximum around noon and a nocturnal minimum, depending on the sea breeze regime).

Dieminger:

Because of the influence of sea backscatter care must be exercised in selecting sites for observing partial reflections. For sites far from the coast it is not too difficult to distinguish between ground reflections and ionospheric reflections because the former are more or less stable in amplitude and range whereas the fading of ionospheric partial reflections is rather violent. It is correct, however, that much care must be exercised in analysing the records.

MESURES DE VENTS PAR METEORES
ENTRE 80 ET 110 KM

A. SPIZZICHINO
Ingénieur, C.N.E.T., France

Abstract. Winds measured between 75 and 110 km are nearly horizontal. their speed can reach 100 m/s: they are strongly variable in speed and direction as a function of altitude. An analysis (sect. 3) shows three main components:
main components:
1) the *steady wind* (3.1) is mainly zonal (East-West), with an eastward component in summer and a westward component in winter, increasing with height: using classical theory this experimental result would lead to the unexpected conclusion that at these heights the atmospheric temperature increases from the summer pole towards the winter pole.
2) the *tides* (3.2) are periodic solar and lunar components. Between 80 and 110 km, the prevailing tides are solar (semi-diurnal and diurnal). The predominance of solar tides shows that they have mainly thermal origin. The semi-diurnal tide can be represented by a wind vector rotating clockwise in the Northern hemisphere and anti-clockwise in the Southern hemisphere. There is a systematic shear corresponding to a propagation downwards with speeds between 4 and 10 km/h. The diurnal tide has more irregular structure. and does not present any clear propagation effect.
3) the *small-scale winds* (3.3) present quick variations with time autocorrelation radius of a few hours and vertical correlation radius of 5 to 10 km. The movements have some regular and organized structure. such that they are not turbulent as formerly assumed. Meteor observations indicate strong systematic wind shears and. generally. a descending motion of wind profiles. After Hines these small-scale winds could result from upward propagation of gravitational waves.

Résumé. Les vents mesurés entre 75 et 110 km d'altitude sont analysés en distinguant trois composantes:
1) une composante continue zonale. vers l'est en été. vers l'ouest en hiver. L'accroissement de la vitesse avec l'altitude peut être expliqué par l'hypothèse d'une température plus élevée au pole d'hiver qu'au pole d'été.
2) des marées solaires (prépondérantes) et lunaires. La composante semi-diurne solaire présente une variation systématique.
3) les vents de petite échelle à variation rapide ayant un rayon d'autocorrelation de quelques heures et un rayon vertical de 5 à 10 km. Ces mouvements ne sont pas aléatoires; il y a des cisaillements "organisés" et, en général, un déplacement vers le bas du profil des vents.

1. INTRODUCTION

On appelle *vent* tout mouvement des molécules non ionisées de l'atmosphère. L'observation par radar des trainées laissées par les météorites n'est qu'une des méthodes possibles de mesure de vent. Les mesures qu'elle fournit concernent la seule région de l'atmosphère comprise entre 75 et 110 km d'altitude, mais les phénomènes qu'elle fait apparaître (marées, ondes de gravité, etc.) existent dans un domaine d'altitude beaucoup plus étendu. Aussi, pour interpréter les résultats des mesures de vent obtenues par l'observation des météorites, nous devrons souvent les confronter avec des résultats obtenus par d'autres méthodes aux mêmes altitudes ou à des altitudes voisines. Par exemple:

a) la méthode "des fadings" *, qui consiste à suivre le mouvement de petites irrégularités des couches ionisées, observées par réflexion des ondes. Appliquée à la région E de l'ionosphère, cette méthode fournit des mesures de vent entre 105 et 110 km d'altitude.
b) la déformation d'une trainée luminescente éjectée d'une fusée donne le "profil" des vents en fonction de l'altitude entre 90 et 160 km d'altitude.
c) l'étude de la propagation du son produit par l'explosion de grenades à haute altitude fournit des mesures de vent au-dessous de 80 km d'altitude; etc...

Dans la première partie de cet exposé, nous étudierons les problèmes posés par la mesure de vent à partir de l'observation radioélectrique de météores, et nous décrirons quelques expériences réalisées. La deuxième partie sera consacrée à l'étude des résultats ainsi obtenus; on examinera les différents phénomènes mis en évidence: vents dominants, perturbations à petite échelle. Pour chacun d'eux, les résultats tirés de l'observation des météores seront confrontés avec ceux obtenus par d'autres méthodes expérimentales, et avec ceux déduits de la théorie.

2. MESURES DE VENTS

2.1. *Principe des mesures*
Les météorites sont des petites particules de matière qui gravitent autour du soleil comme des planètes. La plupart d'entre elles ont des dimensions de l'ordre de quelques μ ou quelques dizaines de μ. Celles qui rencontrent l'atmosphère terrestre s'y échauffent fortement par frottement et sont vaporisées, laissant ainsi une trainée de gaz à température élevée. Les trainées laissées par les plus grosses météorites (100 μ et plus) sont quelquefois incandescentes et peuvent être observées optiquement: ce sont les "étoiles filantes". Les trainées laissées par des météorites plus petites (quelques μ à 100 μ) ne sont pas visibles, mais sont en partie ionisées et par conséquent réfléchissent les ondes radio: on peut donc les observer au moyen d'un radar.

---

* Voir Harnischmacher and Rawer: **W**inds in the D- and E-region observed by the fading method.

On montre que le coefficient de réflexion des trainées météoriques décroit très rapidement lorsque augmente la fréquence de l'onde utilisée.
Aussi, les radars employés pour détecter ces trainées doivent être à des
fréquences les plus basses possibles. Comme au-dessous de 25 MHz la
détection des trainées météoriques serait souvent perturbée par les ondes
réfléchies par les couches de l'ionosphère, on préfère utiliser des ondes
de fréquence comprise entre 25 et 40 MHz (longueur d'onde: 7 à 12 m).

Chaque jour, 10^{11} à 10^{12} météorites assez grosses pour être détectées
par des radars rencontrent l'atmosphère terrestre. Les radars utilisés
jusqu'ici en détectent de quelques dizaines à quelques milliers par jour. En
fait, les météorites les plus petites, qui produisent les trainées les plus
faiblement ionisées, sont beaucoup plus nombreuses que les plus grosses:
par exemple, pour 1 météorite de diamètre supérieur à 1 mm, la terre reçoit 10^3 météorites de diamètre supérieur à 100 μ et 10^6 météorites de
diamètre supérieur à 10 μ. Il en résulte que le nombre de trainées météoriques qu'un radar est capable de détecter dépend d'une manière très
critique de sa sensibilité.

La plupart des météorites commencent à se vaporiser entre 95 et 110 km
d'altitude; ensuite, leur vaporisation s'accélère et, sauf pour quelques unes
de dimensions exceptionnelles, elles sont complètement vaporisées après
un parcours de 10 à 20 km dans l'atmosphère: la plupart des trainées météoriques se forment donc entre 75 et 110 km d'altitude. (La plus grande partie des mesures intéresse la zone comprise entre 80 et 105 km.)

Les ions et les électrons formés lors de la vaporisation d'une météorite
diffusent rapidement dans l'atmosphère*: les échos radar provenant des
trainées météoriques ont donc une durée très courte, le plus souvent de
quelques dixièmes de seconde.

Aussitôt après leur formation, les trainées météoriques sont entrainées
par les vents et se déplacent à la même vitesse V que l'atmosphère neutre.
Il en résulte, par *effet Doppler*, une variation Δf de la fréquence de l'onde
réfléchie par la trainée ou, ce qui revient au même, une rotation de la
phase ϕ de cette onde:

$$\Delta f = \frac{1}{2\pi} \frac{d\phi}{dt} = \frac{2}{\lambda} \frac{dr}{dt} = \frac{2}{\lambda} V_r \qquad (1)$$

où r = RP est la distance du radar R au point de réflexion P des ondes sur
la trainée, λ est la longueur d'onde, V_r la projection de V sur l'axe RP (vitesse radiale), voir fig. 1.

En mesurant la dérive de fréquence Δf (ou la variation de phase $d\phi/dt$),
on peut connaitre une composante V_r du vecteur vent V. Pour déterminer
complètement le vecteur V, il faudrait déterminer les projections V_r de V
sur 3 axes différents: il faudrait donc mesurer Δf en 3 points P_1, P_2, P_3
tels que les directions RP_1, RP_2, RP_3 soient différentes.

2.2. *Principales difficultés des mesures de vents*

Pour que la méthode décrite ci-dessus soit applicable, il faut que le vent

---

* Ce phénomène est examiné plus en détail au § 2.3.1).

A. SPIZZICHINO

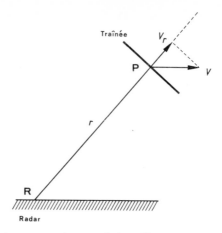

Fig. 1. Observation d'une traînée (réflexion perperdiculaire).

V soit le même au trois points P_1, P_2, P_3. Malheureusement, V varie d'un point à un autre de l'espace.

Les premières expériences ont montré que:

1) le vent V est presque horizontal, ce qui simplifie les mesures: il suffit d'avoir mesuré V_r en deux points P_1 et P_2 pour connaitre V_γ.

2) le vent V varie rapidement en fonction de l'altitude: les variations de V sont du même ordre de grandeur que le vecteur V lui-même pour une variation d'altitude de 5 à 10 km.

3) le vent V varie beaucoup plus lentement le long d'une horizontale: dans la zone observée par un radar, qui s'étend sur une ou quelques centaines de km, on peut en première approximation négliger les variations de V le long d'une horizontale.

4) le vent V peut varier d'une manière appréciable en 1 h.

Pour qu'un expérience fournisse une description à peu près complète des variations du vent V entre 75 et 110 km d'altitude, il faut donc avoir reçu pendant des intervalles de temps plus courts que 1 h des couples d'échos provenant de points P_1 P_2 de même altitude (à ± 1 à 2 km près); de plus, si l'on veut connaître les variations du vent en fonction de l'altitude, de tels couples d'échos doivent être reçus de toutes les altitudes comprises entre 80 et 105 km. Sans entrer dans le détail, on voit que ceci implique la réception d'au moins plusieurs dizaines d'échos météoriques par heure: nous avons vu que la fréquence d'apparition de ces échos dépend de manière critique de la sensibilité du radar; un nombre d'échos aussi élevé ne peut être obtenu qu'avec des radars équipés d'émetteurs puissants et de récepteurs très sensibles.

D'autre part, puisque V varie rapidement avec l'altitude z, la mesure de V n'a d'intérêt que si z peut être déterminée simultanément avec une bonne précision (la détermination précise de z est aussi nécessaire si l'on veut regrouper les échos reçus par couples de même altitude). De plus, la direction de RP doit être connue pour chaque écho, si l'on veut savoir quelle est la composante V_r du vecteur V que l'on a mesurée. Le point P, dont il faut connaître à la fois la direction et l'altitude, doit donc être complètement localisé dans l'espace.

Nous venons d'énumérer les deux principales conditions à satisfaire pour obtenir une bonne mesure de vents: recevoir beaucoup d'échos grâce à une bonne sensibilité des équipements, localiser avec précision le point de réflexion des ondes sur chaque trainée détectée. Ces deux conditions sont difficiles à réaliser, et difficilement compatibles entre elles. Par exemple, la localisation du point de réflexion s'effectue souvent en mesurant sa distance et sa direction (azimut et site); il est classique de déterminer sa distance en émettant des impulsions dont on mesure le temps de retour, mais on doit alors utiliser des récepteurs à large bande passante qui sont peu sensibles; pour connaitre la direction du point de réflexion, il est exclu d'utiliser des antennes très directives, qui ne seraient réalisables qu'à des fréquences élevées où, comme nous l'avons vu, le coefficient de réflexion des trainées météoriques devient très faible, ce qui équivaut à une baisse de sensibilité des équipements.

2.3. *Description de quelques équipements*

La plupart des résultats décrits au § 3 ont été obtenus par l'un des trois équipements que nous allons sommairement examiner. Ils représentent trois solutions différentes pour résoudre les difficultés énumérées ci-dessus (2.2).

2.3.1. Radar de Jodrell Bank (36 MHz)[*]

La localisation des échos repose sur la détermination de l'azimut α, de la distance r et de l'altitude h du point de réflexion.

La détermination de l'azimut est obtenue grâce à des antennes directives, dont le faisceau a une demi-largeur de 12.5° de part et d'autre de son axe. On utilise alternativement une antenne d'axe Nord-Sud et une autre d'axe Est-Ouest, de manière à mesurer alternativement les composantes Nord-Sud et Est-Ouest du vent, V_{NS} et V_{EW}. Celles-ci sont déduites des valeurs mesurées de V_r, z et r par:

$$V_{NS} \text{ (ou } V_{EW}) = \frac{V_r}{\cos \beta},$$

avec: $\sin \beta = h/r$, où β est le site du point P (fig. 2).

La distance du point P est mesurée par la méthode classique du radar à impulsions.

L'altitude h est déduite de la décroissance des échos[**]: on montre que lorsqu'une trainée ionisée de densité d'ionisation suffisamment faible diffuse dans l'atmosphère, la puissance P de l'onde réfléchie par cette trainée décroit exponentiellement au cours du temps t:

[*] Voir Bibliographie I.
[**] Voir Bibliographie IV.

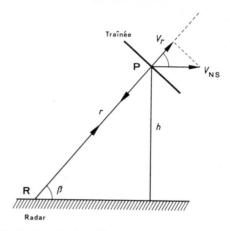

Fig. 2. Altitude du point de réflexion sur une traînée météorique.

$$P = P_0 \exp(-t/\tau) \ ,$$

où la constante de temps τ dépend du coefficient de diffusion D des électrons et des ions dans l'atmosphère:

$$\tau = \frac{\lambda^2}{32\pi^2 D} \ ,$$

(λ: longueur d'onde). Or D dépend de la densité de l'air et, par suite, de
l'altitude h du point de réflexion: celle-ci peut donc être déduite de la mesure de τ.

On observe en général une décroissance exponentielle de la majorité des
échos météoriques reçus par un radar (fig. 3), et τ peut être mesuré avec
précision. Mais si cette méthode a l'avantage d'être simple et de ne néces-
siter aucun équipement particulier, elle ne s'applique qu'à partie des échos
reçus, et elle est peu précise: la fig. 4 montre que l'altitude h_D déduite de
la mesure de τ n'est égale à l'altitude h mesurée directement qu'à ± 3 km
près en moyenne, avec de nombreuses valeurs aberrantes.

La mesure de Δf est obtenue en superposant l'écho de fréquence $f + \Delta f$ et
une onde de fréquence f et de même phase que l'onde émise: l'amplitude du
signal résultant présente des fluctuations sinusoidales à la fréquence Δf
("fréquence de battements"). La mesure n'est précise que si la période
$1/\Delta f$ de ces battements est beaucoup plus courte que la durée d'un écho
météorique, c'est-à-dire la durée pendant laquelle on peut faire une mesure. Prenons par exemple $V_r = 30$ m/s et $\lambda = 10$ m. Il vient d'après l'éq. (1)
$\Delta f = 6$ Hz, la période des battements est 0.17 s. Or la durée de la plupart
des échos météoriques varie entre 0.2 et 1 s: pour une proportion non négligeable de ceux-ci, la mesure de vent est impossible.

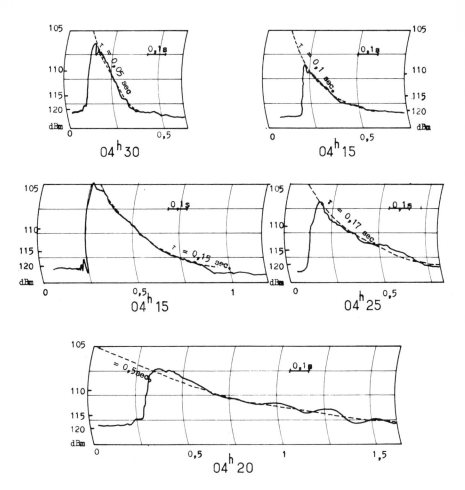

Fig. 3. Exemples d'échos provenant de trainées sous-denses, où l'on peut recon-
naitre la loi exponentielle de décroissance du champ. Ces exemples sont tirés d'un
même enregistrement de champ effectué sur la liaison La Haye-Toulon le 6 Avril
1962. En abscisse, le temps en secondes; en ordonnées, le champ reçu en dBm (décibels au-dessous du milliwatt).

2.3.2. Radar d'Adélaïde (Australie) (27 MHz)*

La localisation des échos repose sur la mesure de la distance r et sur
celle de la direction du point de réflexion.

La distance du point P est mesurée par un radar à impulsions.

La mesure de *la direction* du point P, c'est-à-dire la direction d'arrivée de

* Voir Bibliographie II.

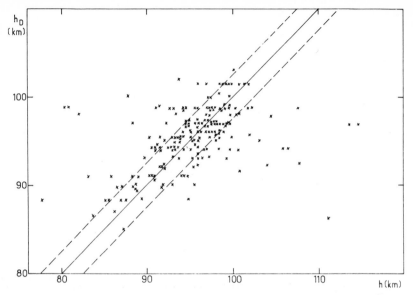

Fig. 4. Comparaison entre l'altitude h_D déduite de la loi de décroissance des échos. et leur altitude h mesurée directement par le radar de Garchy (15-16 Nov. 1965).

l'onde réfléchie, et de *la dérive de fréquence Doppler* Δf utilisent au contraire l'émission d'une onde entretenue. La station de réception, située à 20 km de l'émetteur, est équipée de 3 antennes A1, A2, A3, disposées comme sur la fig. 5 et distantes de A1A2 = λ et A1A3 = λ = 11 m.

Le champ E_i (i = 1, 2, 3) reçu par chacune de ces trois antennes est la somme d'une onde provenant directement de l'émetteur $E_\mathrm{O}\exp(2\pi jft)$ et d'une onde réfléchie par une trainée météorique $E\exp\left[2\pi(f+\Delta f)t+\phi_i\right]$ (fig. 5):

$$E_\mathrm{i} = E_\mathrm{O}\exp(2\pi jft)\left[1 + \frac{E}{E_\mathrm{O}}\exp j(2\pi\Delta ft + \phi_i)\right]. \qquad (2)$$

Le champ E_i reçu par chaque antenne fluctue donc sinusoidalement en fonction du temps; la fréquence Δf de ce battement est égale à la dérive de fréquence par effet Doppler, ce qui permet de la mesurer, et d'en déduire d'après (1) la composante V_γ du vent. De plus, la différence de phase entre les variations sinusoidales des champs reçus par A1 et A2 est:

$$\phi_2 - \phi_1 = \frac{2\pi}{\lambda}\overrightarrow{A_1A_2}. \qquad U = 2\pi\,\boldsymbol{i}\cdot\boldsymbol{U} = 2\pi\cos\delta\ . \qquad (3)$$

et celle entre les champs reçus par A1 et A3 est:

$$\phi_3 - \phi_1 = \frac{2\pi}{\lambda}\overrightarrow{A_1A_3}. \qquad U = 2\pi\,\boldsymbol{j}\cdot\boldsymbol{U} = 2\pi\cos\epsilon\ . \qquad (4)$$

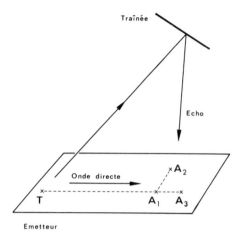

Fig. 5. Disposition des antennes (Adélaïde).

où U est le vecteur unitaire parallèle à la direction du champ réfléchi par la trainée, i et j sont les vecteurs unitaires

$$i = \frac{\overrightarrow{A_1A_2}}{A_1A_2} , \qquad\qquad j = \frac{\overrightarrow{A_1A_3}}{A_1A_3} ,$$

cos δ et cos ε sont deux cosinus directeurs de la direction du champ réfléchie. A partir des valeurs mesurées de $\phi_2 - \phi_1$ et $\phi_3 - \phi_1$, on détermine δ et ε qui définissent complètement la direction du point P.

2.3.3. Radar de Garchy (France)[*] (30 MHz)

Afin d'obtenir la meilleure sensibilité possible et de recevoir ainsi un plus grand nombre d'échos météoriques, on a cherché à éviter l'emploi d'impulsions qui, nous l'avons vu (§ 2.2) nécessitent des récepteurs à large bande passante. L'émetteur utilise donc des ondes entretenues, et la station de réception est située à 30 km de l'émetteur.

Pour mesurer la dérive de fréquence Doppler, on a utilisé un dispositif d'antennes qui permet de recevoir séparément les échos météoriques et une onde directe provenant de l'émetteur. Pour cela, les antennes T_1 et R_1 sont directives, et leurs faisceaux sont dirigés vers une même région de la haute atmosphère; T_2 et R_2 sont dirigées l'une vers l'autre. De plus T_1 et R_1 fonctionnent en polarisation horizontale, T_2 et R_2 en polarisation verticale. De cette manière, R_1 reçoit uniquement un champ provenant de T_1 et réfléchi par des trainées météoriques, tandis que R_2 ne reçoit qu'une onde provenant directement de T_2 (fig. 6). La différence de phase ϕ entre les ondes reçues par les deux antennes R_1 et R_2 peut être mesurée à chaque instant, et on en déduit V_r d'après l'éq. (1). En ramenant ainsi la mesure de l'effet Doppler à une mesure de la phase ϕ (au lieu d'une mesure de la fré-

[*] Voir Bibliographie III.

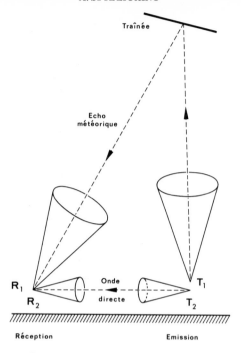

Fig. 6. Influence de la directivité des antennes (Garchy).

quence Δf), on rend la mesure possible même si la durée de l'écho n'est pas grande par rapport à la période $1/\Delta f$ (cf. § 2.3.1.).

La localisation des échos repose, comme pour le radar d'Adélaide, sur la détermination de la distance r et des deux angles δ et ϵ définissant leur direction.

Les angles δ et ϵ sont obtenus en comparant les phases ϕ_1, ϕ_2, ϕ_3 des champs reçus par 3 antennes A_1, A_2, A_3 orientées comme l'antenne R_1 de la fig. 6 et disposées aux 3 sommets d'un triangle rectangle comme celles du radar d'Adélaide (fig. 7).

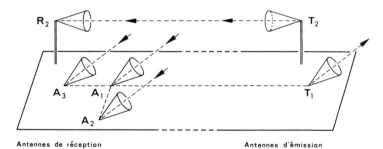

Fig. 7. Plan des antennes d'émission et de réception (Garchy).

On a :

$$\phi_2 - \phi_1 = 2\pi \frac{A_1A_2}{\lambda} \cos \delta \ ,$$

$$\phi_3 - \phi_1 = 2\pi \frac{A_1A_3}{\lambda} \cos \epsilon \ ,$$

relations analogues à (3) et (4), qui permettent de déterminer δ et ϵ à partir des différences de phases mesurées $\phi_2 - \phi_1$ et $\phi_3 - \phi_1$.

N.B. - Malgré l'analogie des relations utilisées, les méthodes employées à Adélaide et à Garchy sont différentes : dans le premier cas, le champ E_i reçu par chaque antenne est donné par (2) et ϕ_i est la phase d'un battement ; dans le second cas, les antennes ne reçoivent que les échos météoriques

$$E_i = E \exp[j(\omega + \Delta\omega)t + \phi_i] \ ,$$

et ϕ_i est la phase de l'onde reçue. Nous avons vu que la phase d'un battement ne peut être correctement mesurée pendant la durée d'un écho météorique que si celle-ci est grande par rapport à la période de battement : en ramenant la mesure de δ et ϵ à la comparaison entre les phases de deux ondes, qui peut être mesurée instantanément, on a cherché à s'affranchir de cette condition.

Pour mesurer la distance r, deux ondes de fréquences voisines f et $f + \delta f$ sont simultanément émises. Les ondes reçues ont respectivement pour phase (en négligeant la distance entre les stations d'émission et de réception)

$$\phi = \frac{4\pi}{c} f r \quad \text{et} \quad \phi + \delta\phi = \frac{4\pi}{c} (f + \delta f)r \ .$$

En ramenant ces deux ondes à une même fréquence et en mesurant leur différence de phase :

$$\delta\phi = \frac{4\pi}{c} \delta f \ r \ ,$$

on détermine r.

Le tableau 1 résume les principales caractéristiques et les performances des trois expériences que nous venons de décrire. Les radars de Jodrell Bank et d'Adélaide, qui ont respectivement fonctionné pendant 7 ans et plus de 2 ans, ont fourni la quasi-totalité des connaissances que l'on a sur les mouvements à grande échelle (vents dominants et marées, voir §§ 3.1 et 3.2), qui nécessitent une observation continue de très longue durée. Le radar de Garchy représente au contraire une tentative récente pour améliorer à la fois la sensibilité et la précision des équipements, mais qui n'en est qu'à ses débuts. Ces deux qualités le rendent en particulier plus adapté pour l'étude des phénomènes à petite échelle, sur lesquels il a déjà donné quelques résultats (§ 3.3).

Tableau 1
Caractéristiques et performances de quelques radars météoriques.

	Jodrell Bank	Adélaïde	Garchy
Composante mesurée	Nord-Sud Est-Ouest	Nord-Sud Est-Ouest	Est-Ouest
Puissance émise	Impulsions: 50 kW	Impulsions: 4 kW Ondes entretenues: 0.25 kW	Ondes entretenues: 1.5 kW (pour chaque fréquence émise)
Largeur de bande des récepteurs	Impulsions: 100 kHz	Impulsions: 100 kHz Ondes entretenues: 2 kHz	Ondes entretenues: 0.2 kHz
Sensibilité des récepteurs	Impulsions: 5×10^{-11} mW	Impulsions: $\simeq 5 \times 10^{-11}$ mW Ondes entretenues: $\simeq 10^{-12}$ mW	Ondes entretenues: $\simeq 10^{-13}$ mW
Rapport puis./sensibilité	Impulsions: $\simeq 10^{18}$	Impulsions: $\simeq 10^{17}$ Ondes entretenues: $\simeq 2 \times 10^{17}$	Ondes entretenues: $\simeq 1.5 \times 10^{19}$
Nombre d'échos reçus par jour	1000-3000 échos	200-300 échos	3000 échos
Nombre d'échos utilisables par jour	?	50-75 échos	500-1000 échos
Précision sur l'altitude	± 3 km	± 2 km	± 0.5 km
Précision sur la direction des échos	Azimut: ± 12.5° Site: ± 1.5°	± 2°	± 0.3°
Années de fonctionnement	1953-1958	1952-1955 [*]	1965-1966

[*] L'expérience semble avoir été poursuivie jusqu'en 1961 mais les caractéristiques statistiques du vent n'ont pas été publiées après 1955.

3. RESULTATS

En général, les vents observés entre 80 et 105 km d'altitude ont des vitesses beaucoup plus élevées qu'au niveau du sol: elles peuvent atteindre et même dépasser 100 m/s. Le vent est presque horizontal, sa composante verticale ne dépasse pas quelques m/s.

Nous allons voir que le vent résulte de la superposition de phénomènes physiques différents, qui se distinguent les uns des autres par la rapidité de leurs variations au cours du temps: on peut donc les séparer par une analyse de Fourier. On distingue:

le vent dominant, que l'on présente généralement comme la composante constante du vent, bien qu'on y inclue les termes très lentement variables, de période supérieure à un mois environ.

les ondes planétaires, ondes se propageant dans l'atmosphère, dont la période est de quelques jours. On soupçonne leur existence au-dessus de 80 km d'altitude, mais on n'en a guère de preuve jusqu'ici (leur étude ne sera pas abordée dans cet exposé).

les marées, provoquées principalement par le mouvement relatif du soleil; ces oscillations ont des périodes de 24 h, 12 h, 8 h, etc.

les mouvements à petite échelle, qui présentent un spectre continu de périodes variant entre une demi-heure et quelques heures, ont été attribués à des *ondes de gravité**.

3.1. *Le vent dominant*

Pour calculer le vent dominant, la plupart des auteurs font la moyenne des valeurs du vent mesurées pendant un mois. Le vent moyen ainsi obtenu présente presque toujours une forte composante Est-Ouest et une composante Nord-Sud beaucoup plus faible.

3.1.1. Composante Est-Ouest

Elle présente des variations saisonnières qui se reproduisent de manière à peu près similaire toutes les années. La fig. 8 montre sa variation moyenne au cours d'une année pour les deux seules stations qui aient donné des résultats sur une longue période: Jodrell Bank et Adélaide. Ces deux stations sont toutes deux situées aux latitudes moyennes, l'une dans l'hémisphère Nord, l'autre dans l'hémisphère Sud. Malgré la différence entre les latitudes (respectivement 53° N et 35° S), on aurait pu s'attendre à ce que les variations du vent dominant en ces deux stations se ressemblent, avec un décalage de 6 mois: en effet, au bout de 6 mois, la position du soleil par rapport à ces deux stations est à peu près intervertie. Ceci est assez mal confirmé par la fig. 8. Les ordres de grandeur du vent dominant sont même très différents: autour de 10 m/s à Jodrell Bank, et de 30 m/s à Adélaide.

Cependant, on remarquera qu'en été le vent dominant est dans les deux cas dirigé vers l'Est et augmente avec l'altitude. En hiver, il est difficile de tirer une conclusion simple des données de Jodrell Bank, mais les résultats d'Adélaide et ceux obtenus par d'autres méthodes (méthode des "fadings") semblent s'accorder à montrer que le vent dominant souffle vers l'Est vers 80 km d'altitude, et vers l'Ouest au-dessus de 100 km.

3.1.2. Composante Nord-Sud

Comme la composante Est-Ouest, elle présente des variations saisonnières qui se reproduisent de manière à peu près similaire toutes les années. La fig. 9 montre sa variation moyenne au cours d'une année pour les stations de Jodrell Bank et Adélaide. Pour ces deux stations, les variations du vent sont à peu près en phase: il souffle vers le Sud en été et vers le Nord en hiver.

En extrapolant ces résultats, on peut penser qu'il existe un vent per-

---

* Voir Gille et Hines sur les ondes de gravité.

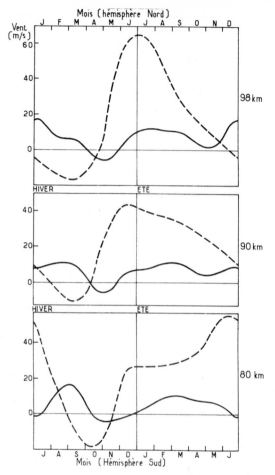

Fig. 8. Composante Ouest-Est du vent dominant en fonction de l'altitude et de la période de l'année. En traits pleins: Jodrell Bank. En traits discontinus: Adélaide. Pour les résultats d'Adélaide, les abscisses ont été décalées de 6 mois par rapport à Jodrell Bank, pour faire coincider les saisons.

manent soufflant du pôle d'été vers le pôle d'hiver, entre 80 et 100 km d'altitude.

L'existence de ce courant n'est cependant pas vérifiée entre 105 et 110 km par la méthode des "fadings".

3.1.3. Discussion

Les météorologistes rendent compte d'une manière assez satisfaisante des vents dominants dans la basse atmosphère en admettant que le vent V satisfait à l'équation d'un *mouvement permanent**:

* En supposant négligeable le terme de transport de vitesse $V \cdot (\nabla V)$.

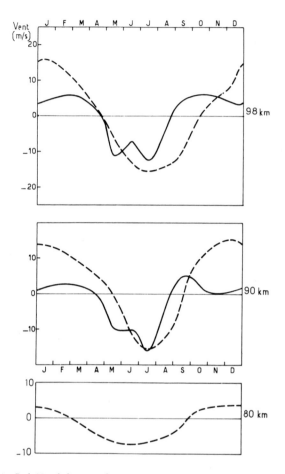

Fig. 9. Composante Sud-Nord du vent dominant en fonction de l'altitude et de la période de l'année. En traits pleins: Jodrell Bank. En traits discontinus: Adélaide.

$$\rho \; \frac{\partial V}{\partial t} = -\rho g - \nabla p - 2\rho\omega \times V = 0 \qquad (5)$$

où ρ est la densité de l'air, p la pression, $-g$ l'accélération de la pesanteur, ω le vecteur rotation de la terre. Le dernier terme représente la force de Coriolis, et l'éq. (5) exprime que la somme des forces qui agissent sur chaque élément de volume d'air est nulle.

On admet en outre que la densité ρ est donnée par l'équation des gaz parfaits,

$$\rho = p/RT$$

en fonction de p et de la température T, et que le vent V est horizontal. On démontre que les deux composantes u et v du vent V, comptées positivement vers l'Est et vers le Nord respectivement, varient avec l'altitude suivant la loi dite du "*vent thermique*":

$$\frac{\partial}{\partial z}\left(\frac{u}{T}\right) = \frac{g}{2\,\omega\,\sin\phi}\,\frac{\partial}{\partial y}\left(\frac{1}{T}\right)$$

$$\frac{\partial}{\partial z}\left(\frac{v}{T}\right) = -\frac{g}{2\omega\,\sin\phi}\,\frac{\partial}{\partial x}\left(\frac{1}{T}\right)$$

(6)

(ϕ est la latitude, les axes ∂x, ∂y, ∂z sont orientés positivement vers l'Est, vers le Nord, et vers le zénith). Ces équations sont déduites de (5) par dérivation (on annulle le rotationnel du premier membre de (5)).

Les équations (6) montrent que le vent Ouest-Est u augmente si la température augmente vers le Sud, et que le vent Sud-Nord v augmente si la température augmente vers l'Est.

Appliquée au domaine d'altitude où l'on observe les météores, cette méthode permet d'expliquer pourquoi la composante Est-Ouest du vent dominant est prépondérante: le long d'une ligne Nord-Sud, l'intensité et la durée de l'éclairement solaire varient fortement, et il en résulte nécessairement une variation de la température; au contraire, le long d'une ligne Est-Ouest, l'éclairement moyen, et par suite la température moyenne ne doivent pas varier (il s'agit de moyennes calculées sur un grand nombre de jours, comme pour la définition du vent dominant). En première approximation, le vent Sud-Nord v, qui est beaucoup plus faible que u au-dessous de 70 km, et dont d'après (6), les variations en fonction de l'altitude doivent être petites, doit rester faible à toutes les altitudes.

Nous avons vu que, d'après les mesures du vent Est-Ouest, entre 80 et 110 km, le gradient $\partial u/\partial z$ doit être positif l'été et négatif l'hiver: d'après l'équation "du vent thermique" (6), cela conduit à un résultat surprenant: en été, la température augmente des pôles vers l'équateur; en hiver, elle augmente de l'équator vers les pôles. L'hémisphère d'hiver est donc plus chaud que l'hemisphère d'été entre 80 et 110 km. Bien que ce résultat ait semblé confirmé par quelques mesures de température (Stroud et al, 1960), il doit être accueilli avec quelques réserves, puisque: le signe de $\partial u/\partial z$ en hiver n'est pas confirmé par les mesures de Jodrell Bank (voir ci-dessus); la méthode "du vent thermique" qui conduit à l'équation (6) consiste à négliger les composantes variables du vent, ou à admettre qu'elles n'ont aucune interaction avec le vent dominant, que l'on traite comme s'il était seul (éq. (5)). Cette méthode, satisfaisante à basse altitude, est d'une application plus discutable au-dessus de 80 km où les composantes variables du vent ont, nous le verrons, une amplitude très élevée.

3.2. *Les marées*

L'analyse de Fourier du vent mesuré à une altitude fixe fait apparaitre des termes périodiques de périodes égales à: un jour solaire et ses sous-multiples (24, 12 et 8 h); un jour lunaire et ses sous-multiples. Par analogie avec les phénomènes océaniques et atmosphériques observés au niveau du sol, on appelle *marées* ces composantes du vent.

Ces marées existent à toutes les altitudes entre le sol et la basse ionosphère. Mais, alors qu'au niveau du sol elles représentent une composante presque négligeable de l'ensemble des vents, leur amplitude augmente rapidement avec l'altitude, et, au niveau des trainées météoriques, leur énergie est comparable à celle de l'ensemble des autres composantes du vent.

3.2.1. Composantes des marées entre 80 et 105 km d'altitude

On peut se rendre compte de l'importance des marées dans ce domaine d'altitude, d'après l'exemple de la fig. 10, qui montre les variations du vent observées à une altitude fixe par le radar météorique de Garchy. Le tableau ci-dessous donne les ordres de grandeur des différentes composantes des marées observées par les radars météoriques de Jodrell Bank et d'Adélaide:

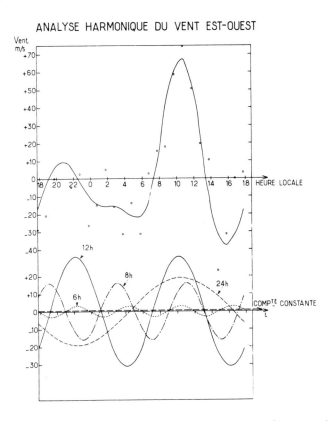

Fig. 10. Analyse harmonique du vent Est-Ouest. Enregistrement fait à Garchy. 16 au 17 Novembre 1965, 95-100 km.

		Jodrell Bank	Adélaide
Marées solaires - Période:	24 h	2-10 m/s	10-40 m/s
	12 h	5-25 m/s	20-50 m/s
	8 h	2-4 m/s	0
Marées lunaires - Période:	1 jour lunaire	0	0
	$\frac{1}{2}$ jour lunaire	< 2 m/s	0

(la mention 0 indique que la marée était trop faible pour être observée).

Pour ces deux stations, les marées solaires sont largement prépondérantes. Mais, alors que la marée de période 12 h l'emporte à Jodrell Bank, celles de périodes 12 h et 24 h ont à Adélaide des amplitudes comparables. Malgré le manque de résultats expérimentaux, on peut penser que cette divergence est dûe à la différence de latitude entre ces deux stations (respectivement 53°N et 35°S). En effet: 1) les mesures de vents par observation des météores faites à Kharkov et à Garchy, qui ont des latitudes voisines de celles de Jodrell Bank, indiquent également une forte prépondérance de la marée semi-diurne; 2) les observations faites à une altitude plus élevée (105-110 km) par la méthode des fadings semblent confirmer la prépondérance de la marée semi-diurne aux latitudes moyennes, et de la marée diurne aux latitudes basses. On peut en avoir une confirmation (plus ou moins nette) sur la fig. 11, où l'on a porté, en fonction de la latitude le rapport A_{24}/A_{12} des amplitudes des marées de périodes 24 et 12 h observées par un grand nombre de stations réparties sur la surface du globe.

3.2.2. Discussion. Origine des marées

Le soleil et la lune peuvent agir de deux manières sur l'atmosphère terrestre: soit par leur force gravitationnelle, soit, dans le cas du soleil, en échauffant l'atmosphère.

Si les marées atmosphériques étaient dûes à des forces gravitionnelles, les marées lunaires seraient prépondérantes (c'est le cas pour les marées des océans): en effet, l'action gravitationnelle de la lune est environ 2.5 fois plus élevée que celle du soleil. Nous avons vu que la marée solaire l'emporte: les marées doivent donc provenir principalement de l'échauffement de l'atmosphère par le soleil.

Mais cet échauffement présente au cours de la journée un seul maximum de jour et il est nul de nuit: si on décompose ses variations en série de Fourier, on conçoit qu'elles présentent une forte composante de période 24 h et une composante de période 12 h beaucoup plus faible. Pour expliquer que l'échauffement solaire donne naissance à une marée semi-diurne plus forte (Jodrell Bank) ou comparable (Adélaide) à la marée diurne, Wilkes (1949) a admis que des oscillations résonnantes de période 12 h peuvent apparaître, amplifiant sélectivement la marée semi-diurne. Le mécanisme de cette résonance est en principe simple: les oscillations de l'atmosphère peuvent être réfléchies par le sol et par une couche située à 30 km d'altitude où il existe un fort gradient vertical de température; dans la région comprise entre 0 et 30 km d'altitude, qui joue le rôle de cavité résonnante, s'établit un système d'ondes stationnaires, dont l'énergie est entretenue par l'échauffement de l'atmosphère par le soleil. La réflexion des oscilla-

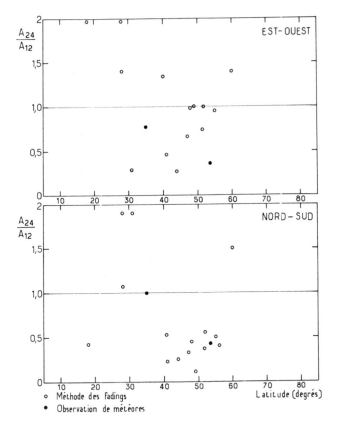

Fig. 11. Rapport A_{24}/A_{12} des amplitudes des marées diurne et semi-diurne en fonction de la latitude, pour 17 stations des deux hemisphères (d'après les données recueillies par Rao (1965), Kazimirovski (1963), etc.).

tions à 30 km n'étant que partielle, une onde progressive se propage audessus de cette altitude. On montre que son amplitude augmente[*] jusque vers une altitude de 120 km, à partir de laquelle elle se dissipe progressivement.

Nous allons voir que cette explication théorique est presque en accord avec les propriétés de la marée semi-diurne déduites de l'observation des météorites.

3.2.3. La marée semi-diurne

On définit en général une marée par son amplitude A_T, et sa phase Φ_T ou l'instant t_T de passage par un maximum. On écrit par définition une composante de période T sous la forme

[*] Voir Gille et Hines sur les ondes de gravité.

$$A_T \sin(2\pi \frac{t}{T} + \Phi_T) = A_T \cos \frac{2\pi}{T} (t - t_T)$$

avec:

$$\Phi_T = \tfrac{1}{2}\pi - 2\pi f t_T$$

La fig. 12 donne les variations de A_{12} et t_{12} ($T = 12$ h) pour les deux composantes Nord-Sud et Est-Ouest du vent observées à Jodrell Bank et Adélaide, au cours de l'année, à une altitude de 93 km.

Les résultats de Jodrell Bank font clairement apparaître les propriétés de la marée semi-diurne:

a) Les amplitudes A_{12} des composantes Nord-Sud et Est-Ouest restent sensiblement égales.

b) L'instant t_{12} où la composante Nord-Sud est maximale (et dirigée vers le Nord) précède d'environ 3 h celui où la composante Est-Ouest est maximale (et dirigée vers l'Est).

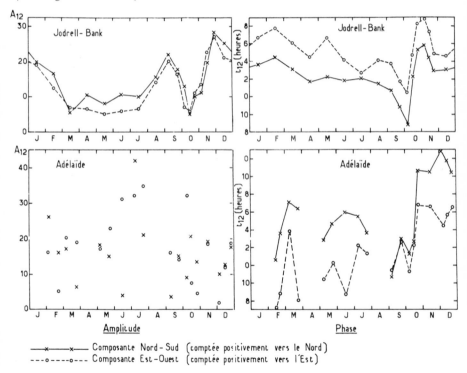

Fig. 12. Comparaison de la marée semi-diurne à Jodrell Bank et à la Adélaide. En abscisse: la période de l'année. En ordonnée: l'amplitude A_{12} de la marée semi-diurne et l'instant t_{12} de passage par un maximum. N.B. Les droites joignant les points de mesure du radar d'Adélaide ont pour but de faciliter la lecture de la figure: elles n'impliquent nullement une variation continue du vent entre deux points de mesure consécutifs.

D'après a) et b) le vecteur vent représentant la marée semi-diurne résulte de deux composantes Nord-Sud et Est-Ouest d'égale amplitude et déphasées de $\frac{1}{2}\pi$: son extrémité décrit un cercle dans le sens rétrogarde (sens des aiguilles d'une montre).

c) Pout chacune des deux composantes Nord-Sud et Est-Ouest, l'amplitude A_{12} augmente avec l'altitude z

$$\frac{dA_{12}}{dz} = 1 \text{ m/s/km en moyenne}$$

$$2 \qquad \text{en hiver}$$

$$0 \qquad \text{en été}$$

d) Pour chacune de ces deux composantes, l'instant t_{12} de passage au maximum décroît lorsque l'altitude z augmente:

$$\frac{dt_{12}}{dz} = -0.17 \text{ h/km en moyenne, soit } \frac{d\Phi_{12}}{dz} = 5°/\text{km}$$

$$-0.23 \qquad \text{en hiver} \qquad\qquad 7°/\text{km}$$

$$-0.10 \qquad \text{en été} \qquad\qquad 3°/\text{km}$$

Ce résultat, établi à partir de l'observation des météores entre 85 et 100 km au-dessus de Jodrell Bank, est confirmé par d'autres observations faites dans une région voisine par la méthode des 'fadings', entre 105 et 110 km d'altitude (Jones, 1958).

e) Les variations saisonnières de A_{12} et t_{12} données sur la fig. 12 se reproduisent toutes les années d'une manière à peu près similaire.

Les résultats du radar météorique d'Adélaide sont moins nets: cela serait dû à leur imprécision plus grande, par suite du nombre plus faible d'échos détectés (voir tableau 1). Ils confirment assez mal (a), un peu mieux (b), (c), (e), avec une différence: la composante Nord-Sud est en retard de 3 h sur la composante Est-Ouest, au lieu d'être en avance comme à Jodrell Bank; le vecteur vent tourne donc dans le sens direct.

A ces résultats, on peut comparer ceux obtenus par la méthode des 'fadings' aux latitudes moyennes, qui confirment (a) et (b) en indiquant une rotation dans le sens rétrograde dans l'hémisphère Nord et dans le sens direct dans l'hémisphère Sud.

Dans l'ensemble, ces données expérimentales s'accordent avec le modèle théorique proposé par Wilkes: les propriétés (a), (b), (c), (d) sont bien celles d'une onde progressive du type 'onde de gravité' qui, comme l'annonce la théorie, doit se propager de bas en haut au-dessus de la couche réfléchissante située à 30 km d'altitude. Pour une telle onde, le vecteur vent doit tourner d'un mouvement uniforme, dans le sens rétrogarde dans l'hémisphère Nord, et dans le sens direct dans l'hémisphère Sud. On montre * que l'amplitude du mouvement doit augmenter avec l'altitude, et qu'une propagation de l'énergie de bas en haut - c'est-à-dire une vitesse de groupe dirigée vers le haut - entraîne nécessairement une vitesse de phase

---

* Voir Hines et Gille sur les ondes de gravité.

dirigée vers le bas: en effet, nous avons vu que les valeurs expérimentales de dt_{12}/dz sont négatives.

Il reste cependant des propriétés de la marée semi-diurne dont le modèle simple proposé par Wilkes ne rend pas très bien compte: la valeur de dt_{12}/dz trouvée expérimentalement ne paraît pas compatible avec les profils de densité et de température généralement admis. On n'a pas fourni jusqu'ici d'explication sûre des variations saisonnières de A_{12}, t_{12} et dt_{12}/dz.

3.2.4. Marée diurne

Nous avons vu que cette composante des vents a une amplitude moyenne très différente à Jodrell Bank (2-10 m/s) et à Adélaïde (10-40 m/s). A chacune de ces deux stations, elle a présenté au cours du temps de grandes et rapides variations d'amplitude et de phase. Les amplitudes des deux composantes Nord-Sud et Est-Ouest sont très inégales. Lorsqu'on fait la moyenne d'un grand nombre d'observations, on trouve que le déphasage entre ces deux composantes varie autour de $\frac{1}{2}\pi$, la marée diurne tournant le plus souvent dans le sens rétrograde dans l'hémisphère Nord, et dans le sens direct dans l'hémisphère Sud. Aucun effet de propagation verticale (c'est-à-dire de variation continue de la phase et de l'amplitude le long d'une verticale) n'a pu être mis en évidence.

Ces propriétés sont à l'opposé de celles de la marée semi-diurne. Alors que celle-ci apparaît comme une oscillation régulière à l'échelle planétaire prenant naissance dans les couches denses de l'atmosphère, la marée diurne semble avoir une structure plus complexe; l'absence d'effet de propagation, ses variations irrégulières laisseraient plutôt penser que des influences locales y jouent un rôle important.

Des observations récentes (mais malheureusement peu nombreuses) faites à Garchy ont montré que la marée diurne a, le long d'une verticale, une structure analogue aux vents à petite échelle: la corrélation entre les marées observées en deux points tombe à une valeur très faible si leur différence d'altitude devient supérieure à 6 km.

3.3. *Les vents à petite échelle*

Comme on peut le voir sur la fig. 10, le vent dominant et les marées ne suffisent pas à rendre compte des variations au cours du temps des vents observés entre 80 et 105 km d'altitude. On désignera par 'vents à petite échelle' un ensemble de composantes de périodes allant d'une à quelques heures en formant un spectre continu. Leur énergie totale est comparable à celle des marées. Ces mouvements, qui sont les plus rapides au cours du temps, sont aussi ceux qui varient le plus vite dans l'espace: ceux que l'on observe en deux points distants de 6 km d'une même verticale ne présentent qu'une faible corrélation (ce qui justifie l'appellation de 'vents à petite échelle').

Pour obtenir une description satisfaisante des vents à petite échelle à l'aide d'un radar météorique, il faut:
a) disposer d'un grand nombre d'échos météoriques, pour pouvoir suivre les rapides variations du vent dans le temps et dans l'espace.
b) déterminer leur altitude avec une grande présision, puisque cette composante des vents varie très rapidement avec l'altitude.

Or ces deux conditions sont précisément les plus difficiles à satisfaire par un radar météorique (2.2.). Ceci explique qu'à partir de simples mesures de vents telles que nous les avons décrites ci-dessus (2.2., 2.3.), le radar de Jodrell Bank n'ait fourni que peu de données[*], et que le radar d'Adélaide n'en ait donné aucune sur les vents à petite échelle.

3.3.1. Description statistique des vents à petite échelle

La première description assez complète des vents à petite échelle a été fournie par Greenhow et Neufeld (1959). Pour cela, une deuxième station de réception R_2 a été associée au radar météorique de Jodrell Bank (fig. 13) de cette manière, chaque traînée météorique donnait naissance à deux échos reçus à chacune des deux stations de réception R_1 et R_2, provenant de deux points d'altitudes voisines P_1 et P_2. Le vent pouvait ainsi être mesuré en P_1 et P_2. Même si les altitudes h_1 et h_2 de ces deux points ne pouvaient pas être connues avec précision, la différence $\triangle h = h_1 - h_2$ pouvait être déterminée de manière assez précise en tenant compte de la géométrie de la traînée. Les auteurs ont pu disposer ainsi d'un millier de couples de valeurs de vent V_1 et V_2, mesurées simultanément en deux points dont on connait avec précision la différence d'altitude $\triangle h$, ainsi que la distance $P_1P_2 = L$.

A partir de ces données, on peut calculer les fonctions d'autocorrélation:

$$\rho = \frac{1}{\sigma^2} \sum (V_1 - \overline{V})(V_2 - \overline{V})$$

où $\overline{V}$ est la valeur moyenne du vent et σ son écart quadratique moyen ($\overline{V}$ et σ sont calculés sur un intervalle de 1 h).

Dans un premier essai, les auteurs ont fait l'hypothèse d'une distribution *isotrope* des vents, où la corrélation des vents observés en deux points ne dépend que de leur distance L: la somme $\sum$ a été étendue à tous les termes $(V_1 - \overline{V})(V_2 - \overline{V})$ tels que P_1 et P_2 soient à une même distance L. On a obtenu la fonction d'autocorrélation $\rho(L)$.

Dans un deuxième essai, ils ont fait au contraire l'hypothèse d'une distribution *stratifiée* des vents, où le vent ne dépend que de l'altitude h: la somme $\sum$ a été étendue à tous les termes $(V_1 - V)(V_2 - V)$ tels que la différence d'altitude entre P_1 et P_2 ait une même valeur $\triangle h$. On a obtenu une autre fonction d'autocorrélation $\rho'(\triangle h)$.

Alors que la fonction $\rho(L)$ ne présentait pas de variations régulières facilement interprétables, $\rho'(\triangle h)$ décroissait uniformément lorsque $\triangle h$ augmentait (fig. 13). Les auteurs en ont déduit qu'une distribution stratifiée des vents, définie par la fonction d'autocorrélation $\rho'(\triangle h)$ représentée par la fig. 14, rend mieux compte de la réalité.

Cette interprétation a pu être confirmée par une comparaison des valeurs de V_1 et V_2 pour des couples de points P_1 et P_2 ayant presque la même altitude ($\triangle h \cong 0$), mais séparés par une distance horizontale $\triangle x$ relativement grande. On a trouvé que V_1 et V_2 restaient presque égales pour

---

[*] Voir Greenhow et Neufeld (1960). Bibliographie I.

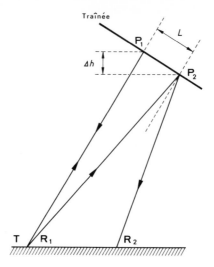

Fig. 13. Observation des vents à petite échelle par Greenhow et Neufeld (1959)

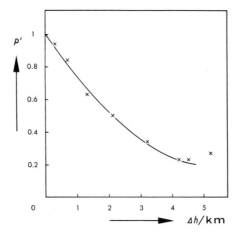

Fig. 14. Corrélation en fonction des différences d'altitude (d'après Greenhow et Neufeld, 1960).

toutes les valeurs de $\triangle x$ observées, qui ne dépassaient pas une vingtaine de
km [*]. Par extrapolation, les auteurs ont montré que la fonction d'autocorrélation $\rho''(\triangle x)$ entre les vents mesurés en deux points distants de $\triangle x$ et de
même altitude doit s'annuler pour des valeurs de $\triangle x$ de l'ordre de 150 km.

[*] Les valeurs possibles de $\triangle x$ sont limitées par le fait que P_1 et P_2 doivent être
sur une même traînée météorique. Rappelons que la longeur de ces traînées dépasse rarement 20 km (cf. 2.1.).

Greenhow et Neufeld ont en outre montré que:
1) la valeur moyenne du vent à petite échelle est de 28 m/s de jour et 25 m/s de nuit; elle ne présente pas de variations significatives suivant l'heure de la journée.
2) le vent à petite échelle fluctue constamment autour de sa valeur moyenne; sa valeur instantanée n'est corrélée ni avec les autres composantes du vent, ni avec leur gradient vertical.
3) le gradient vertical du vent à petite échelle peut varier entre 0 et 70 m/s par km.

3.3.2. Les forts cisaillements de vents

D'autres études de vents à petite échelle reposent sur la comparaison des valeurs du vent en deux (ou plusieurs) points d'une même traînée météorique. Les observations des fluctuations des échos météoriques de longue durée entrent dans cette catégorie[*].

En particulier, Révah et Spizzichino (1963, 1964) ont remarqué que les échos météoriques de durée suffisamment longue (0.8 à 10 s) présentent fréquemment des fluctuations sinusoidales (fig. 15). La seule explication possible de ce phénomène est l'existence de zones de forts cisaillements de vents, c'est-à-dire de couches horizontales de quelques km d'épaisseur où le vent subit une variation beaucoup plus brusque que dans les régions environnantes.

L'effet d'un fort cisaillement de vent sur une traînée météorique est schématisée sur la fig. 16: la partie supérieure et la partie inférieure de la traînée étant entraînées à des vitesses différentes V_1 et V_2, la traînée est déformée. Supposons la traînée observée par un radar: à l'instant $t = 0$ où elle se forme, elle est rectiligne et ne peut présenter qu'un seul point de réflexion des ondes P_0. Puis, tandis que la traînée se déforme, on montre que deux autres points de réflexion P_1 et P_2 apparaissent dans la zone de cisaillement, puis se déplacent rapidement vers les extrémités de cette zone: alors, l'un des points de réflexion, P_1 par exemple, se déplace à la même vitesse V_1 que P_0, l'autre se déplace à vitesse V_2. Les champs réfléchis en P_1 et P_0 ont, d'après eq. (1), une dérive de fréquence par effet Doppler:

$$\Delta f_1 = (2/\pi)V_1 \cos \beta \, ,$$

où $V_1 \cos \beta$ est la composante radiale de V, tandis que le champ réfléchi en P_2 a une dérive:

$$\Delta f_2 = (2/\lambda)V_2 \cos \beta \, .$$

Le champ total reçu par le radar, qui résulte du battement de ces deux champs de fréquences légèrement différentes, présente alors de fluctuations sinusoidales de fréquence:

$$\Delta f = \left| \Delta f_2 - \Delta f_1 \right| = (2/\lambda)\left| V_2 - V_1 \right| \cos \beta \, .$$

On a ainsi un moyen de mettre en évidence les forts cisaillements de

[*] Voir Bibliographie V.

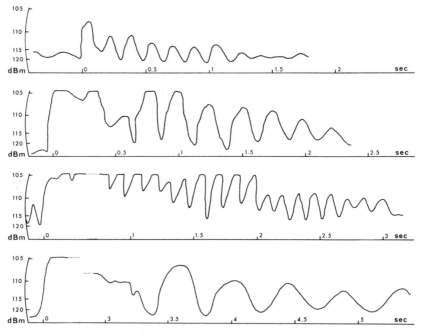

Fig. 15. Exemple d'échos météoriques de longue durée présentant des fluctuations sinusoïdales (Liaison La Haye-Toulon). En ordonnées, le champ reçu, en décibels par rapport au mW.

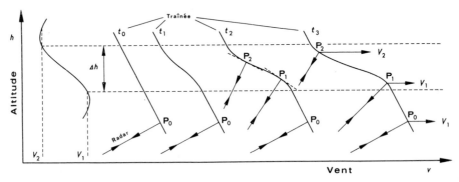

Fig. 16. Developpement dans le temps d'une traînée météorique (temps t_0, t_1, t_2, t_3). à gauche profile de vent.

vents et de déterminer la différence de vitesse $|V_2 - V_1|$. De plus, on montre que l'on peut déterminer l'épaisseur $\triangle h$ de la tranche d'altitude où apparaît le cisaillement en utilisant deux antennes de réception voisines: les fluctuations sinusoïdales des champs reçus par ces deux antennes ont entre elles un déphasage Φ qui dépend de $\triangle h$. A partir des valeurs expérimentales de Φ et $\triangle f$, on a pu établir les propriétés suivantes:

1) les cisaillements de vents fréquemment observés représentent des variations de vent $|V_2 - V_1|$ de 40 à 120 m/s dans des intervalles d'altitude $\triangle h$ de 1 à 7 km (valeur la plus probable: 3 km).

2) de tels cisaillements de vents sont isolés, c'est-à-dire qu'on n'en rencontre en général qu'un seul dans la zone de 20 km d'épaisseur où, à une heure donnée, apparaissent la plupart des échos météoriques.

3) leur probabilité d'apparition passe par un maximum entre 105 et 110 km d'altitude, elle est très faible audessous de 90 km.

4) la fréquence d'apparition de ces cisaillements ne varie guère d'une heure à l'autre de la journée; elle est plus forte en hiver qu'en été.

Ces données sur les cisaillements de vents, qui représentent un phénomène particulier, complète la description statistique de l'ensemble des vents à petite échelle fournie par Greenhow et Neufeld (1959).

3.3.3. Mouvements de descente des profils de vent

Récemment, la mise au point du radar de Garchy, qui fournit des données plus nombreuses et plus précises (2.3.3.), a permis d'obtenir une description plus complète des vents à petite échelle. La fig. 17 en donne un ex-

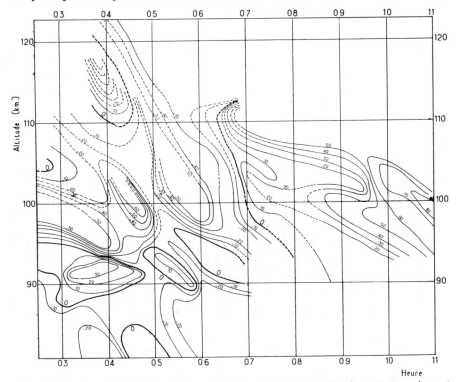

Fig. 17. Composante Est-Ouest du vent le 17 nov. 1965. Exemple de variations du vent Est-Ouest en fonction du temps et de l'altitude, d'après des mesures faites par le radar de Garchy.

emple: on peut voir comment varie, au cours de quelques heures, la composante Est-Ouest du vent en fonction du temps (en abscisses) et de l'altitude (en ordonnées). En général, les variations du vent ainsi obtenues confirment la description statistique de Greenhow et Neufeld (1959) et l'existence de forts cisaillements de vent (fig. 17, à 4 h et 94 km d'altitude). De plus, elles montrent une tendance des profils de vents à descendre au cours du temps.

L'existence de ce mouvement descendant peut être confirmée en calculant la fonction d'autocorrélation $\rho(\triangle t, \triangle z)$ du vent $V(t, z)$, où $\triangle t$ et $\triangle z$ représentent des variations du temps t et de l'altitude z. La fig. 18 en donne un exemple; la fonction ρ a été calculée sur une durée de 3 journées en novembre 1965 et pour l'intervalle d'altitude 90-100 km. Pour cet intervalle, on trouve en général que:

a) Pour $\triangle t = 0$, $\rho(0, \triangle z)$ présente une décroissance comparable à celle de la fonction d'autocorrélation donnée par Greenhow et Neufeld (1959), et tombe à des valeurs très basses pour $\triangle z = 5$ à 10 km.

b) Au bout d'un temps $\triangle t$ positif, la fonction d'autocorrélation $\rho(\triangle t, \triangle z)$ passe par un maximum pour une valeur négative de $\triangle z$: il y a donc une descente général des profils, à une vitesse variant entre 1 et 3 km/h.

c) A altitude constante ($\triangle z = 0$), $\rho(\triangle t, 0)$ tombe à une valeur faible au bout d'un temps $\triangle t$ de l'ordre de 1 h: ce chiffre donne un ordre de grandeur moyen de la demi-période du vent à petite échelle.

d) En suivant le mouvement général de descente, la fonction d'autocorrélation tombe à une valeur faible pour des valeurs de $\triangle t$ de 2 à 3 h: ce chiffre représente un ordre de grandeur moyen de la durée d'une perturbation qui se déplace de haut en bas.

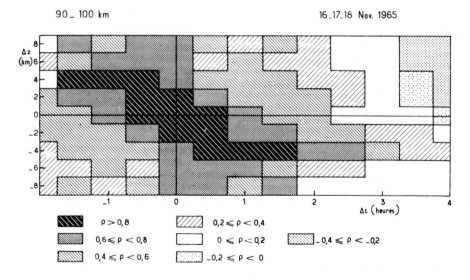

Fig. 18. Fonction d'autocorrélation $\rho(\triangle t, \triangle z)$.

3.3.4. Comparaison avec d'autres méthodes

La seule autre méthode de mesure de vents qui ait fourni d'importants résultats sur les vents à petite échelle est celle qui consiste à lacher d'une fusée un nuage luminescent. Cette méthode, qui n'est utilisable que de nuit, confirme à la fois la description statistique de Greenhow et Neufeld (1959), l'existence des forts cisaillements de vents, et le mouvement de descente des profils (bien que celui ci n'ait été mis en évidence jusqu'ici que sur un petit nombre d'exemples) *. L'observation des nuages luminescents permet en outre d'observer les vents à petite échelle dans la région comprise entre 110 et 150 km d'altitude: leurs propriétés sont similaires à celles observées au-dessous de 110 km, mais: leur diamètre d'autocorrélation vertical croît proportionnellement à l'échelle de hauteur; leur amplitude, qui croît avec l'altitude jusque vers 120-130 km passe par un maximum, puis décroît à des altidudes plus élevées.

3.3.5. Interprétation des résultats

Les premières descriptions des vents à petite échelle (par exemple celle de Greenhow et Neufeld, 1959) représentaient ceux-ci comme des mouvements purement aléatoires, qui ne pouvaient être décrits que statistiquement (par exemple par des fonctions d'autocorrélation). Cette présentation des résultats a certainement contribué à faire croire que ces mouvements étaient l'effet d'une turbulence analogue à celle que l'on rencontre dans la basse atmosphère.

Cette interprétation paraît aujourd'hui erronnée: si des mouvements turbulents existent effectivement jusque vers 100 km d'altitude - ils ont été observés par d'autres méthodes - leur échelle est trop petite (quelques dizaines à quelques centaines de mètres) pour qu'un radar météorique puisse les observer directement.

En tentant d'expliquer les mouvements de l'air qu'ils avaient observés par de la turbulence, Greenhow et Neufeld (1959) s'étaient déjà heurtés à quelques difficultés: la basse ionosphère, où les mouvements à petite échelle atteignent leur plus grande amplitude, est une région de grande stabilité atmosphérique **, où par conséquent la turbulence peut difficilement apparaître; d'autre part, nous avons signalé l'absence de corrélation entre l'amplitude des vents à petite et à grande échelle: or ce sont toujours les mouvements à plus grande échelle qui engendrent une turbulence; etc.

De plus, les découvertes plus récentes - forts cisaillements de vents, descente des profils de vents - paraissent tout à fait inconciliables avec le caractère aléatoire de la turbulence, et suggèrent l'existence de mouvements organisés.

Pour expliquer les vents à petite échelle, Hines *** avait dès 1960 proposé de les attribuer à la propagation d'ondes de gravité. De telles ondes

* Voir Rosenberg et Justus (1966); Bibliographie V.
** On montre que la stabilité atmosphérique est liée au gradient vertical de température: lorsque la température augmente avec l'altitude. comme dans la basse ionosphère. l'atmosphère est stable.
*** Voir Hines (1960) Bibliographie V. ainsi que les exposés de Gille et Hines sur les ondes de gravité.

peuvent en effet prendre naissance dans les basse couches de l'atmosphère et se propager vers le haut. On montre que: leur amplitude augmente très rapidement avec l'altitude, ce qui explique qu'elles puissent atteindre une amplitude élevée vers 100 km; si elles se propagent vers le haut, leur vitesse de phase est dirigée vers le bas [*], c'est-à-dire que les profils de vents sont animés d'un mouvement de descente.

Ces deux faits sont confirmés par l'experience, et, de plus, la théorie des ondes de gravité peut fournir une explication cohérente de l'ensemble des propriétés des vents à petite échelle [**].

DISCUSSION

Anastassiades:

Est-ce que la descente est localisée seulement aux heures du lever du soleil?

Spizzichino:

Non. Le mouvement de descente apparaît à d'autres heures de la journée.

Ilias:

Comme la sensibilité de la méthode C.W. que vous utilisez est bien élevée et la fréquence de 30 MHz relativement basse, des interférences dues à la propagation ionosphérique anormale semble de ne pas être exclus. Carman (1964, Bibliographie VI) en étudiant la propagation des fréquences supérieures à 30 MHz entre Corée-Australie, a trouvé que la réception de signaux était possible pendant certaines périodes et que la liaison Corée-Australie était presque périodique avec un effet journalier et saisonier. Il n'a pas tiré une conclusion ferme; les expériences vont, du reste, continuer entre Athènes-Basutoland, ces villes étant situées à peu près aux points conjugés geomagnétiques.

Je voudrais savoir si M. Spizzichino durant ses mesures n'était pas gêné par des interférences de ce type et quel est le pourcentage du temps, pendant lequel les conditions de réception étaient propres pour des mesures de météorites?

Spizzichino:

De telles interférences peuvent apparaître, mais ne gênent les observations que pendant une très faible proportion du temps. Deux autres facteurs de gêne sont beaucoup plus importantes: en été, de jour, des échos provenant probablement d'une diffusion par E-sporadique; pendant toute l'année, des échos d'avions.

Stilke:

It might be added that there is a well expressed period of 12 h in air pressure at ground level, most distincly in lower latitudes, with maximum

---

[*] Un effet analogue a déjà été décrit à propos de la propagation des marées (3.2).
[**] Voir Hines (1960) Bibliographie V. ainsi que les exposés de Gille et Hines sur les ondes de gravité.

pressure at about 10.00 and 22.00 LT. As perhaps is known, Bartels has been successful in detecting a lunar tide from air pressure recordings at ground level.

Lalonde:

We have made measurements in Arecibo by the incoherent backscatter technique of the history of two simultaneous layers of ionization (E_S), one in the 100-110 km range and the other in the 130-150 km range of heights. These both appear to move downward, but with very different velocities. The lower layers have a downward velocity of 1-2 km/h, while the upper layers drift downward at a rate of about 10 km/h. I note that the vertical velocity of your wind profiles is somewhat higher in the lower altitudes than the drift of the E_S-layers at the same height.

I also point out that E_S-layers seem to have a relatively constant downward drift over the entire range of altitude from 110-90 km, while your wind profiles apparently have different velocities in the 100-110 and 90-100 km regions; I believe your rates were 5-10 km/h at the higher level, and 2-5 at the lower level. This should point out the importance of a good simultaneous measurement of wind profile history and E_S history in the same volume of the ionosphere, in order to determine just how the layers of ionization move with respect to the shear planes of wind profiles.

Spizzichino:

An ionosonde located in Dijon was used to observe E_S-layers in the same region and in the same time as winds were measured by the meteoric radar at Garchy since June 1966. The data are not yet analyzed. A preliminary series of measurements using an ionosonde located in Dijon showed a downwards motion of E_S-layers (Spizzichino and Taieb, 1963, 1964, Bibliographie VI). The observed descending speed of E_S-layer is of the same order of magnitude as those described by Mr. Lalonde.

Rawer:

En ce qui les marées les résultats d'une série d'observations d'environ 12 mois effectuées au cours de deux années (Jacobs, pas encore publié) confirment l'importance de la marée de 12 h par rapport à celle de 24 h. Mais ii en résulte aussi, suivant l'analyse faite, une composante verticale du mouvement matériel, qui n'est pas négligeable.

Au sujet de la 'vitesse verticale apparente' déduite de la fonction de corrélation il parait que la signification de sa variation avec l'altitude puisse être étudiée en recalculant pour des intervalles d'altitudes de 85... 95... 105 km.

Spizzichino:

Ceci a été fait. De 95 à 105 km on obtiendrait suivant la théorie de Hines deux vitesses en même temps (à savoir celle de l'onde de gravité et celle de l'onde de marées), mais pas une vitesse intermédiaire. Or, ce que l'on a trouvé est une très grande dispersion ne permettant pas une décision.

Rawer:

Y-a-t-il une différence entre jour et nuit concernant les mouvements à petite échelle?

Spizzichino:

A première vue, le même mouvement de descente est observé de jour et de nuit. (Une étude très détaillée n'a pas encore été faite.) Ceci est donc bien différent des perturbations transitoires (ou itinérantes) qui n'apparaissent que de jour en général.

Anastassiades:

Je me demande pourquoi on a abandonné pour réaliser l'antenne de Garchy, l'antenne en dent de scie de Chireix-Mesny, qui présente pour un nombre suffisamment grand de dents, un diagramme de rayonnement de quelques minutes (demi-angle) dans le plan horizontal, et de 180° dans le plan vertical. (Angle des dents corrigé 90°.) Une telle antenne était réalisée, voilà quelques années, à Meudon, aussi pour l'étude des météorites.

Spizzichino:

Le radar de Garchy nécessitait une antenne de caractéristiques différentes: ouverture de ± 15° en site et en azimut, faibles lobes secondaires, et surtout très faible rayonnement vers l'arrière (c'est-à-dire dans la direction de la station de réception).

Robert:

Dans ces méthodes on suppose que la trainée météorique n'est entrainée que par le vent ambiant.

Le fait que la trainée est ionisée et qu'elle se produit dans un milieu ionisé et magnétique, ne peut-elle être soumise à une force autre que celle du vent ambiant? Si oui, peut on l'évaluer et en tenir compte?

Spizzichino:

Des études théoriques ont montré qu'un colonne ionisée est pratiquement entraînée sans dérive au-dessous de 100 km d'altitude (Clemmow et al., 1954, Bibliography VI).

Rawer:

L'hypothèse p. 228 indiquant une constante de temps d'une heure me semble douteuse.

Spizzichino:

C'est un ordre de grandeur. Si l'on en juge d'après les quelques enregistrements dont nous disposons, elle paraît très variable: parfois inférieure à $\frac{1}{2}$ h, d'autres fois supérieure à 1 h.

Rawer:

J'ai l'impression que la plus grande difficulté de mesures en Europe est la présence d'avions. Pour un procédé automatique les avions lointains peuvent sérieusement limiter les observations.

Spizzichino:

Les échos dûs aux avions entraînant effectivement une interruption des enregistrements pendant $\frac{1}{6}$ du temps en moyenne, malgré la protection que constituent des antennes très directives. Ces échos sont en général faciles à distinguer des échos météoriques.

Dieminger:

The distinction between meteor echoes and airplane echoes is not too difficult when taking into account the amplitude variation of the echo versus time. The meteor echo raises very steeply in amplitude and decays exponentially. The airplane echo begins with a high beating note which goes to zero and increases again. In addition there is a trick to distinguish between both phenomena: the frequency dependence is completely different. The amplitude of the meteor echo decreases as $1/f^2$, the airplane echo is stronger on high frequencies. Thus using two widely different frequencies (e.g. 30 and 120 MHz) one can assume nearly with certainty that it is an airplane echo when the amplitude of the echo is larger on the higher frequency.

Rawer:

Je pense qu'ici nous avons un avantage majeur de la méthode de Garchy. Etant donné que la phase est mesurée instantanément, on n'y a pas besoin de plusieurs périodes de battement comme dans la méthode de Jodrell Bank (où on a seulement des points isolés par l'interruption des impulsions) et dans celle d'Adélaide (où on fait la triangulation à l'aide de la phase du battement sur plusieurs antennes).

Dieminger:

It sounds somewhat surprising that the duration of an echo depends only on the reflection height taking into account that the amplitude of the echo depends strongly on the size of the meteorite. This, however, is a matter of definition. Measuring the time delay until the amplitude of the echo decays to $A_0(1/e)$, where A_0 is the original amplitude of the echo, as a matter of fact this time delay is independent of the size of the meteorite. This, however, is true only as long as one has to deal with 'underdense' trails which show an exponential decay of amplitude. For 'overdense' trails the amplitude remains constant and finally decreases exponentially. In this case the 'duration' strongly depends on the electron line density of the trail.

Spizzichino:

In my lecture, the term 'duration of the echo' was only used for the sake of simplification. The altitude h_D was deduced from the exponential decay of the amplitude *of only underdense echoes.*

Dieminger:

The question whether C.W. or pulse transmission is more sensitive is a very old one. As a matter of fact one can demonstrate that the only parameter which matters is the *mean power* independently whether it is spent in short burst of high power or continuously on low power. A pulse transmitter of 1000 kW with a duty cycle of 1 : 1000 is as efficient as a C.W.-transmitter of 1 kW. The reason is the different bandwith which is needed in both cases.

Spizzichino:
I do not ignore that the sensitivity of a radar only depends, as Prof. Dieminger said, on the mean transmitted power. For the radar of Garchy, a 5 kW C.W. transmitter is used. To obtain the same sensitivity with a pulse transmitter having a duty cycle of 1/1000, a peak power of 5000 kW would be needed: much more technical difficulties would arise in constructing such an equipment rather than in constructing a 5 kW C.W. transmitter. Than, it appears that, for the same difficulties (or for the same price), a better sensitivity can be obtained by a C.W. radar.

BIBLIOGRAPHIE

I. Radar météorique de Jodrell Bank
Greenhow, J.S., 1952a, A radio echo method for the investigation of the atmospheric wind at altitudes of 80 to 100 km. J. Atm. Terr. Phys. 2, 282.
Greenhow, J.S., 1952b, Characteristics of radio echoes from meteor trails: III. The behaviour of electron trails after formation, Proc. Phys. Soc.(London) B 65, 169.
Greenhow, J.S., 1954, Systematic wind measurements at altitudes of 80-100 km using radio echoes from meteor trails, Phil. Mag. 45, 471.
Greenhow, J.S. and J.F.Hall, 1960, Diurnal variations of density and scale height in the upper atmosphere, J. Atmos. Terr. Phys. 18, 203.
Greenhow, J.S. and E.L.Neufeld, 1955, Diurnal and seasonal wind variation in the upper atmosphere. Phil. Mag. 46, 549.
Greenhow, J.S. and E.L.Neufeld, 1956, The height variation of upper atmosphere winds, Phil. Mag. 1, 1157.
Greenhow, J.S. and E.L.Neufeld, 1959a, Measurement of turbulence in the upper atmosphere, Proc. Phys. Soc. 74, 1.
Greenhow, J.S. and E.L.Neufeld, 1959b, Turbulence at altitudes of 80-100 km and its effect on long-duration meteor echoes. J. Atm. Terr. Phys. 16, 384.
Greenhow, J.S. and E.L.Neufeld, 1960, Large scale irregularities in high altitude winds, Proc. Phys. Soc. 75, 228.
Greenhow, J.S. and E.L.Neufeld, 1961, Winds in the upper atmosphere, Quart. J. Roy. Met. Soc. 87, 472.

II. Radar météorolique d'Adélaïde
Robertson. D.S., D.T.Liddy and W.G.Elford, 1953, Measurement of winds in the upper atmosphere by means of drifting meteor trail (I). J. Atmos.Terrest Phys.4. 255.
Elford, W.G. and D.S.Robertson, 1953, Measurements of winds in the upper atmosphere by means of drifting meteor trail (II). J. Atmos. Terrest. Phys. 4, 271.
Elford, W.G., 1959a, A study of winds between 80 and 100 km in medium latitudes. Plan. Space Sci. 1, 94.
Elford, W.G., 1959b, Winds in the upper atmosphere, J. Atmos. Terrest. Phys. 15, 132.
Weiss. A.A. and W.G.Elford, 1963, An equipment for combined geophysical and astronomical measurements of meteors. Proc. Inst. Rad. Engrs. Austr. 24, 197.

Roper, R.G. and W.G.Elford, 1963, Seasonal variation of turbulence in the upper atmosphere, Nature 197, 963.

III. Radar météorique de Garchy

Spizzichino, A., J.Delcourt, A.Giraud and I.Revah, 1965, A new type of C.W. radar
for the observation of meteor trails, Proc. IEEE 53, 1084.
Revah, I. et A.Spizzichino, 1966, Résultats de mesure continue des vents ionosphériques à partir de l'observation de traînées météoriques, Compt. Rend. (Paris)
262 B, 378.
Spizzichino, A., 1967, in: Space Research VII, R.L.Smith-Rose, ed. (North-Holland,
Amsterdam) p. 73.

IV. Discussion des mesures de vents par météores. Comparaison avec d'autres méthodes

Haurwitz, B., 1961, Comments on tidal winds in the upper atmosphere, Plan. Space
Sci. 5, 196.
Haurwitz, B., 1964, Tidal phenomena in the upper atmosphere, Techn. Note 58,
World Meteorological Organization.
Jones, I.L., 1958, The height variation of drifts in the E region, J. Atmos. Terrest.
Phys. 12, 68.
Kazimirovsky, E.S., 1963, Wind system in the lower ionosphere, Geomagnetism
and aeronomy 3, 380.
Kochanski, A., 1963, Circulation and temperatures at 70 to 100 km height, J. Geo-
phys. Res. 68 (1), 213.
Mirkotan, S.F., 1961, Rapport au Symposium U.R.S.I. - C.I.G. de Nice.
Murgatroyd, W., 1957, Winds and temperatures between 20 and 100 km. A review,
Quart. J. Roy. Met. Soc. 83, 417.
Rao, G.L.N., 1965, Horizontal drifts and anisotropy of irregularities in the lower
ionosphere. A review. Aeronomy Rep. - Dep. of Electronic Engineering, Univ. of
Illinois, Urbana.

V. Etude des vents à petite échelle utilisant la réflexion des ondes en plusieurs points d'une même traînée

Greenhow, J.S., 1950, The fluctuation and fading of radio echoes from meteor trails,
Phil. Mag. 41, 682.
Greenhow, J.S. and E.L.Neufeld, 1959, Measurement of turbulence in the upper at-
mosphere, Proc. Phys. Soc. 74, 1.
Hines, C.D., 1960, Internal atmospheric gravity waves at meteor lights, Canad. J.
Phys. 38, 1441.
Kent, G.S., 1960, The fading of radio waves reflected obliquely from meteor trails,
J. Atmos. Res. 19, 272.
Manning, L.A., 1959, Air motions and the fading diversity and aspect sensitivity of
meteoric echoes, J. Geophys. Res. 64, 1415.
Revah, I. et A.Spizzichino, 1963, Etude des cisaillements de vents dans la basse
ionosphère par l'observation radioélectrique des traînées météoruques, I. Etude
théorique, Ann. Géophys. 19, 43.
Revah, I. et A.Spizzichino, 1964, Etude des cisaillements de vents dans la basse
ionosphère par l'observation radioélectrique des traînées météoriques, II. Résultats expérimentaux, Ann. Géophys. 20, 248.
Rosenberg, N.W. and C.G.Justus, 1966, Space and time correlations of ionospheric
winds, Radio Sci. 1, 149.

VI. Observation des météores (en général)

Carman, E.H. and B.C.Gibson-Wilde, 1964, J. Atmos. Phys. 26, 1231.

Clemmow. P.C. et al., 1954, Rep. Phys. Soc. Conf. (Cambridge) 136.
MacKinley. D.W.R.. 1961, Meteor science and engineering (MacGraw Hill. New York).
Spizzichino, A. and C.Taieb. 1963, Compt. Rend. (Paris) 257. 206.
Spizzichino. A. and C.Taieb. 1964. Ann. Géophys. 20. 197.

FIRST GENERAL DISCUSSION
ON MOTIONS IN THE UPPER ATMOSPHERE

1. EQUATION OF MOTION

Rawer:

One most important point which came up in our discussion is that of the equation of motion. In plasma physics and in meteorology rather different equations are used. Taking account of the most important influences these are:

$$\text{'plasma'}: \frac{d v_{ie}}{dt} \equiv \frac{\partial v_{ie}}{\partial t} + v_{ie} \cdot \nabla v_{ie} = \frac{1}{\rho_{ie}} J \times B_{\circ} + g - \frac{1}{\rho_{ie}} \nabla (p_i + p_e) - \nu v_{ie}$$

where

$$v_{ie} = \frac{m_i v_i + m_e v_e}{m_i + m_e}$$

is the averaged speed of the charged particles relative to neutrals.

$$\text{'meteorology'}: \frac{d v}{dt} \equiv \frac{\partial v}{\partial t} + v \cdot \nabla v = -2\omega \times v + g - \frac{1}{\rho} \nabla p + \frac{1}{\rho} F(v).$$

First of all we should clarify the approximations used at the application of the last equation in most of all meteorological work. The stationary approximation neglects $\partial v / \partial t$ but not necessarily $v \cdot \nabla v$. Most often a rather extreme simplification is used, namely the geostrophic approximation which equates two force terms on the right side: the pressure gradient and the Coriolis-term. The 'thermal wind' seems to be deduced with three terms, viz. yet considering the gravity term.

Maenhout:

Meteorological approximation neglects the vertical components for which the hydrostatic equation is simply used. So one considers the *vertical component* only of the earth's rotation ω.

Erkmen:

The hydrostatic equation is given by the third component of the vectorial equation, neclecting the other terms. This third component contains the gravitational term which is so large that the vertical components of the Coriolis-term and acceleration are negligible. In the x-component of the equation of motion $2\omega \cos \varphi_w$ has been neglected because the vertical wind component w is negligible for large scale motion, but not for small scale motions (for example in cumulonimbus clouds).

Rawer:

But the gravity term is almost cancelled by the hydrostatic pressure gradient, so that in the third component the Coriolis-term may not be negligible. The Coriolis term in the third component is $-2\omega u \cos \varphi$, so that it introduces a coupling between horizontal and vertical motion - this could be very important for ionospheric drifts.

$$2\omega \times v \equiv \begin{pmatrix} x & y & z \\ 0 & 2\omega \cos \varphi & 2\omega \sin\varphi \\ u & v & w \end{pmatrix}$$

$$\equiv \begin{cases} 2\omega(w \cos \varphi - v \sin \varphi) \\ 2\omega\, u \sin \varphi \\ -2\omega\, u \cos \varphi \end{cases}$$

Erkmen:

In the troposphere the term $v \cdot \nabla v$ may be neglected together with the term $\partial v/\partial t$ for the large scale motion between the top of the surface frictional layer and just below the first jet level which, in the average, almost coincides with the tropopause.

Hoult:

With $\omega \sim 10^{-4}$ s^{-1} the Coriolis term becomes smaller than the $v \cdot \nabla v$ term:
1) at 30 km height if the scale corresponding to the velocity gradient is < 1000 km.
2) at 100 km if this scale is $< 10^4$ km.
So the nonlinear term should be considered above 30 km of height.

Rawer:

The difficulty with the nonlinear term is that the total velocity must be known to its determination - including all effects together. In fact this is another coupling term, not only between the different geometrical components but also with respect to different tidal harmonies, solar and lunar tides, the dominant ('steady') motion and even small scale motions.

Spizzichino:

The importance of these terms depends not only on the scale of the gradients but also on the scale of the motion considered.

Bolgiano:

Vertical coupling is probably mainly produced by the Coriolis term.

Rawer:

As the geostrophic approximation applies only to temperate and high latitudes, but not near the equator (and the same is true for the three term approximation used to compute the 'thermal wind'), what are the methods applied by meteorologists at the equator and at low latitudes?

Misme:

We have to take account of the friction force $F(v)$ which has the negative direction of the motion. This term is small at higher latitudes. There we consider an equilibrium between three forces: the pressure gradient force and the small firction force combined must cancel the Coriolis force. Therefore at temperate latitudes the direction of motion is nearly perpendicular to the pressure gradient, and this is the geostrophic approximation. Approaching the equator the horizontal Coriolis force goes to zero and in the horizontal plane the friction force alone must now cancel the pressure gradient. Therefore here the direction of motion is parallel to the pressure gradient. (Nature simplifies the work of meteorologists insofar as rather small pressure gradients use to appear in the equatorial region.) In the transition range (at low latitudes) meteorologists apply intermediate directions which, generally, are only estimated between the limiting cases.

Rawer: Conclusion

The geostrophic approximation has only a limited validity range, even in the troposphere. At greater heights, even if conditions are stationary $(\partial v/\partial t = 0)$ the wind gradient term on the left side should be considered. As it is a nonlinear term, it introduces coupling between different phenomena. Also the vertical component of the Coriolis-term results in some coupling between horizontal (west-east) and vertical motion. Finally the friction-term is probably important, at least in equatorial regions, and it is rather difficult to determine this term, which should consist of a contribution from laminar motion plus one from turbulence.

2. DISTINCTION OF DIFFERENT TYPES OF MOTION

Rawer:

The distinction used by Spizzichino was: 'dominant' (probably better than 'steady'), 'tidal' and 'small scale' motions. What is the parameter after which 'dominant' (i.e. 'large scale') and 'small scale' motions are distinguished?

Maenhout:

In meteorology after the dimensions on the globe.

Spizzichino:

For the ionospherists after the time scale. This for the simple reason that data are not available from enough stations to determine a geometrical scale.

Rawer:

So at any case the distinction is made in some way arbitrarily on a continuous scale of phenomena underlying essentially to the same influences, but with variable importance of the different forces.

Which is now the situation for the tidal motions?

Neubauer:

Tidal motions can be considered as long period gravity waves. At these calculations the Coriolis-term is not negligible for periods longer than about one hour, so for all interesting tidal components. The nonlinear velocity gradient term is mostly neglected, or approximated by linearization; but this is mainly done for convenience and probably coupling should not be neglected. The different tidal harmonics differ by the way how the energy input is distributed along the height axis. In particular the solar tide can be explained to a large amount by heating by solar radiation; there is an important input in the layers near the ground, but also one in the ozonosphere.

Rawer:

And probably also one in the thermosphere resulting from the ionization processes.

Neubauer:

It is certain that the combination of these different inputs makes the computation more difficult. The calculations for the thermal drive below 100 km have been carried through by Lindzen for the diurnal tide. The results are considered to be valid below 105 km and show considerable agreement with observational features.

3. VERTICAL MOTIONS

Rawer:

Our last subject concerns a phenomen which has mostly been neglected in the past for the simple reason that vertical motions do not really appear in the meteorological approximation considering precisely stationary motion in a surface of constant geopotential (and not at constant height). We should at least enlist those observations in which vertical motion seems to appear at mesopheric or ionospheric altitudes.

Lalonde:

There are ionospheric observations with different echo techniques showing that the phenomenon called E_S (or sporadic E) has a tendency to descend with a vertical speed of the order of 1 km/h near the 100 km level, but with about 10 km/h in the height range 130 to 150 km. These values describe the vertical displacement of a very thin, ionized layer.

As to the D-region it is an open question whether the partial echoes from this layer are produced by steep gradients in the ionization profile, or by a phenomenon similar in character to E_S, though of smaller electron density.

Rawer:

May I ask Mlle Baguette which are her conclusions from the observations of sodium vapour traces?

Baguette:

We feel that we have observed vertical displacements, however these are at the limit of our observational accuracy. Anyhow as a crude rule we may say that 10% of the average horizontal speed could exist as vertical speed after our observations.

A SIMPLE DESCRIPTION OF IONOSPHERIC DRIFTS IN THE E REGION AS OBTAINED BY THE FADING METHOD AT BREISACH

E. HARNISCHMACHER and K. RAWER
Ionosphären-Insitut Breisach, Germany *

Abstract. The observations of the period 1955 through 1963 have been analyzed by a special program of harmonic analysis using only three terms of development with 'variation of the constants'. The results for the direction statistics are given in figs. 9 through 11. The seasonal influence is introduced as statistical difference with respect to the annual mean value. A strong influence of the solar declination is stated. Arranging the data after the lunar phase, a similar influence of the lunar declination is found. There exists also an important influence of the lunar phase which is shown by diagrams of differential statistics.

Résumé. Les observations de la période 1955 à 1963 ont été analysées suivant un programme particulier d'analyse harmonique, utilisant seulement 3 termes du developpement avec variation des constantes. Il en résulte une description de la statistique des directions présentée dans les figures 9 à 11. L'influence saison-nière est introduite comme différence statistique par rapport à la moyenne annuelle. Il apparait ainsi une forte influence de la déclinaison solaire. Par arrangement des données suivant la phase lunaire une influence pareille de la déclinaison lunaire est trouvée. Il y a aussi une influence importante de la phase lunaire qui est démontrée par des diagrammes de statistique différentielle.

1. SERIES OF OBSERVATIONS

During an 8 years period of observations from 1955 through 1963 E-region drifts have been determined with the method of similar fades (Harnischmacher and Rawer, 1961) at Breisach (Germany). The program of observations was such that in the average half of the time of a day was covered with observations during 5 min, with 30 min intervals. The total number of days of observations is of the order of 1200 whilst the number of individual determinations of the drift vector is about 0.5×10^6. This seems to be the most intense series of observations obtained until now.

2. DEFINITION OF PARAMETERS

It has been shown (Harnischmacher and Rawer, 1958a) that solar and lunar tidal influences are very important factors in ionospheric drifts. On the other side there is experimental evidence that conditions are really different for day and night time. The classical way for describing the observed

* Research sponsored in part by Air Force Cambridge Res. Labs. through European Office OAR under contracts AF61(052)-81 and -672.

features is the Fourier analysis, either in cartesian coordinates or in polar ones. In such an analysis the difference between day and night conditions appears as a 24 h component. Also if the Fourier analysis is made in solar time then the lunar influence is a disturbing influence which is not directly expressed but becomes visible by a certain amount of higher harmonic components, apparently depending on solar, instead of lunar time. There is another experimental difficulty given by the fact that with the fading method directional data are considerably more accurate than are speed data.

For all these reasons it appears to be rather doubtful to apply straightforward Fourier analysis to ionospheric drift data. For these reasons we have developped a special system which is mainly based on directional data and gives a simple description in terms of only three Fourier 'quasi-components'.

In fact the Fourier analysis is applied at the explanation of observational data under very different conditions. There are cases where the Fourier components are really selected by the experimental device (e.g. by a tuned receiver); in these cases the Fourier components have a physical reality and it makes sense to describe one of the components as an individual. In other cases, however, the decomposition of a natural time sequence into Fourier components is rather artificial so that only the composition of all components to the overall time sequence is physically significant, but not individual components. We feel that our case is of the second kind so that the Fourier series is only one and not the only possible way to describe the observed facts. We found that in our case, in view of the small difference of the periods for solar and lunar effects a better readable description was given by combining solar and lunar periods and considering only the lowest harmonics up to the second one. In this analysis a 'sliding phase' had been used, and a rotational drift change was thought to be the most natural case (for temperate and high latitudes at least). The parameters are therefore a probability (called 'engagement', replacing the amplitude of a classical Fourier component) and a phase of each of the three first harmonics, each being dependent on time inside the period considered. The method is in some way comparable with methods of 'variation of constants' in the mathematical theory of differential equations.

3. BASIC DATA

The basic data of our analysis are the individual determinations of the drift vector obtained from the recordings. The median drift vector is determined from all observed drift vectors for a given 5 min interval. All such 5 min median data obtained during a month are statistically presented in a diagram giving the probability for certain directions or speeds to appear during that month at a given hour. To this end all E-region observations which we have obtained in 5 years are presented in cumulative diagrams which have been established individually for each month. Fig. 1 gives an example for such a typical monthly diagram. A more general sur-

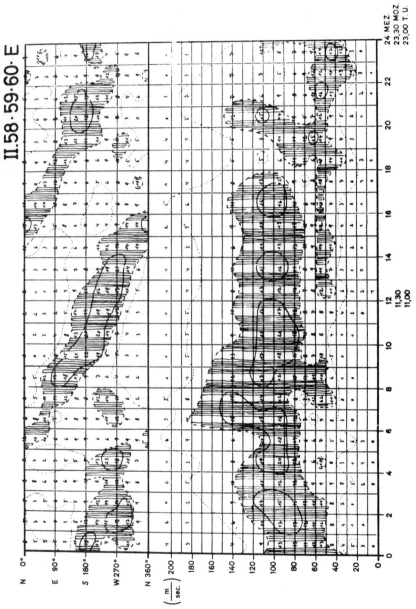

Fig. 1. Probability diagram for the month of February over three years (1958–1960). The upper diagram describes the direction of the drift vector while the lower diagram is concerned with the absolute speed value. Probabilities are indicated in per cent, regions with probability higher than 10% are hatched. The limit of the zone with more than 15% is given as a fat line.

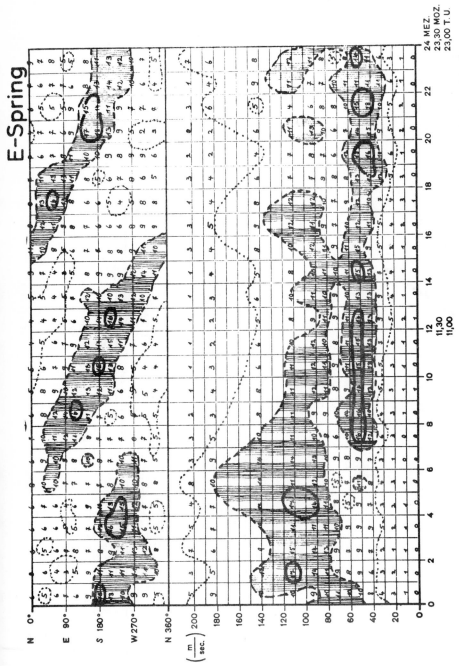

Fig. 2a. Probability diagram (see caption to fig. 1) over the whole eight years period of observations established for spring (February through April).

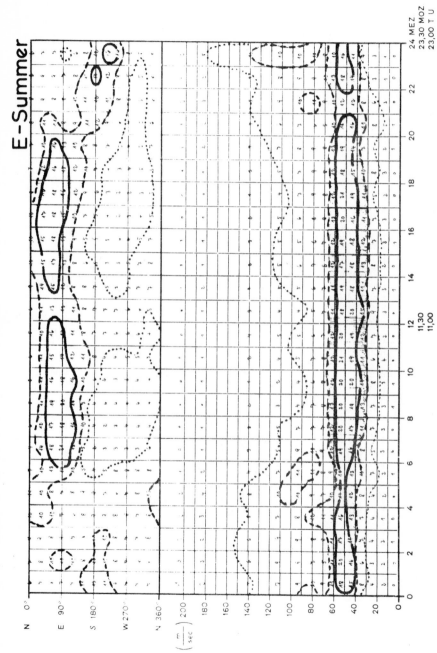

Fig. 2b. Probability diagram (see caption to fig. 1) over the whole eight years period of observations established for summer (May through July).

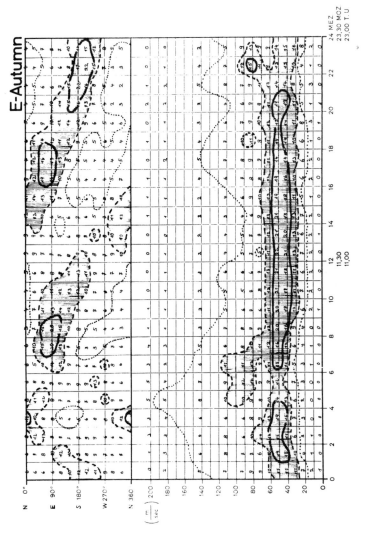

Fig. 2c. Probability diagram (see caption to fig. 1) over the whole eight years period of observations established for autumn (August through October).

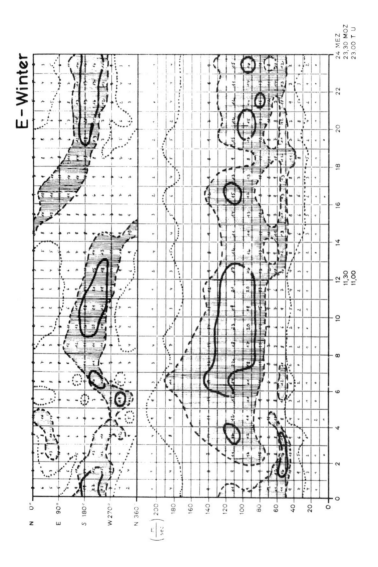

Fig. 2d. Probability diagram (see caption to fig. 1) over the whole eight years period of observations established for winter (November through January).

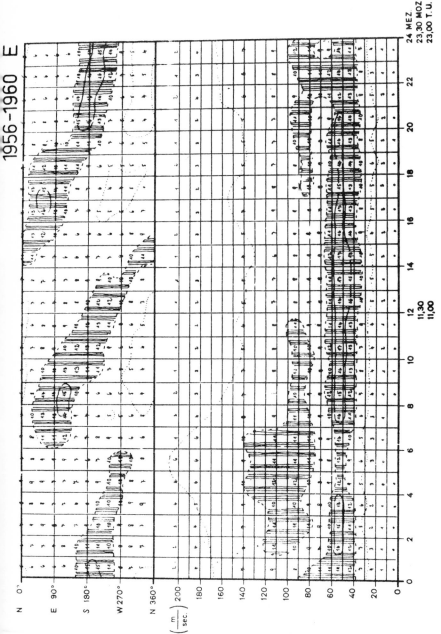

Fig. 3. Probability diagram (see caption to fig. 1) covering all observations of the whole eight years period, so that an average over all seasons is obtained. The seasonal particularities do not completely disappear in this diagram. For example in the lower (speed–) diagram the high speed maximum is only due to winter and spring data, but the lower speed range mainly to summer and autumn data.

vey is given by seasonal diagrams. Such average diagrams for the four
seasons are given in figs. 2a-d. Finally an overall diagram grouping all
observations of E-region drifts during the period 1955 through 1960 is given
in fig. 3.

Each of these diagrams contains two parts. In the upper one the drift direction is presented (direction of the drift vector - opposite to the meteorological definition concerning the direction from which the wind comes); the
diagram gives the direction as ordinate, the solar hour as abscissa and
probability is indicated for each case in this field in per cent. (Zones of
probability higher than 10% are hatched, a thick line encloses the zone of
more than 15%.) The lower diagram is a similar presentation of the statistics of apparent speeds, however in this case we use a division which is only linear between 0 and 100 m/s, larger divisions being used for the higher
velocities.

The analysis was first restricted to the direction. Afterwards the corresponding velocity values were also investigated. Looking for solar and lunar rotational components, we obtained the following results: A 'dominant'
(or 'prevailing') drift exists with more or less constant direction (and velocity) lasting for approximately 6 to 8 hours; rather important differences
occur between day and night. Rotating components could be identified with
periods of 24, 12, 8, 6 and 4.8 h, in both, solar and lunar time. The importance of these phenomena depends mainly on solar and lunar declination,
and this is the reason why 'seasonal' effects are observed. Its influence on
the 'dominant' drift is such that high positive declination goes with a tendency for easterly direction, while for negative declination westerly drifts
occur preferentially. The corresponding velocity is large for negative and
small for positive declination (figs. 4-7). (Similar behaviour has besides
been stated at Puerto Rico.) This explains the seasonal variation.

As to the 12-h solar rotational component, it appears most clearly in
winter during daytime, but also in late summer for nighttime. The phase of
the solar and lunar 12-h component is controlled by the declination, shifting
towards late with increasing declination of the sun or the moon. This is
proved by fig. 8 where systematic phase variations of the effective 12-h oscillation are shown. Values are given in hours on the abscissa (see top at
right) as function of the declination of sun or moon. The four curves at the
left side identify the phase against Lunar Time for the four seasons (F =
spring, S = summer, H = fall, W = winter). The curve along the 'Lunar
Time' axis is the yearly average phase of the 12-h oscillation against Lunar Time. It shows the *solar influence* on the *lunar tide*. It should be compared with the curve right along the 'Solar Time' axis, giving the yearly
average phase of the 12-h oscillation against Solar Time. It shows the *lunar
influence* on the *solar tide*. The latter is only slightly smaller than the
first. If higher tidal harmonics are considered, the lunar influence seems
to be increasing with the order, particularly in summer. Possibly 12-h rotational components with variable phase are better adapted to describe most
of the complicated features of combined solar and lunar control than does
straightforward Fourier analysis (see section 4).

The observed drifts certainly depend on the height. The zonal system

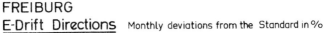

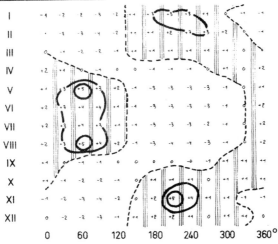

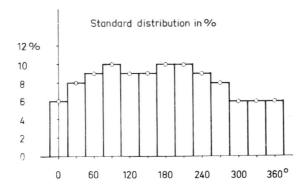

Fig. 4. The upper diagram is the difference diagram of the 'dominant' drift component for Freiburg as function of the solar declination as identified by the month (ordinate). The drift direction is found on the abscissa. Numerical indications are
probability differences against the average dominant drift as given by the 'standard
distribution' in the lower diagram. Regions of positive difference values are
hatched, the full curves identify 3 and 5% while zero difference is indicated by the
broken curve.

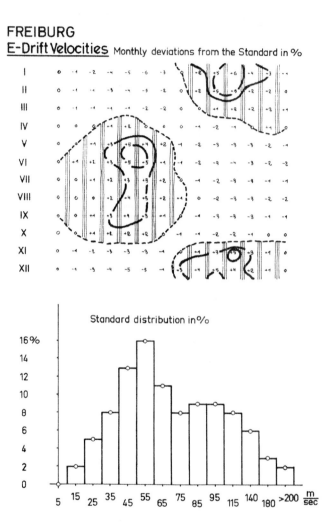

FREIBURG
E-Drift Velocities Monthly deviations from the Standard in %

Standard distribution in %

Fig. 5. The upper diagram is the difference diagram of the 'dominant' drift component for Freiburg as function of the solar declination as identified by the month (ordinate). The drift speed is found on the abscissa. Numerical indications are probability differences against the average dominant drift as given by the 'standard distribution' in the lower diagram. Regions of positive difference values are hatched, the
full curves identify 3 and 5% while zero difference is indicated by the broken curve.

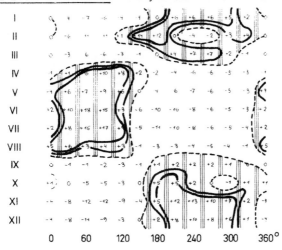

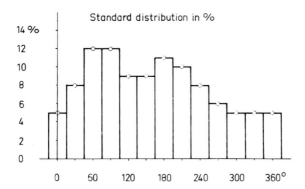

Fig. 6. The upper diagram is the difference diagram of the 'dominant' drift component for Puerto Rico as function of the solar declination as identified by the month
(ordinate). The drift direction is found on the abscissa. Numerical indications are
probability differences against the average dominant drift as given by the 'standard
distribution' in the lower diagram. Regions of positive difference values are
hatched, the full curves identify 3 and 5% while zero difference is indicated by the
broken curve.

E. HARNISCHMACHER and K. RAWER

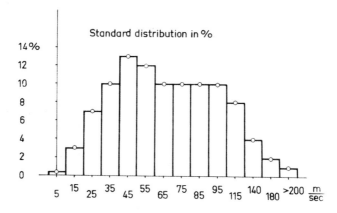

Fig. 7. The upper diagram is the difference diagram of the 'dominant' drift component for Puerto Rico as function of the solar declination as identified by the month
(ordinate). The drift speed is found on the abscissa. Numerical indications are probability differences against the average dominant drifts as given by the 'standard distribution' in the lower diagram. Regions of positive difference values are hatched.
the full curves identify 3 and 5% while zero difference is indicated by the broken
curve.

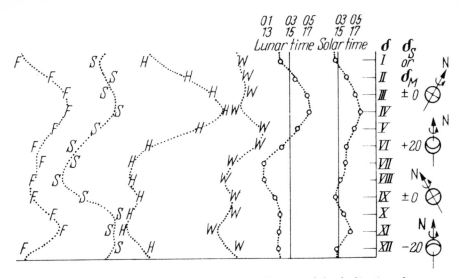

Fig. 8. Phase of the different 12 h components as function of the declination of sun or moon. The scale 'δ_S or δ_M' is given on the ordinate in degrees of declination as a cyclic variable. The corresponding position of the earth's axis is shown by the small figures at extreme right hand. (The solar declination is also indicated by the order number of the corresponding month; see δ on the right side.) The phases have been determined from different diagrams of the 12 h component. The curve under 'solar time' describes the solar declination or seasonal influence. The curve under 'lunar time' describes the pure lunar influence (averaged over all seasons). The four curves in the left side field give combined influences, viz. the lunar declination influence during each of the seasons, thus for a given solar declination value. The indications F, S, H, W identify the seasons spring, summer, fall and winter respectively; thus S designates high positive declination of the sun and W negative one. (To avoid confusion the zeros of these curves are displaced along the abscissa.)

revealed by low frequency sounding is typical for low altitude; higher up the 12-h tidal rotations appear more and more clearly. As the E region is found at slightly lower height in summer, tidal drifts appear only rarely in summer; also they are not observed when E_S is present in daytime, the corresponding reflection level being yet lower. On the contrary tidal phenomena clearly appear in winter, when the E layer is some 5-8 km higher up.

Other findings after which the phase of the tidal 12-h component varied systematically with the height have not been verified by these observations. However, at certain seasons the individual fades often show two accumulation points at opposing directions, and this is the undiscutable result of a large mass of observations. This finding may eventually be explained by inconsistencies of the 'similar fade' evaluation but we feel that drifts of opposite direction may really exist at different heights as a consequence of wind shears.

4. EXTRACTION OF THE TIDAL COMPONENTS

In the following the monthly average statistics are used as the standard, and individual effects are described as deviations from this standard. For example, the lunar influence is obtained by grouping the observational data after the lunar phase, determining the statistical distribution for an individual lunar phase and computing its difference with respect to the standard distribution. The standard itself is decomposed into the three main tidal components in the sense described above, namely: a 'dominant drift' (formerly often called 'prevailing drift'), a 12-h component and a 24-h component. Each of these must be considered as a statistical distribution and not as a simple unique function of the hour.

The first term of the decomposition is that of zero order, which is independent on the hour in the strict Fourier analysis. It could be obtained from the diagrams of figs. 1, 2 or 3 by averaging the probability over each line of the diagram over 24 h. This gives distribution curves describing the 'preference' for each direction or speed to occur - without indicating a certain direction and speed as being representative.

In our new analysis (Harnischmacher, 1964) this procedure is 'softened' to one which conserves a certain dependence on the hour: instead of averaging horizontally the basic diagrams over 24 h we compute sliding averages over 7 h only (i.e. ± 3 h). This gives us a statistical distribution depending on the hour in which the tendency for 'horizontal' connections is increased. An algebraic description can be obtained by defining a 'quasi-dominant' directional probability distribution, C_1, out of the original one, P, by the equation:

$$C_1(\varphi;t) = \frac{1}{7} \sum_{\tau=t-3h}^{t+3h} P(\varphi;\tau) ,\tag{1}$$

φ being the center of a directional interval, t being the hour.

The following operations are based on the difference

$$P_{11}(\varphi;t) = P(\varphi;t) - C_1(\varphi;t) .\tag{2}$$

(This difference contains positive and negative probability values.) The corresponding diagram should have a smaller tendency for horizontal connections than the original one, $P(\varphi;t)$, so that in this diagram the oblique features corresponding to the rotating harmonics appear to be more important.

From this diagram the 12-h component could be obtained by summing up not along an horizontal line but along an oblique line with inclination 30^0/h. By this operation we obtain diagrams in which all components are almost averaged out, except for that of 12 h. The averaging is made over 3 hours only, i.e. by the equation:

$$V_1(\varphi;t) = \frac{1}{3} \sum_{\tau=t-1h}^{t+1h} P_{11}(\varphi + \frac{\tau}{h} \cdot 30^0;\tau) .\tag{3}$$

Now V_1 is deduced from the remaining distribution P_{11} by computing:

$$P_{12}(\varphi;t) = P_{11}(\varphi;t) - V_1(\varphi;t)$$
$$= P(\varphi;t) - C_1(\varphi;t) - V_1(\varphi;t). \tag{4}$$

The main influence which is yet contained in the probability distribution P_{12} is the variable 24-h component. It is obtained by the same procedure as applied to deduce the 12-h component V_1, i.e. by summing up along an oblique line with inclination $15^o/h$ this time. The corresponding equation is:

$$W_1(\varphi;t) = \tfrac{1}{9} \sum_{\tau=t-4h}^{t+4h} P_{12}(\varphi + \tfrac{\tau}{h} \cdot 15^o; \tau). \tag{5}$$

The 3 components C_1, V_1, W_1 may already be considered as to give a rather good description of the main solar influences. It was, however, felt that the establishment of these features should be improved by an iteration procedure. This can be done in the following manner: for the second iteration step we begin with

$$P_{20}(\varphi;t) = P(\varphi;t) - V_1(\varphi;t) - W_1(\varphi;t) \tag{6}$$

and apply to P_{20} the operation of eq. (1) in order to obtain a better representation of the 'quasi-dominant' directional probability distribution which is now called C_2 and replaces C_1 in the following. Then the operation of oblique summing with $30^o/h$ after eq. (3) is applied to the difference

$$P_{21}(\varphi;t) = P(\varphi;t) - C_2(\varphi;t) - W_1(\varphi;t). \tag{7}$$

This gives us a better distribution function for the 12-h component which may be called V_2. The 24-h component is similarly obtained with eq. (5) applied to the difference

$$P_{22}(\varphi;t) = P(\varphi;t) - C_2(\varphi;t) - V_2(\varphi;t) \tag{8}$$

and so $W_2(\varphi;t)$ is obtained and the second step of the iteration is finished. Normally a two step iteration was found to be sufficient, in some cases a third step of iteration was made in a manner analogic to the procedure described above. In this way finally the mainly significant content of the original probability distribution is described by the three functions

$C(\varphi;t)$ for the dominant component,
$V(\varphi;t)$ for the 12-h component,
$W(\varphi;t)$ for the 24-h component.

Results have been obtained for the monthly statistics as well as for seasonal statistics. Here we reproduce only the results of the seasonal statistics in fig. 9 for $C(\varphi;t)$, fig. 10 for $V(\varphi;t)$ and fig. 11 for $W(\varphi;t)$. The numerical values in these diagrams are again probability values in per cent. However, there is a difference as compared with the original representation in so far as the diagrams for the variable components contain now positive and negative probability values. The diagrams of fig. 9 for the dominant component C contain positive probability values only. On the other side the diagrams for V in fig. 10 and for W in fig. 11 contain positive and

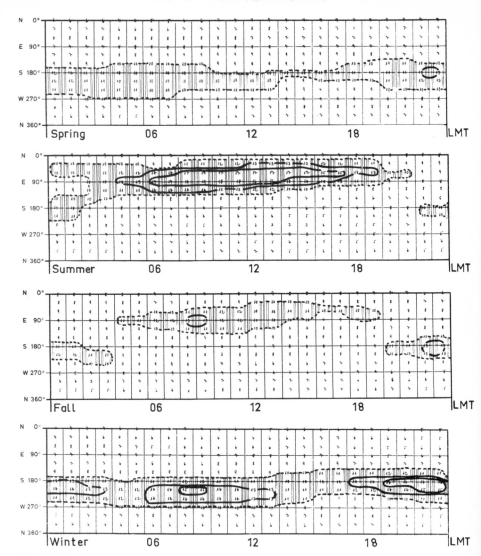

Fig. 9. Dominant drift component, C, obtained by iteration from the directional statistics (as explained in the text). Separate diagrams for the four seasons.

negative probability values in equal number so that the total probability sum over each of these diagrams is zero. In figs. 10 and 11 the whole region where positive probabilities occur has been hatched and the region with more than 3% positive probability is indicated by crossed hatching. (Hatching was not applied in the regions of negative probability.

The higher the concentration of high (or low) probability values in these

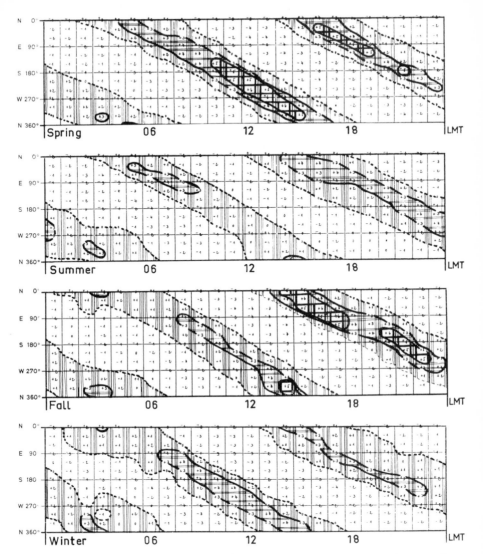

Fig. 10. Variable solar 12 h component, V, deduced by iteration from the directional
statistics (as explained in the text). Separate diagrams for the four seasons.

diagrams the clearer appeared the corresponding influence in our observational data. We may therefore define the importance of this concentration
as *'engagement'* of the corresponding influence. We may for example state
from fig. 9 that the quasi-dominant component has a particularly strong engagement in summer with a direction around $80°$, but only for sunlit hours.
The engagement is rather weak in the equinox seasons, it is higher again in

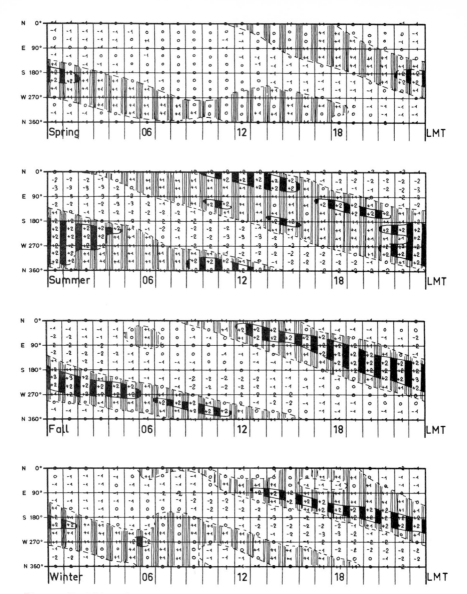

Fig. 11. Variable solar 24 h component, W, deduced by iteration from the directional statistics (as explained in the text). Separate diagrams for the four seasons.

winter but for directions around 210° nearly opposed to the representative summer value. The main result of fig. 10 may be formulated as follows: the engagement of the 12-h solar component is particularly strong in the equinox

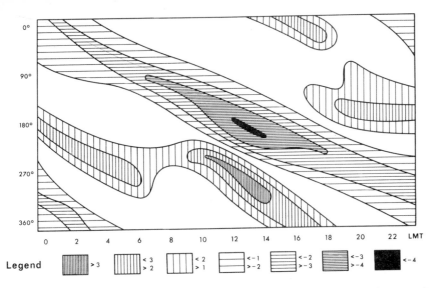

Fig. 12. Variable solar 24 h component, W, deduced by iteration from the directional statistics (as explained in the text), for one month only (January). Zones of positive and negative differential probability are hatched, as indicated in the legend.

seasons, with preference for the hours between 10 h and 22 h, however, with slightly different phases in spring and autumn. Fig. 12 is one example of a monthly diagram for the 24 h component showing 'secondary' features.

The basis of our data-analysis are the observed drift directions. These are certainly more significant than the absolute speed values obtained with the method of similar fades (Harnischmacher and Rawer, 1958b). It is well-known that different reduction methods give different absolute speed values and that, in the average, reduction by the correlation methods gives considerably lower speed than obtained with the method of similar fades, and that metal vapour rocket observations have a tendency to give even higher speeds. However, the relative variations of the speed are probably well defined. We felt that by discriminating the speeds in classes one can obtain from the diagram describing the directional features a corresponding one, describing the relevant speed variations. An example is given in our figs. 13a and b in which the seasonal variation of the dominant component is shown, in fig. 13a for the directions and in fig. 13b for the speed values.

5. SEASONAL AND RELATED EFFECTS

These figures are a first result where we have presented average seasonal changes. They have been obtained from the corresponding monthly data. We feel that another presentation of the statistical data conserves more information, in particular for the rotating components. Instead of indicating

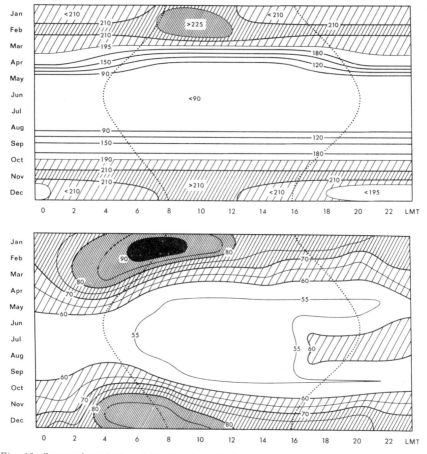

Fig. 13. Seasonal variation of the dominant drift vector as function of local mean time (abscissa) and month (ordinate). Fig. 13a is for the direction. fig. 13b for the speed. The regions corresponding to different values are distinguished in steps (bold lines for 30° and 10 m/s. thin lines for 15° and 5 m/s in figs. 13a and b respectively). The zones of extreme values are hatched. The dotted line identifies sunrise and sunset at ground level.

one phase and one engagement value per month, as it is done in the classical Fourier analysis, our sliding averaging process leaves more detailed information (e.g. in the graphs figs. 9-12).

Another way to look after the seasonal effects starts from a representation giving the probability of a fixed direction to be observed with one of the variable components. The corresponding graph is obtained as a section of the monthly graph of $V(\varphi;l)$ or $W(\varphi;l)$. For example, from the V-graph for January (fig. 14), putting $\varphi = 180° \pm 15°$, we get the uppermost horizontal line of fig. 15 indicating the probability to have V in southern direction. This

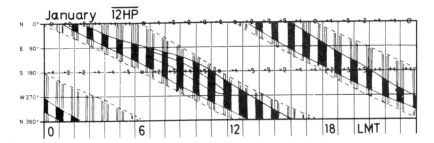

Fig. 14. Difference probability diagram of the average solar 12 h component (directions) for January: Numerical indications in the field identify positive and negative differences in per cent. Positive regions are hatched with fat hatching for values above + 2%. Abscissa: local mean time, ordinate: direction.

gives a distribution with two clear maxima at 09 and 1930 h LMT. (The time difference is not exactly 12 h as a consequence of different conditions by day and by night which are revealed by our sliding averaging method.) Composing such strips for the 12 months we get the diagram of fig. 15. If

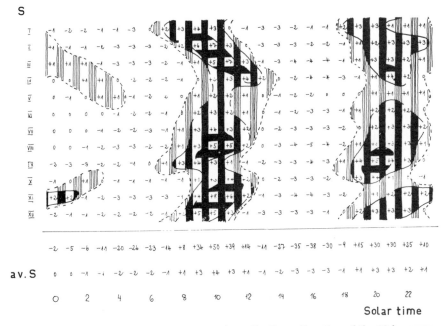

Fig. 15. Difference probability diagram to have Southern direction of the 12 h component V. (The values have been obtained from intersections with the line 180° in smoothed monthly diagrams like fig. 14.) Abscissa: solar time (= local mean time), ordinate: month. Numerical indications in the field and hatching like in fig. 14. (The numerical indication below December gives column sums, the next line contains column averages.)

no seasonal effect was present the maxima should be at the same time
hours all year over. One sees from fig. 15 that this is not so: the position
of the maxima is variable by a few hours with earlier values in winter. Also the engagement (here: the concentration of the high probability values) is
variable through the year with flattest forms in May and Obtober. A corresponding diagram for the probability of V to have a northern direction
$(\varphi = 0 \pm 15^{o})$ is given by fig. 16. This figure is rather similar to fig. 15 if
the signs are inverted; even small features (like in the lower left-hand corner) are appearing in both diagrams so that both are supplementary. We
are therefore quite sure that the apparent irregularities are physically
meaningful. On the other side to a first approximation the graphs 15 and 16
show a nearly symmetric behaviour with respect to mid-summer and midwinter. These features could be represented by using solar declination as
independent variable. This result will be used later, in sect. 6.

The probability graphs like figs 15 and 16 can be described as being
composed of an average probability distribution, valid for the whole year,
plus a seasonal term, so that by combination of both the original graph is
obtained. The all year average has been indicated numerically below each
of the originals (see figs. 15 and 16). By this procedure we get diagrams

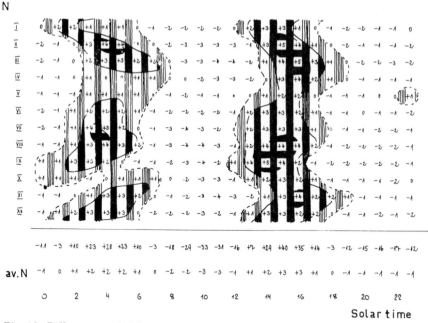

Fig. 16. Difference probability diagram to have Northern direction of the 12 h solar
component V. (The values have been obtained from intersections with the line $0/360^{o}$
in smoothed monthly diagrams like fig. 14.) Abscissa: solar time (= local mean time),
ordinate: month. Numerical indications in the field and hatching like in fig. 14. (The
numerical indication below December give column sums, the next line contains column averages.)

2nd Diff.

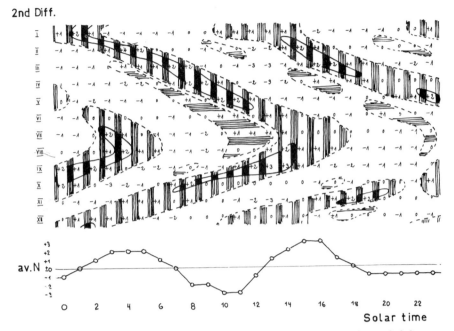

Fig. 17 Seasonal effect obtained as second difference from fig. 16. The probability difference values written in the field are obtained by subtracting the average (lower curve in the present figure) from the values in the corresponding line of fig. 16. (The lower diagram is identic with the numerical values given in the average difference line at the bottom of fig. 16.) Numerical indications and hatching like in fig. 14.

like fig. 17 describing the seasonal effect alone. (It is, of course, understood that such diagrams cannot be taken as directly describing observable variations; they only give the additional probability values which are needed to bring about the original graph by adding the average probability distribution which is shown as a curve below the main part of fig. 17. Rather similar features have been established by comparing such graphs. Our example, fig. 17, refers to northern direction, so that, combined with the average curve below it gives the original graph of fig. 16. The fact that a certain flattening occurred in April-May and October in the original graph is shown by higher values in the seasonal chart near the lines corresponding to these months. Here again we feel that the large mass of our basic data allows us to find out significant details. It should be mentioned that in these graphs a 'counterphase' appears sometimes, with small but non-negligible probability. (These domains are indicated by horizontal hatching in fig. 17.)

6. SOLAR AND LUNAR DECLINATION

The declination of the sun is slowly variable during a year. Its maximum

values are ± 23°, the inclination of the earth axis against the ecliptic. As
to the moon its orbital plane is inclined by 5° against the ecliptic and we
have a variation of the moon's declination through the year which depends
on the season and the lunar phase μ (see sect. 7). For example full moon
in winter corresponds to a high declination while full moon in summer occurs with a small one.

As the seasonal influence can be described as to be mainly one of solar
declination we have looked after a possible influence of the lunar declination. Such an influence can be derived from our data if lunar declination is
used for description instead of solar one.

For example for our quasi-dominant component T_0 we have established
a diagram of the deviations from the standard values as function of the
lunar declination. The corresponding graph is fig. 18 giving the differential
probability as function of the direction of T_0 (abscissa) and the lunar declination δ_L (ordinate). There appears a very clear lunar declination effect
which is of the same order of magnitude as the corresponding solar (seasonal) effect. Even for the speed values the lunar declination appears quite
clearly. In a similar presentation as used in fig. 18, fig. 19 gives the probability for the quasi-dominant component as a function of its speed (abscissa)
and lunar declination (ordinate).

The results may be summarized by saying that for high positive lunar
declination the quasi-dominant component has a tendency to be towards
East, while for lunar declinations around zero the preference is to the
western direction and for large negative declination it is to the South. The
speed values show a more complicated behaviour with higher values during
the period of increasing lunar declination and considerably lower values
during that of decreasing lunar declination.

7. INFLUENCE OF THE LUNAR PHASE

In the preceding analysis we took advantage of the fact that effects of lunar phase are quite well averaged out in monthly statistics as we have used
in sect. 4 and 5. In order to obtain that lunar phase influence we must subdivide our material according to this phase and average over the different
solar phases, i.e. the solar hour. This has been done with the whole observational material, distinguishing 8 lunar phases for every month. This
gives us a total of 96 basic diagrams which have then been treated with the
methods described above in sect. 4, using lunar instead of solar time. One
set of results obtained for the 12-h period, V_L, is presented in figs. 20a-d.
The parameter μ used for the identification of the lunar phase is the same
as used by Bartels and Fanselau (1938), namely the time difference between
solar and lunar culmination in hours. This parameter has been taken from
Fanselau's tables. By inspection of these figures quite important differences are seen. In particular there are some phases for which the engagement is rather small ($\mu = 20 \ldots 22$), while it is pretty large for the phase
values around 8 h. All these results are significant and need some explanation.

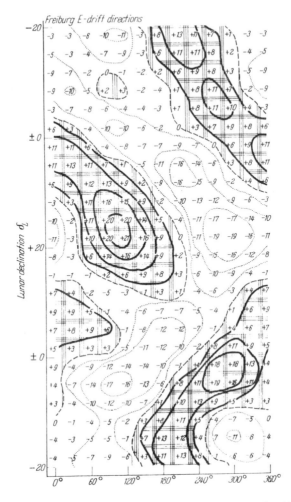

Fig. 18. Difference diagram of the 'dominant' drift component as function of the lunar declination δ_L (ordinate as a cyclic variable). The drift direction is found on the abscissa. Numerical indications are probability differences against the average dominant drift statistics in $\frac{1}{24}\%$. Regions of positive differences values are hatched. the lines identify multiples of $\frac{5}{24}\%$.

The data so obtained can be presented in a manner similar to figs. 15 and 16, namely by arranging sections for a given direction after the μ-value. An example is shown in fig. 21, giving the probability for southern direction ($\varphi = 180^\circ \pm 15^\circ$). Here again the average over all phases is given by numerical values below the diagram. This diagram is yet in solar time,

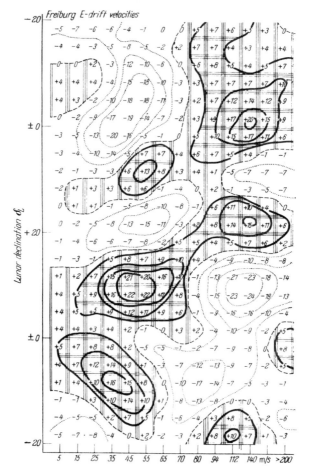

Fig. 19. Difference diagram of the 'dominant' drift component as function of the lunar declination δ_L (ordinate as a cyclic variable). The drift speed is found on the abscissa. Numerical indications are probability differences against the average dominant drift statistics in $\frac{1}{24}\%$. Regions of positive difference values are hatched, the lines identify multiples of $\frac{5}{24}\%$.

$t_\odot$, it gives the variations of the solar 12-h component as a function of the lunar phase.

Now, knowing lunar phase and solar hour these diagrams can be transformed into diagrams depending on lunar time t_L using the simple relation

$$t_L = t_\odot + \mu \ .$$

With this procedure a basic material is obtained which can be analyzed in lunar hour. In this way diagrams of the additional lunar influence as function

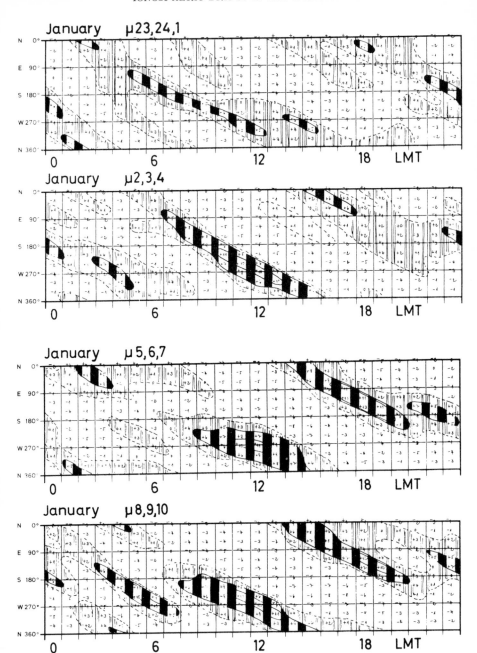

Fig. 20a, b.

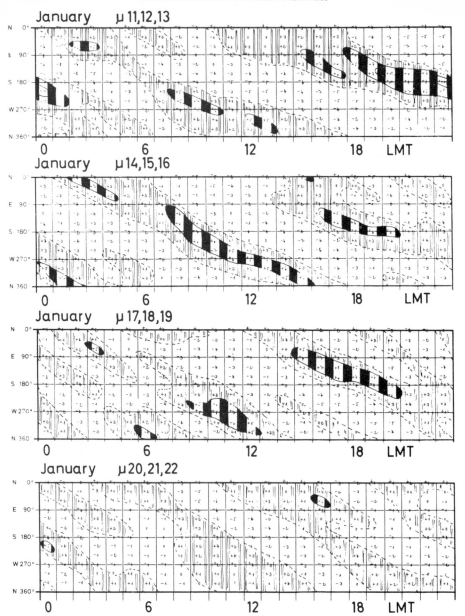

Fig. 20a–d. Difference probability diagrams of the average solar 12 h component (directions) for January, like in fig. 14 but distinguishing the lunar phase. μ is the time difference of the culminations of sun and moon in hours. The eight diagrams correspond to μ-groups of three hours. Numerical indications in the field identify positive and negative differences in per cent. Positive regions are hatched with fat hatching for values above + 4%. Abscissa: local mean time, ordinate: direction.

January ΔP 12HP S

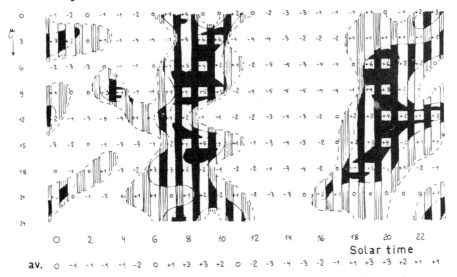

Solar time

av. 0 -1 -1 -1 -1 -2 0 +1 +3 +3 +2 0 -2 -3 -4 -3 -2 -1 +1 +3 +3 +2 +1 +1

Fig. 21. Difference probability diagram to have Southern direction of the 12-h component V in January. Abscissa: solar time (= local mean time), ordinate: lunar phase
μ(= time difference between solar and lunar culmination in hours). Numerical indications in the field and hatching like in fig. 14. (The numerical indications in the bottom
line are column averages.)

I II III IV

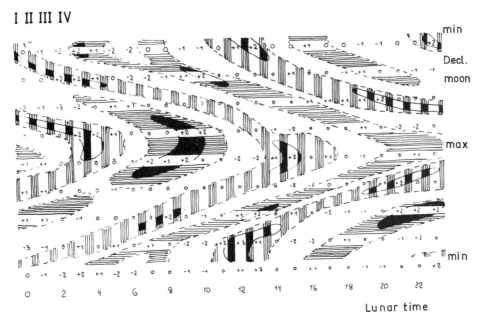

Lunar time

Fig. 22a.

V VI VII VIII

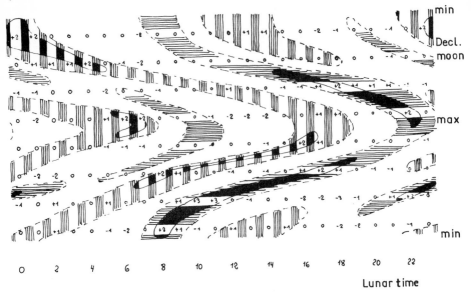

IX X XI XII

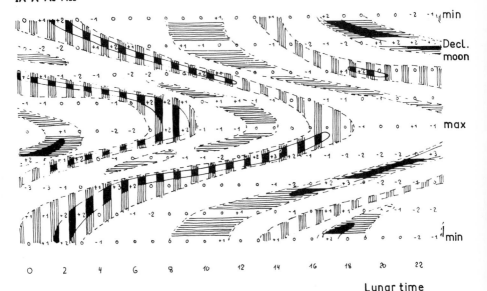

Fig. 22a–c. Lunar declination effect obtained as second difference from a set of monthly figures like figs. 20 after transforming from solar to lunar hour (using μ). The probability difference values written in the field are obtained by subtracting the average lunar time effect from the values corresponding to a given lunar declination (ordinate). Positive regions in the field are hatched (fat hatching for values above + 2%).

The three diagrams a. b. c refer to groups of four solar months each.

of lunar declination (ordinate) and lunar time is obtained similarly to the graphs of the seasonal influence shown e.g. in fig. 17. Such results are shown in figs. 22a-c. The parameter of these figures is the season; subdivision has been made for 3 periods of 4 months each. It appears quite clearly that in the course of the year the effect of lunar declination is variable and this is probably the incluence of the declination of the sun. Looking at figs. 17 and 22 we may state that the influence of solar declination (normally called seasonal influence) and that of lunar declination are rather similar. This statement confirms the conclusions obtained in sect. 5. This should be an interesting piece of evidence for a future theory of ionospheric tides.

REFERENCES

Bartels, J. and G. Fanselau, 1938, Geophysikalische Mondtafeln 1850-1975 (Springer, Berlin).
Harnischmacher, E., 1964, Ann. Géophysique 20, 425.
Harnischmacher, E. and K. Rawer, 1958a, Geofis. Pura Appl. 39, 216.
Harnischmacher, E. and K. Rawer, 1958b, J. Atmos. Terrest. Phys. 13, 1.
Harnischmacher, E. and K. Rawer, 1961, Contribution to the URSI-CIG Conference on ionospheric results of IGY, Nice 1961.

COMMENT

Rawer:

A large mass of data exists from the fading drift observations. Vol. 33 of Annals of the IGY gives the probably most complete set of statistical data, which have been obtained during the IGY. It is certainly not known, whether this method describes neutral air motions, it is even not known, whether it does this for the plasma motion, because only the motion of irregularities is seen by this method. It is probable that a part of the observed field strength fluctuations be due to 'travelling disturbances', so that the displacement of gravity wave 'crests' at the reflection level in the ionospheric plasma may be at the origin of many of the observed fades. One is then perhaps inclined to expect only very limited physical significance from fading drift results. However, the data obtained in the few series of observations which were intense enough to be statistically reliable showed, that clear physical relations exist. Even if the 'dominant drift' were only apparently produced - which I do not believe - even then it has to be explained why the wave crests have such preferred directions in the ionosphere. And the tides are certainly a physical phenomenon, so that one should look for the possibility that the wave crests 'go with the wind'.

Harnischmacher's analysis seems to be particularly important here. It is his idea that the conventional Fourier analysis may be physically misleading, even if it is mathematically correct. For example a strict Fourier analysis in terms of solar effects brings the lunar influence into the higher solar orders. This was the reason why Harnischmacher came to his uncon-

ventional analysis, allowing for phase and amplitude changes during the
period. His main (temperate latitude) results may be described by saying:
There is an apparent dominant drift (which may only be due to a preferred
direction of the crests), but it is different by day and by night, and in different seasons. In the classical analysis that day/night change is described
as a 24-h tide; however, this is not a rotating drift vector but a 'switching'
of the direction in the evening and morning. On the other side the 12-h tide
is a clear rotation of a vector of nearly constant amplitude. This tide suffers systematic phase delays different for the 'day' and the 'night' branch.
The lunar 12-h influence is nearly hidden in monthly analysis, but it comes
clearly out in a special analysis after lunar phase, particularly if the solar
influence has first been removed statistically. All these features are to be
explained by a future theory of drift phenomena in the E region.

DISCUSSION

Spizzichino:
    Une comparaison faite par Jones de la phase des marées semi-diurnes
observées 1) à Jodrell Bank par les météores (x); 2) en Angleterre (?) par
la méthode des fadings (o) en utilisant 2 fréquences réfléchies semble indiquer une variation continue de la phase de cette marée en fonction de l'altitude, les 2 méthodes se recoupant parfaitement.

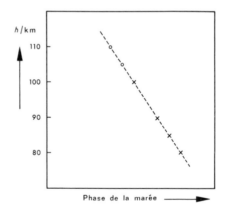

Harnischmacher, Rawer:
    Nous n'y croyons pas.

Spizzichino:
    Dans ce cas, je propose de tenter la même comparaison entre les ré-
sultats de Breisach et ceux du radar météorique de Garchy. La distance
entre ces deux stations parait petite par rapport à la longueur d'onde de la
marée semi-diurne. La comparaison doit donc être valable.

Pouvez-vous récapituler les ordres de grandeur relatifs des marées de periode 24 h, 12 h et des marées lunaires?

Harnischmacher:

1) The average occurrence of the different directions is not the same. There is a clear preference for E and W directions, S direction is rarer and N direction is the rarest. This distribution is different in winter and summer because of the existence of the dominant component.

2) Taking the 12-h solar component from our statistical analysis it passes through N and S at the following local hours:

	W	N	E	S	W	N	E	S	
hour		4		10		15		20	observed (over all average)
hour		3		9		15		21	theoretical (90° shifted against direction to subsolar point)
difference		+1		+1		0		-1	h

At noon the drift is normally from East to West, i.e. at 90° to the direction towards the subpolar point - but in the *opposite direction* as given by the Coriolis force in the case where a pressure 'High' is supposed at the subpolar point. The rule with the Ciriolis force would be right of a 'Low' occurred at the subpolar point. (Another possible way to explain the 90° shift would be by a Lorentz-force.)

3) The statistical engagement of the solar and lunar tidal 12-h components is as follows:

	Solar (S_2)	Lunar (L_2)
Yearly average	22%	9%
Declination changes	± 11%	± 9%
Range as produced by variable declination	11...33%	0...18%

Bolgiano:

I should like to ask a question of clarification. Are we to interpret the motion deduced as an average over the 90 to 120-km layer or should we expect a preferential indication of motion at different altitudes as a function of season and of diurnal cycle (because of the variations of reflection altitudes)?

Rawer:

The latter is true. The method observes preferentially the levels where a sharp vertical gradient of ionization is existing.

Baguette:

Les mouvements déduits de l'observation des fadings représentent peut-être les mouvements des couches E-sporadiques. Dans la théorie dite des 'cisaillements de vent' ces mouvements sont couplés à ceux du vent mais ne sont pas exactement ceux des particules neutres.

Rawer:

C'est vrai. Il y a encore le problème de la sélection statistique que nous effectuons, parce que de nuit nous pouvons seulement effectuer nos mesures s'il y a E-sporadique. Donc il est bien possible que nous sélectionnons systématiquement des cas qui correspondent à des conditions particulières. De jour, par contre, nous mesurons soit à l'aide de la couche E-normale, soit à l'aide de E-sporadique. Nous avons effectué une comparaison de ces cas sans trouver des résultats sensiblement différents en statistique.

Kriester:

(Discussion on remark of a diagram of a paper by Sprenger and Schmieder (1966) presented by Prof. Rawer:)

The authors have drawn attention to a remarkable anomaly of drift direction in the lower ionosphere during January/February 1963, i.e. during a period of strong stratospheric warming. A drift direction towards ESE which was considered to be normal, has been measured at Kühlungsborn until 15 January, then changing rapidly to a direction towards SW. The normal direction was re-established at about 5 February.

This change of drift direction in the lower ionosphere coincides well with the change of wind direction in the mid-stratosphere during this period. In mid-January the circumpolar circulation pattern of the 10 mb surface (31 km) was changed to a bipolar circulation system with the two troughs extending to America and Siberia. During this period north-westerly winds were found over the European area. In the following days the Atlantic anticyclone strengthened considerably while moving towards the north, thus initiating north to north-easterly winds over Europe. In the beginning of February the anticyclone has weakened, cyclonic flow was re-established over the eastern part of the northern hemisphere and the wind direction over Europe was changed to north-westerlies.

Daily data are necessary to compare the velocities of both the ionospheric drift and the stratospheric winds. It may be concluded, however, that an anomalous circulation has existed throughout the stratosphere and the lower ionosphere during the second half of January 1963, although one must bear in mind the large altitude differences of the two phenomena observed.

RESULTS OF AN EXPERIMENT CONCERNING THE FADING PATTERN

E. HARNISCHMACHER
Ionosphären-Institut Breisach, Germany *

Abstract. A new model for explaining drift observations supposes incurved extremal lines moving and expanding (or contracting) at the same time, and with a rather short average life time. Using a simplified Monte Carlo computation technique one obtains the statistics of indication errors; these are minimum for the central triangle, and show typical distributions for the outer ones. Comparison with observational data shows priority of imploding forms in winter, but of exploding forms in summer. This explains certain aspects of the observed statistics of the error distribution.

Résumé. Pour expliquer les observations de vent on introduit un nouveau modèle contenant des lignes extrémales courbes dont la courbure varie durant le mouvement. La durée de vie moyenne d'une telle constellation est supposée assez brève. Appliquant une technique simplifiée de calcul Monte Carlo on obtient la statistique des erreurs d'indication. Elles sont minimum pour le triangle central, on obtient des distributions typiques des triangles extérieures. Par comparaison avec les observations une priorité des 'formes à implosion' est trouvée en hiver, mais une des 'formes à explosion' en été. Ceci explique certains aspects de la statistique observée de la distribution des erreurs.

1. INTRODUCTION

A receiving site with 6 antennae situated at the corners and side-centers of an equilateral triangle together with a pulse transmitter are a good tool to investigate, on a fixed frequency, structure and time variations of the fading pattern in the horizontal plane.

The present study deals with such cases where the fadings are very similar on all six antennae. In this condition it is not difficult to mark the fading maxima or minima and to evaluate the time difference on the 6 aerials. In 1959 we obtained in this way some thousands of fading patterns on an operating frequency of 2 and 3 MHz. The reflecting level, determined by an electronic gate, was in the E region, so that the reflection came either from the normal or the sporadic E layer.

The upper part of fig. 1 is a plan of the aerials on the receiving site. The distance between neighbouring antennae was 60 m. The lower part of fig. 1 is a schematical diagram representing the changes during a typical fading pattern; the drawing indicates at which time the 'extremal values' of the field strength pattern (i.e. fading maxima or minima) are crossing over the different aerials. In the example shown

* Research sponsored by Air Force Cambridge Res. Labs. through European Office OAR under contracts AF61(052)-81 and 672.

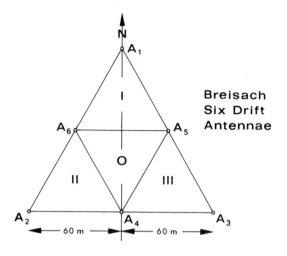

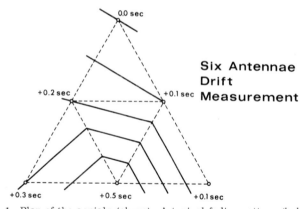

Fig. 1. Plan of the aerials (above). A typical fading pattern (below).

at time 0.0 sec: A_1 is crossed,
at time 0.1 sec: A_5 and A_3 are crossed,
at time 0.2 sec: A_6 is crossed,
at time 0.3 sec: A_2 is crossed,
at time 0.5 sec: A_4 is crossed.

2. ANALYSIS OF RAW DATA

In order to learn something about the behaviour of the fading pattern we may use one or the other of the following procedures:
Procedure one is to draw the 'extremal lines' and their displacement with

the time in a more or less 'artistic' manner. We chose as time difference
between neighbouring lines or curves 0.1 sec.

Procedure two is to evaluate independently, for each of the four small triangles, velocity and direction of the moving pattern, and then determine
the combined behaviour by statistical means thus giving a statistical description of the 'coherency' of the apparent drift of the pattern.

Fig. 2 gives an example of the 'artistical' procedure. All samples shown
are quite normal cases. As the times evaluated for the crossing over each
antenna are given, the 'artistic liberty' is rather limited. The real configuration cannot be very different from the lines indicated in fig. 2. There
can be no doubt that 'expanding' and 'compressing' forms are very often
present; they will be referred to as 'exploding' and 'imploding'. It is difficult to explain these phenomena with existing theories, but the phenomena
are certainly real. We have to change the theory in order to obtain a reasonable explanation of these observed features.

We may retain from a review of such examples that a suitable model of
the pattern configuration should explain forms and changes similar to those
shown by these 'artistic' drawings. Their main features are: a) rather
small scale compared with Fresnel zones, b) important curvature of 'extremal lines', c) variations of the 'exploding' and imploding' type.

With the second procedure the first step is to establish an error statistics for the directions of the apparent motion, and the corresponding histo-
gram of the velocities. This is done for the whole measuring period of
5 min duration each. First of all from the individual data we determine the
mean drift direction for all four triangles together. In our case, we accepted only very similar fades so that with relatively small antennae distances it was easy to find the mean direction. The 'directional error' of
each triangle is defined as the difference against this mean direction. Statistical distributions of direction or velocity errors given in the following
refer always to the above defined mean direction.

For a given month or season, and for the different triangles we calculate
direction error data and corresponding velocities, and present them in tab-
ular form. In each of the four graphs of fig. 3 the abscissa is the mean direction varying from 0° to 360°. The ordinate in the upper graphs is the directional error, its statistical distribution being given by the numerical indication, which is a probability in percent. Similar data for the corresponding velocity are given on the lower graphs. In each column on the left the sum
must always be 100%. The results directly obtained are given by the different
lines on the left-hand tables and for each of these the average is calculated.
The right-hand table gives the difference between the left-hand table and
the corresponding line average (in the middle). (The particular example of
fig. 3 is valid for the month of January and triangle I.) Very characteristic
features appear on the right-hand tables. Positive deviations are hatched.
The numerical indications are given in %, in each of the four graphs.

Such tables containing statistical distributions and differences with respect to averages as function of the mean drift direction are the rough material for the following statistical treating. Let us first consider all directions and all triangles together, i.e. line averages of the left-hand graphs

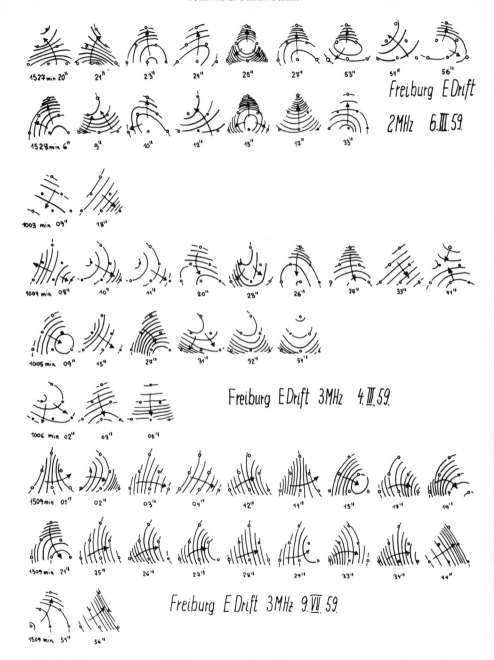

Fig. 2. Three sequences of fading patterns for different measuring periods (time for each pattern is indicated in sec).

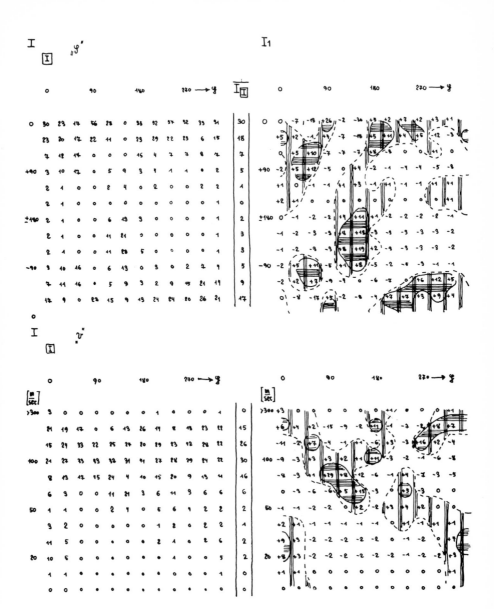

Fig. 3. Characteristic features for a given month and a given triangle. Distinguish:
I = January, Ⅱ = triangle I.) Above: a) Table for the distribution of direction errors
for the different mean-directions. b) The mean direction error. c) Table for the
differences between table a) and b). Below: a) Table for the distribution of velocities
for the different mean directions. b) The mean velocity distribution. c) Table for the
differences between table a) and b).

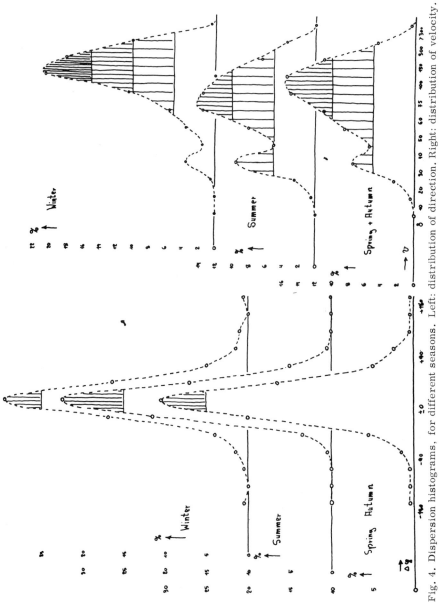

Fig. 4. Dispersion histograms, for different seasons. Left: distribution of direction. Right: distribution of velocity.

in fig. 3 but averaged over the four triangles. Fig. 4 gives the results for the different seasons. The direction errors (left side) are distributed quite symmetrically. For all seasons the result may be summarized by saying that

$\frac{1}{3}$ of the individual measurements were on the mean direction,
$\frac{1}{3}$ gave errors of $\pm 30^{\circ}$
$\frac{1}{3}$ gave errors greater than $\pm 60^{\circ}$.

The seasonal influence is quite small; only a few % is the difference between summer and winter. It appears clearly that winter has larger direction errors (particularly the higher positive ones). Summer has smaller errors than any other season.

As to the velocity distribution we observe two peaks and this for all seasons. The lower peak is near 30 m/sec. Its probability is very low in winter (4%), it reaches 10% in summer. The higher peak reaches 14% at a velocity of 60 to 75 m/sec in summer. In winter this maximum reaches 20% at velocities between 100 and 150 m/sec. The values for spring and autumn lie just between those of summer and winter.

3. MODEL COMPUTATIONS

In the following we report on results obtained with a particular theoretical approach. The direction errors and the velocity distribution have been computed for different models specifying shape and average variation of the extremal lines. Considering the observed patterns (see for example fig. 2) we felt it appropriate to describe an extremal line by a circle, first, making different assumptions concerning the development with time, see fig. 5. As to the development five cases ranging from pure translation to pure expansion have been considered. The development is described at the right-hand side of each line by a full curve valid for t_0 and a broken curve for t_1. We find that in the second case, where the ratio of the 'spreading velocity', v_R, to the translatorial motion, v_T, is $1:2$, the agreement with our experimental results is good. In particular the double-bump in the velocity distribution appears in the corresponding second case of fig. 5 similarly to the observed distributions of fig. 4 (right side). It should be stated that in wintertime the corresponding ratio may be larger: between $1:2$ and $1:1$.

4. DETAILED ANALYSIS OF INDIVIDUAL TRIANGLES

In fig. 4 the seasons have been considered separately but averages for the four triangles were taken. In another consideration we will mix the seasons but consider the 4 triangles separately, i.e. take account of observed differences between an individual triangle and the average. It is to be expected that the inner triangle gives different statistical data than the outer ones. Also anisotropy, if present, could so be studied. Fig. 6 brings the results. In fig. 6a histograms of the direction errors are shown, and in

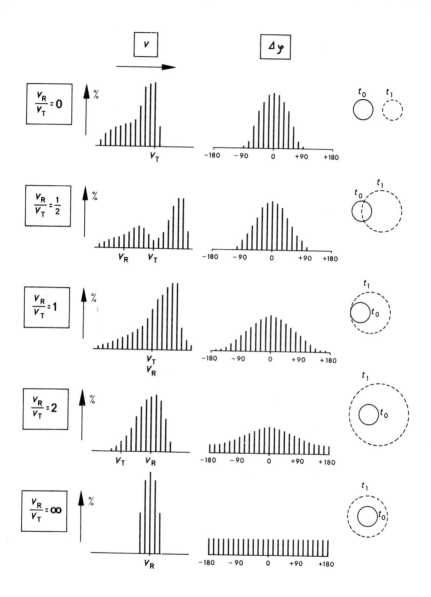

Fig. 5. Influence of the ratio v_R/v_T on velocity and direction distribution. v_R is the spreading velocity, v_T is the translatorial motion. The figures are calculated histograms. left: for the velocity distribution, right: for the direction error distribution. The ratio v_R/v_T varies from 0 to ∞.

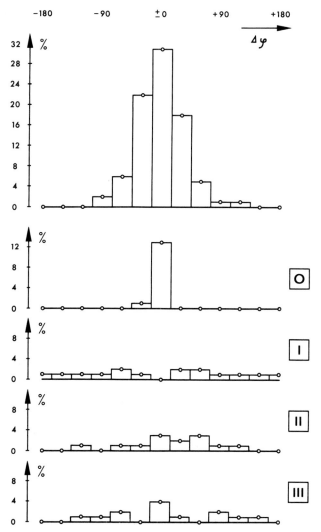

Fig. 6a. Differences between individual triangles concerning the distribution of direction.

fig. 6b the corresponding velocity distribution. Instead of presenting four different histograms, fig. 6 gives the cross section of all four statistics in each upper diagram, and four individual 'correction histograms' below. The total statistics (100%) for one of the triangles is given by the sum of the cross section and the corresponding correction. The big mass of the cases is similar in all four triangles: 87% of all measurements are contained in these upper histograms. Four supplementary histograms are

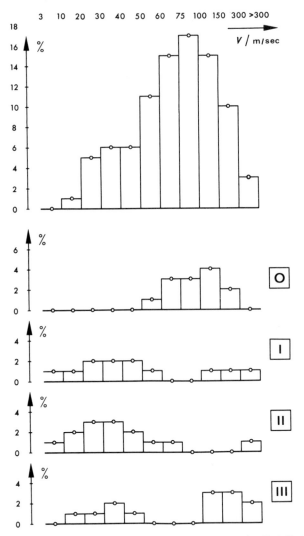

Fig. 6b. Differences between individual triangles concerning the distribution of velocity.

given below; they contain the individual deviations not appearing in the other triangles. Each diagram covers the remaining 13% of all cases, for the triangle indicated individually. Therefore, the total statistics of all triangle 0 observations is the sum of the uppermost line and the second one; for triangle I it is obtained by summing the uppermost line and the third one, and so on. There appears in these statistics a clear difference between the inner triangle and the outer ones. Triangle 0 has the smallest particular differences, it gives in most cases values which are very near to the mean direction and the mean velocity.

The meaning of fig. 6a and fig. 6b is different. Fig. 6a gives the statistics of direction errors, i.e. deviations from the mean direction, thus relative values. Fig. 6b, however, shows absolute velocity values and their statistics. One should think this statistics should be identic for all four triangles. But this is not so because we could not accept all fades passing over triangle II for example (antennas A_2, A_4, A_6), but only those which are seen in all four triangles (i.e. also on antennas A_1, A_3, A_5). This is a certain selection because a few fades die out in the antenna field. The selection is such that triangle 0 is privilegiated; here only fades are accepted which can be observed in a certain 'concentric' neighbourhood (given by antennas A_1, A_2, A_3). The situation is different for the other three triangles, for which a unilateral neighbourhood is claimed. Therefore the velocity statistics is 'flatted out' for the outer triangles I, II, III, but it is better centred for triangle 0. It is interesting to note that the velocity distribution for this triangle is slightly shifted towards higher velocity. This is a rather trivial result, because the location of triangle 0 just in the middle of I, II, III gives a better chance for its data to approach the mean value. These results confirm that the fading pattern has a fine structure with non-negligible curvatures of the extremal lines.

As the 'centre-effect' comes out so clearly we may hope that the features contained in the lower typical histograms of fig. 6, viz. those concerning triangles I-III, have some physical significance. These triangles give larger direction errors, in some cases more than $\pm 90^{\circ}$. In the histograms for the velocity distribution a peak appears around 30 m/sec for each of the triangles I, II and III. It is not at all visible in the diagram for triangle 0 which shows an increased probability near the peak of the cross section.

5. INTRODUCTION OF FADING LIFETIME

We feel again that we can explain these features with a model of moving extremal lines, for example exploding and imploding circles, provided that we introduce a new feature, viz. a 'fading lifetime'. An individual extremal line in the fading pattern will then die out after a certain time. We believe that this lifetime, T_L, is quite short, shorter than the quasiperiod with which the fadings appear. Thus we have

$$T_L \lessgtr 1/f_f ,$$

where f_f is the average fading frequency. If this is so, we have expanding and imploding motions, but not with a large range the individual existing only for a short time. In other words the motion of an individual configuration does not go very far. The maximum distance, R_L, over which a certain feature can be identified is of the order of

$$R_{L\ max} \lessgtr v/f_f$$

where v is the propagation speed of this feature. As now v depends on the direction, also $R_{L\ max}$ varies with direction. If for a certain direction v is very small it may happen that one of the outer antennae is never reached by a fade appearing at the opposite end. In this case similar fades were visible for example at the five antennae $A_2, \ldots, A_6$, but no comparable feature appeared at antenna A_1.

From our abundant material fig. 7 gives a few examples of such cases. In all these cases we realize that there occur big differences for the direction as well as for the velocities between the central triangle and one of the outer triangles. As a consequence of the limited lifetime we can not exclude rather strongly encurved circles or ellipses as extremal lines. If this is so the fine structure of the pattern is comparable with the distances between our antennae, as shown in fig. 7. In all cases where a fade is 'lost' we get a high velocity for triangle 0, but for at least one outer triangle a rather low velocity. Indeed when observing features which have a small lifetime the selection indicated above gives priority to those cases where the origin lies in front of the inner triangle when we observe exploding forms; it lies behind the inner triangle when we have imploding fading shapes. Those cases where all four triangles are crossed by fading shapes with high velocity have the best chances to be seen on all six antennae. This

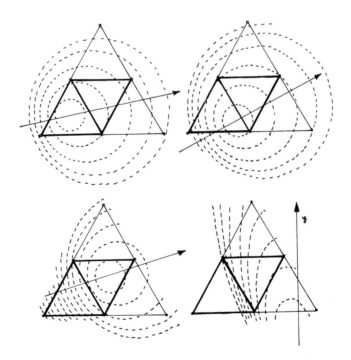

Fig. 7. Model fading patterns constructed in order to explain the differences in velocity and directional distribution for the individual triangles.

gives a preference for the direction of the translatorial movement of the pattern. With this in mind we find from our improved model the same features as found in the histograms of fig. 6 viz:
a) small direction errors for the inner triangle,
b) large direction errors for the outer triangles,
c) higher velocity to be determined from the inner triangle,
d) low and high additional velocities for the outer triangles.

In the case where radial and translatorial velocities are opposite, the motion is slow and the pattern has no chance to reach the other side of the configuration. If this is the case, the fades are not similar enough on all six aerials (and therefore they are not evaluated). Our selection rule to account only for cases where a certain fade appeared on each of the six traces is the reason why we cannot find in our statistics low velocities for the inner triangle.

6. IMPROVED MODEL COMPUTATIONS

As next step in our model calculations we have made a test program considering four types:
1) concave fading front with translatorial motion,
2) convex fading front with translatorial motion,
3) exploding fading pattern,
4) imploding fading pattern.

With these models we calculated the direction errors and the velocity distribution for an outer triangle. We supposed that the 0° direction goes through the outer corner of triangle I. Magnitude and sense of the direction errors for different drift directions can be seen from fig. 8. The sense of the errors is the same for types 1 and 3 but opposite for type 2 and 4. The magnitude of the errors is greater for types 3 and 4, i.e. for exploding and imploding forms.

A 'synthetic statistical result' obtained by a simple 'Monte Carlo' method considering possible combinations of types is given in the upper part of fig. 9 (types 2 and 4: left side; types 1 and 3: right side). The types are marked by different symbols. The graphs are complementary and we may state that:
1) Convex fading fronts or imploding fading patterns produce nearly no direction error when the drift direction is around 180°, but large errors in the range 270° over 360° to 90°.
2) Concave fading fronts or exploding fading patterns produce nearly no direction error when the drift direction is around 0°, but large errors in the range 90° over 180° to 270°.

As the two groups of types give quite different statistics, this latter could be used to distinguish between types. This theoretical result can be compared with drift measurements more precisely with the abnormal cases found in these. The lower part of fig. 9 gives the statistical results concerning ex- and imploding types observed in winter (left) and in summer (right). By comparison we may conclude that winter has a surplus of imploding fading patterns. The ratio of occurrence for imploding and exploding types (i and e) is:

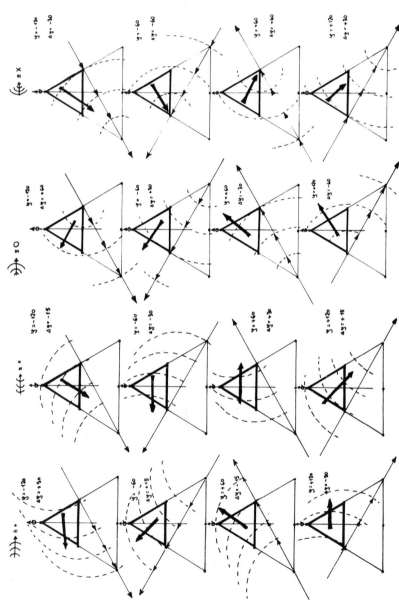

Fig. 8. Comparison of real drift vector (thin arrow) with observed one in an outer triangle (bold vector) for different direction against the orientation of the basic triangle. The four columns concern different models for the time sequence of extremal lines.

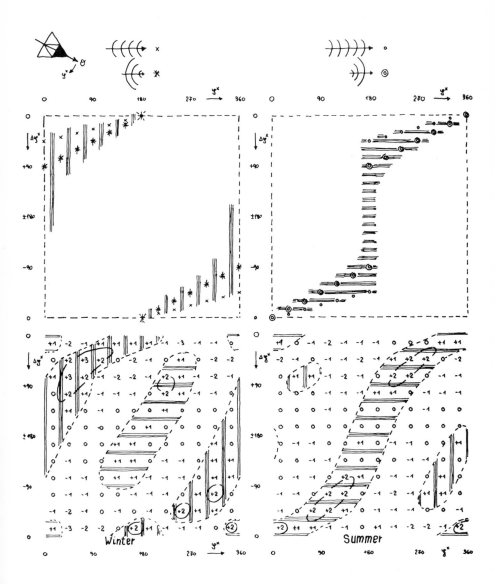

Fig. 9. Above: calculated error distribution of the observed direction for different models of fading development. Below: observed distributions for winter (left) and summer (right).

$$\frac{N_i}{N_e} \approx \frac{3\%}{1\%} = 3 \; .$$

It is clear that the big mass of fades is simply translatorial, but the remaining cases are not equally distributed. In summer we find more exploding fading patterns:

$$\frac{N_i}{N_e} \approx \frac{0.5\%}{3\%} = \frac{1}{6} \; .$$

In spring and autumn the ratio for the two types is roughly equal

$$\frac{N_i}{N_e} \approx \frac{3\%}{3\%} = 1 \; .$$

and the total occurrence of queer cases is now 6%.

Let us now consider the velocity distribution. As example we take type 4, the imploding fading pattern. We state that the velocity measured in an outer triangle depends also in a critical way on the position of the 'centre' to which the implosion goes. Be 0° or 180° the mean drift direction for all four triangles. Successive positions of the 'centre' are shown in fig. 10.

If the centre of the imploding type is yet outside the outer triangle the resulting velocity is high. If the centre lies on the outer triangle the velocity for this triangle is extremely high. But if it lies inside the inner triangle the velocity slows down to a low velocity-value. If the centre passes over the side of the great triangle the mean direction has changed to 180°. Going further out, the pattern can no more be evaluated because of the limited life time of the fades.

Similar features are obtained in the case where the drift direction is 180° at the beginning. Extremely high velocities occurred for 0° mean direction, if the centre was just over the outer triangle. But there is no chance to have an extremely high velocity for a mean drift direction of 180° in the case of an imploding fading pattern.

On the other side if the mean drift direction is at $\pm 90^o$ for imploding and exploding patterns we always find values which are in between. The whole result of a Monte Carlo model calculation is shown in the upper diagram of fig. 11. The left side is for imploding pattern, so applies best to winter. In agreement with the above we find:

extremely high velocities for drift direction 0°,
low velocities for drift direction 180°,
median velocities for drift direction near $\pm 90^o$.

For comparison we give statistical results of our measurements in fig. 11 bottom. The winter side (left) confirms our model calculations. However, we see from the results of our summer measurements (bottom, right hand) that also in summer the velocity distribution is very similar to the winter distribution and not shifted by 180° as expected. Only a few measurements mark very high velocities as expected for 180°. The lack of agreement may be due to an influence of the anisotropy which has not yet been taken into account in our model calculation.

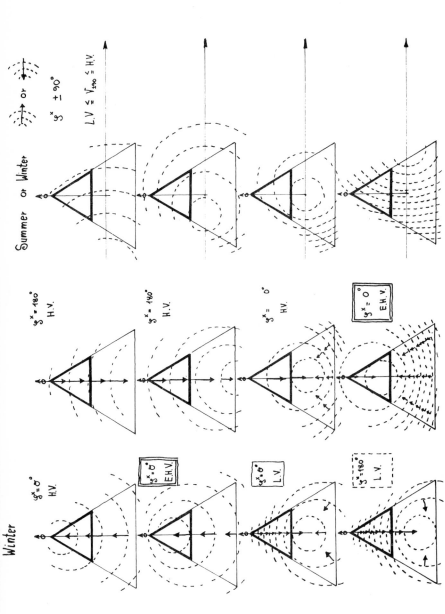

Fig. 10. Influence of the feature of the fading pattern (different models for time sequence) on the observed velocity distribution.

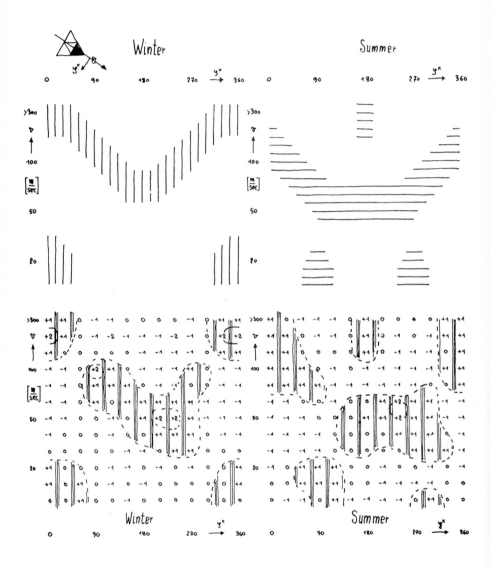

Fig. 11. Above: calculated error distribution of the observed velocity for different fading features and different seasons (compare fig. 9). Below: observed distributions for winter (left) and summer (right).

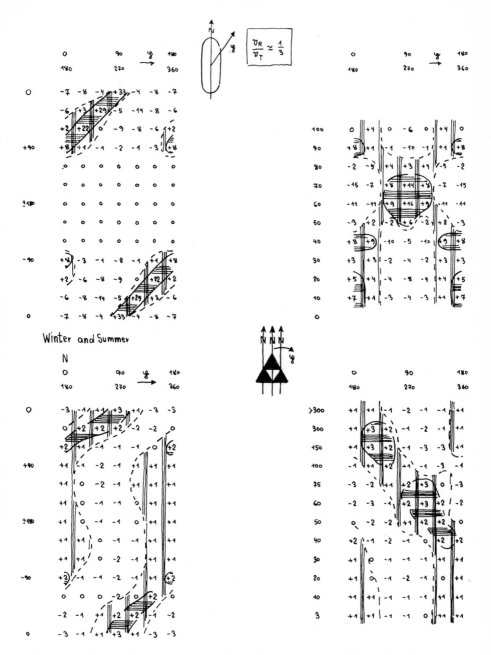

Fig. 12. Influence of an anisotropic fading pattern model on calculated distributions of direction (left) and velocity (right).

7. ANISOTROPY

A last consideration intends to look after the anisotropy of the fading pattern. Replacing our circular extremal lines by a set of different ellipses with different translatorial and radial velocities we calculated again the direction errors and the velocity distribution by a Monte Carlo technique. The results are shown in the upper diagrams of fig. 12 for direction errors (left side) and velocity distribution (right side). We may compare with the bottom diagrams of the same figure giving the results of experimental data. Calculation and measurement agree very well. In about 7% of all measurements the model ellipses had to be oriented with the long axis to the north (in summer and in winter). Also the distributions of the velocities coincide very well here, for calculation and measurement.

Result. Drift measurements with the fading method are significant at an angle accuracy of about $\pm 30^{\circ}$ and a velocity accuracy of about 15 m/sec. Different error statistics are observed in summer and in winter.

REFERENCES

[1] B.H.Briggs and M.Spencer, 1955, The Physics of the Ionosphere (The Physical Society, London) 123.
[2] E.Harnischmacher, 1963, Research on ionospheric structure and motion. IIB-Rep. 6 (USAF Contract No. 61(052)-81).
[3] I.L.Jones, 1958, J. Atmos. Terr. Phys. 12, 68.
[4] J.Krautkrämer, 1943, Deut. Luftfahrtforsch. FB 1761; 1950. Archiv. Elektr. Übertragung 4, 133.
[5] A.J.Lyon and A.J.G.Moorat, 1956, J.Atmos. Terr. Phys. 8, 309.
[6] G.J.Phillips, 1955, J. Atm. Terr. Phys. 6, 124.
[7] H.St.Pütter, 1955, The Physics of the Ionosphere (The Physical Society, London) 191.
[8] K.Sprenger, 1960, Z.Meteorol. 14, 6.

DISCUSSION

Baguette:

Ce qu l'on appelle 'implosion' et 'explosion' correspond-il systématiquement à un déplacement de matière?

Harnischmacher:

Non, ce sont seulement les lignes de fading au sol. J'utilise comme modèle l'interférence entre deux rayons seulement ce qui produit un système de franges d'interférence (suivant les zones de Fresnel). Si maintenant la surface réfléchissante (ou l'irrégularité sur laquelle est réfléchi le second rayon) fait un mouvement vertical, même faible, le système des franges subit un mouvement 'explosif' au cas d'un mouvement réel vers le haut, tandis que le mouvement est 'implosif' pour un mouvement réel vers le bas.

Gille:

What ratios of ellipse axes, and what orientation did the major axis have in the Monte Carlo calculation discussed at the end of your talk? How sensitive are your calculated results to these quantities?

Harnischmacher:

The ratio of the ellipse axis is 2 : 1, the orientation of the major axis was to the NNW. To speak about sensitivity we should have more values evaluated, for the sensitivity is changing with the seasons.

Lalonde:

The question concerns technique of measurement - that is what do you measure, the amplitude of the echo only, or is it gated in height?

Harnischmacher:

The amplitude of a gated echo from the E region (90-120 km) is measured on 3 antennas by switching one receiver from one antenna to the other in time.

Lalonde:

Is it not true then, that at 2.4 MHz your data are much more dense in the daytime than at night?

Harnischmacher:

This is true because E_S is not very frequent at night during 00 - 06 h, particularly in winter and therefore gaps exist in the data.

THE GENERAL NATURE OF
ACOUSTIC-GRAVITY WAVES

John C. GILLE

Department of Meteorology, Florida State University,
Tallahassee, Florida

Abstract. The equations governing acoustic-gravity waves in an infinite isothermal atmosphere are developed by the perturbation method. Physical insight is obtained by considering simple cases and graphical representations. From the boundary conditions between two semi-infinite atmospheres, the possibilities of boundary waves and total reflection are shown. The implications of total reflection for ducting in the atmosphere are explored qualitatively.

Résumé. Les équations décrivant des ondes acoustiques et de gravité dans une atmosphère isothermique infinie sont développées applicant la méthode des perturbations. Considérant des exemples simples et des graphiques on peut se procurer une idée des relations physiques. L'existence possible d'ondes de surface et de réflection totale sont montrées à l'aide des conditions aux limites au cas de deux atmosphères demi-infinies. Le rôle important de la réflection totale à la formation de 'ducts' dans l'atmosphère est discuté qualitativement.

1. INTRODUCTION

In lectures today and tomorrow, we shall be speaking of the nature, propagation and ducting of infrasonic waves in the terrestrial atmosphere. Clearly, in two to three hours we cannot go into great mathematical detail. We will, therefore, attempt to do three things:
1) To see the basic mathematics and physics upon which the results are based;
2) To develop a physical feeling for the processes going on, and
3) To discuss qualitatively the results of numerical calculations, so that we may understand their implications.
   I hope that with this broad overview of an area of intriguing but difficult problems, some of you will be sufficiently interested to turn to the references and fill in the details which we must here omit.

2. THE PERTURBATION EQUATIONS

To develop the basic equations, let us consider a fluid initially at rest, and stratified in the vertical direction. We assume that the wave amplitudes are small compared to the wavelength, so that the equations of motion may be linearized. Also, we will neglect the effects of viscosity and thermal transfer, whether conductive or radiative. Since we are looking for length scales much less than the radius of the earth, and time scales much less than a day, we will neglect curvature and rotation.

We introduce the following symbols:

x, y, z = rectangular coordinates, z vertical (upwards)
u, v, w = velocities in directions x, y, z, of perturbation order
$\rho_0(z)$, ρ_1 = basic and perturbation density
$p_0(z)$, p_1 = basic and perturbation pressure
$\eta_0(z)$, η_1 = basic and perturbation entropy.

The basic equations are developed by Eliassen and Kleinschmidt (1957).
We have the equations of

1) Momentum

$$\rho \frac{D\boldsymbol{v}}{Dt} = -\nabla p + \rho\boldsymbol{g} \qquad \text{(Euler's equations)}$$

which becomes with our assumptions

$$\frac{dp_0}{dz} = -\rho_0 g \qquad \text{(hydrostatic equation)} \qquad (2.1)$$

as the only zeroth equation, and

$$\rho_0 \frac{\partial u}{\partial t} = -\frac{\partial p_1}{\partial x} \qquad (2.2)$$

$$\rho_0 \frac{\partial w}{\partial t} + g\rho_1 = -\frac{\partial p_1}{\partial z} \ . \qquad (2.3)$$

2) Continuity

$$\frac{D\rho}{Dt} + \rho\nabla \cdot \boldsymbol{v} = 0$$

which yields

$$-\frac{\partial \rho_1}{\partial t} = w \frac{\partial \rho_0}{\partial z} + \rho_0 \left(\frac{\partial u}{\partial x} + \frac{\partial w}{\partial z}\right) ; \qquad (2.4)$$

3) Entropy conservation (adiabatic motion)

$$\frac{D\eta}{Dt} = 0$$

which becomes

$$\frac{\partial \eta_1}{\partial t} + w \frac{\partial \eta_0}{\partial z} = 0 \ . \qquad (2.5)$$

To this we add the equation of state

$$p = \rho RT \qquad (2.6)$$

where R = gas constant for air and T = temperature.

The state of a pure fluid can be specified by any two of the four variables ρ, p, η and temperature T. Thus

$$dp = \left(\frac{\partial p}{\partial \rho}\right)_\eta dp + \left(\frac{\partial p}{\partial \eta}\right)_\rho d\eta$$

Now

$$\left(\frac{\partial p}{\partial \rho}\right)_\eta = c^2 = \frac{\gamma p}{\rho} = \gamma RT$$

where c = (adiabatic) sound velocity and $\gamma = c_p/c_v$, the ratio of specific heat values.

In the stratified equilibrium state,

$$\frac{dp_0}{dz} = -g\rho_0 = c_0^2 \frac{d\rho_0}{dz} + Y_0 \frac{d\eta_0}{dz} \tag{2.7}$$

while for small perturbation from this state

$$p_1 = c_0^2 \rho_1 + Y_0 \eta_1$$

and for adiabatic motion

$$\frac{\partial p_1}{\partial t} = c_0^2 \frac{\partial \rho_1}{\partial t} + Y_0 \frac{\partial \eta_1}{\partial t} \tag{2.8}$$

We can get rid of the entropy terms by combining (2.5), (2.7) and (2.8) to find

$$\frac{\partial p_1}{\partial t} = c_0^2 \frac{\partial \rho_1}{\partial t} - w\left[-g\rho_0 - c_0^2 \frac{d\rho_0}{dz} \right] \tag{2.9}$$

The perturbation density can be removed with (2.4) to give

$$\frac{\partial p_1}{\partial t} = wg \rho_0 - \rho_0 c_0^2 \left(\frac{\partial u}{\partial x} + \frac{\partial w}{\partial z}\right) \tag{2.10}$$

Finally, taking $\partial/\partial t$ of (2.2) and (2.3), we can get rid of the perturbation pressure, and are left with

$$\rho_0 \frac{\partial^2 u}{\partial t^2} = -g\rho_0 \frac{\partial w}{\partial x} + \frac{\partial}{\partial x}\left[\rho_0 c_0^2 \left(\frac{\partial u}{\partial x} + \frac{\partial w}{\partial z}\right) \right] \tag{2.11}$$

$$\rho_0 \frac{\partial^2 w}{\partial t^2} = g\rho_0 \frac{\partial u}{\partial x} + \frac{\partial}{\partial z}\left[\rho_0 c_0^2 \left(\frac{\partial u}{\partial x} + \frac{\partial w}{\partial z}\right) \right] \tag{2.12}$$

This derivation has followed that of Tolstoy (1963) (Appendix). They are also derived in Lamb (1945), in Eckart (1960), and many other places.

We shall look for solutions of the form

$$u = U(z)\exp(i(kx-\omega t))$$
$$w = W(z)\exp(i(kx-\omega t))$$

where k is the horizontal wave number, ω is the angular frequency and t is the time.

Let us also suppress the zero subscript of c and ρ which will be taken hereafter to be the basic state.

On substitution in (2.11), we find

$$U = ik\left(\frac{c^2 W' - g W}{k^2 c^2 - \omega^2}\right) \tag{2.13}$$

where d/dz is indicated by a prime, and from (2.12)

$$W'' + \frac{d}{dz}\ln\frac{\rho}{\omega^2/c^2 - k^2}W' + \left\{\frac{\omega^2}{c^2} - k^2 - \frac{k^2}{\omega^2}\,g\,\frac{d}{dz}\left(\ln\frac{\rho}{\omega^2/c^2 - k^2}\right) - \frac{k^2 g^2}{\omega^2 c^2}\right\}W = 0 \tag{2.14}$$

We may note immediately that for ω large this reduces to the acoustic wave equation, while gravity effects enter in terms important for small ω.

Both coefficients depend on gradients of density and sound velocity. The latter are most important for the high frequency range. We can get a great deal of insight by assuming c = constant.

Then

$$W'' + \frac{d}{dz}(\ln\rho)W' + \left\{\frac{\omega^2}{c^2} - k^2 + \frac{k^2}{\omega^2}\left[-g\,\frac{d}{dz}\ln\rho - \frac{g^2}{c^2}\right]\right\}W = 0 \tag{2.15}$$

The term in square brackets has a particular explanation.

3. THE VÄISÄLÄ FREQUENCY

Consider a single element of fluid, contained within a flexible, insulating membrane, and displaced vertically from its equilibrium position. When released, its motion will obey the equation

$$\rho\,\frac{\partial^2\zeta}{\partial t^2} = -g\Delta\rho \tag{3.1}$$

where ζ is the vertical distance from equilibrium and $\Delta\rho$ is the difference between internal and external density. $\Delta\rho = \Delta\rho$ (internal) $-\Delta\rho$ (environment) where $\Delta\rho$ (environment) is the change of density experienced simply because of motion in a stratified fluid. For an incompressible fluid we would have

$$\Delta\rho = -\Delta\rho(\text{environment}) = -\zeta\,\frac{d\rho}{dz}. \tag{3.2}$$

$\Delta\rho$ (internal) is due to the compressibility of the fluid within the membrane. Since the pressure is the same inside and out,

$$\Delta p\,(\text{internal}) = \zeta\,\frac{dp_0}{dz} \tag{3.3}$$

which, by virtue of (2.2) and (2.5) may be written

$$c^2\Delta\rho(\text{internal}) = -\zeta\rho g \tag{3.4}$$

Combining (3.1), (3.2), and (3.4)

$$\frac{\partial^2\zeta}{\partial t^2} + \left[-g\,\frac{d}{dz}\ln\rho - \frac{g^2}{c^2}\right]\zeta = 0 \tag{3.5}$$

When the term in brackets is greater than zero[*], simple harmonic motion will result, with N

$$N^2 = -g \frac{d}{dz} \ln \rho + \frac{g}{c^2}$$ (3.6)

as the angular frequency. This is the Väisälä frequency, sometimes called the Brunt frequency. Clearly, it must be relevant for gravity waves.

4. WAVES IN AN INFINITE, ISOTHERMAL ATMOSPHERE

An equation of the form of (2.15) may be transformed in a standard manner (see Tolstoy, 1963, Sect. 4) which in this case is

$$W = \rho^{-\frac{1}{2}} h$$ (4.1)

to reduce (2.15) to the form

$$h'' + n^2 h = 0$$ (4.2)

where

$$n^2 = \frac{\omega^2}{c^2} - k^2 + \frac{k^2}{\omega^2} N^2 - \frac{1}{4}\left(\frac{d}{dz} \ln \rho\right)^2 - \frac{1}{2}\frac{d^2}{dz^2} \ln \rho$$ (4.3)

is seen to be a vertical wave number.

We shall sometimes find it convenient to make the additional assumption (equivalent to an isothermal atmosphere) that

$$\rho = \rho_0 \exp(-z/H) = \rho_0 \exp(-2\nu z)$$ (4.4)

ρ_0 density at the origin of z, H scale height, γ specific heat ratio,

$$H = \frac{RT}{g} = \frac{c^2}{\gamma g}$$

and ν is a wave number characteristic of the stratification

$$\nu = \frac{1}{2H} = \frac{\gamma g}{2c^2}$$

With these approximations, (4.3) becomes

$$n^2 = \frac{\omega^2}{c^2} - k^2 + \frac{k^2}{\omega^2} N^2 - \nu^2$$ (4.5)

These assumptions are rather unrealistic, since N and ν vary considerably in the atmosphere. However, consideration of this model will provide us with physical insight which will be helpful in considering more realistic situations.

There are three separate effects in the equation for n^2:
1) Compressibility, which enters in terms ω^2/c^2 and g^2/c^2. Incompressibility corresponds to $c = \infty$.

_____
[*] Stability against convective overturnings requires $N^2 > 0$.

2) Stratification $(d/dz) \ln \rho$, $(d^2/dz^2) \ln \rho$. These terms vanish in homogeneous atmospheres.

3) Gravity. This enters only in the definition of N^2 which disappears for $g = 0$. Let us start with a simple case, and add complexity.

4.1. Incompressible, homogeneous case $(c = \infty, \nu = 0, g \neq 0)$

Eq. (4.5) becomes $n^2 = -k^2$. Thus $h \sim \exp(\pm nz)$, an exponential. No real propagating wave system exists without boundaries. There are the gravity waves at an air-water interface, for example.

4.2. Compressible, homogeneous case, without gravity $(c \neq \infty, \nu = 0, g = 0)$

$$n^2 = \frac{\omega^2}{c^2} - k^2 \tag{4.6}$$

Thus h and W obey the acoustic wave equation, and since

$$\frac{\omega^2}{k^2 + n^2} = \frac{\omega^2}{K^2} = c^2 = \text{constant} , \tag{4.7}$$

wave propagation is isotropic and non-dispersive.

4.3. Density stratified, compressible fluids, with $g = 0$ $(c \neq \infty, \nu \neq 0)$

In our isothermal atmosphere with constant scale height, (4.5) becomes

$$k^2 + n^2 = \frac{\omega^2}{c^2} - \nu^2$$

or $\tag{4.8}$

$$\omega_a^2 = c^2(k^2 + n^2 + \nu^2)$$

Because of the symmetry between k and n, propagation is again isotropic, but note that for $\omega^2 < \nu^2 c^2$ unattenuated propagation is not possible. The limiting frequency

$$\omega_0 = \nu c = \frac{\gamma g}{2c} \sim T^{-\frac{1}{2}}$$

forms a low frequency cut off to these waves. Since they approach the acoustic equation at high frequencies, i.e. for

$$k^2 + n^2 \gg \nu^2$$

these are acoustic type waves.

This cut off ω_0 is a resonant frequency for propagating waves, characteristic of a distributed mass - spring system.

We may graph this result in the ω-K plane as shown in fig. 1 (after Tolstoy, 1963). (Plotting ω versus k would be similar.) Note that the slope of a line from the origin to a point on the curve is $V = \omega/K$, the phase velocity, and is given by $V = \omega/K = c (1 - \omega_0^2/\omega^2)^{-\frac{1}{2}}$. Since the slope changes for different ω, the propagation is dispersive*.

---

* A similar case with radio waves is the Sellmeier dispersion formula.

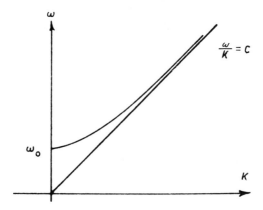

Fig. 1. Dispersion of acoustic waves in an infinite medium with density stratification. (After Tolstoy, 1963.)

Of greater interest than the phase velocity is the group velocity

$$U(K) = \frac{d\omega}{dK} = c\left(1 - \frac{\omega_0^2}{\omega^2}\right)^{\frac{1}{2}}$$

the velocity with which the energy is propagated. It is, of course, the slope of the ω-K curve. As $\omega \to \omega_0$, $V \to \infty$ but $U \to 0$.

The cut-off frequency ω_0 may easily be calculated using $c = 3.3 \times 10^4$ cm/sec, $H = 8 \times 10^5$ cm, to be $\omega_0 = 0.02$ sec^{-1}, corresponding to $P_0 = (2\pi/\omega_0) = 5$ min.

Thus, 'sound' waves of period > 5 min will not propagate.

4.4. *Stratified, incompressible case with gravity (c $= \infty$, $\nu \neq 0$, $g \neq 0$)*
Again, using (4.4), (4.5) becomes

$$n^2 = k^2 \left[\frac{N^2}{\omega^2} - 1\right] - \nu^2$$

or

$$\omega_i = \frac{kN}{(k^2 + n^2 + \nu^2)^{\frac{1}{2}}} \qquad (4.10)$$

where

$$N^2 = 2\nu g \qquad (4.11)$$

We note immediately that we must have $N^2 > \omega^2$, i.e., N is a high frequency cut-off for propagating waves. Also, since k and n are no longer symmetric in the equations, propagation is anisotropic, as well as dispersive.

Graphing as before in fig. 2 (after Tolstoy, 1963) we see the cut-off and also that the largest group and phase velocities occur near $\omega = 0$, while V, $U \to 0$ as $\omega \to N$.

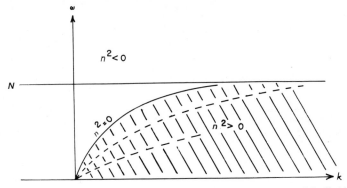

Fig. 2. Dispersion of plane interval waves in an infinite incompressible fluid due to density stratification. (After Tolstoy, 1963.)

4.5 *Compressible stratified fluid with gravity ($c \neq \infty$, $\nu \neq 0$, $g \neq 0$)*
   Eq. (4.5) becomes

$$n^2 = \frac{\omega^2}{c^2} - k^2 + k^2 \frac{N^2}{\omega^2} - \nu^2 \qquad (4.12)$$

where

$$N^2 = 2\nu g - \frac{g^2}{c^2} \qquad (4.13)$$

(For the values used previously, this leads to a period of about 7 min.)
   Eq. (4.12) may be written with the aid of (4.8) and (4.10),

$$\frac{\omega^4}{\omega_a^2} - \omega^2 + \omega_i^2 = 0$$

Acoustic and internal type solutions are both present, and may be written

$$\omega_A^2 = \omega_a^2 \left[1 - \left(\frac{\omega_i}{\omega_a}\right)^2 + \dots \right],$$

$$\omega_I = \omega_i^2 \left[1 + \left(\frac{\omega_i}{\omega_a}\right)^2 + \dots \right]. \qquad (4.14)$$

   The effect of gravity on acoustic waves and of compressibility on internal waves is of order ω_i^2/ω_a^2, which Tolstoy (1963), shows to be only 0.2 at its maximum. To compare these solutions, we must first compare

$$\omega_0 = \frac{\gamma g}{2c} \text{ and } N = (\gamma - 1)^{\frac{1}{2}} \frac{g}{c}.$$

Since $\gamma \sim 1.4$ in the atmosphere, $\omega_0 > N$. The results are shown in fig. 3 (after Tolstoy, 1963). We see that the effect of the gravity on the acoustic waves or compressibility on the internal gravity waves is to move the solu-

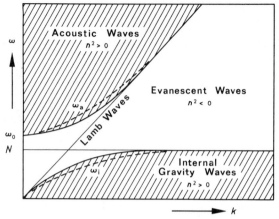

Fig. 3. Regions of solutions for a compressible, stratified fluid in a gravity field. Dashed curves correspond to neglect of gravity (ω_a) and compressibility (ω_i). (After Tolstoy, 1963.)

tions slightly toward each other. Again propagation is anisotropic and dispersive. We have therefore 3 regions separated by curves of $n^2 = 0$, which delimit the acoustic type solutions, the internal gravity type solutions, and the region between where no propagating body waves exist in an infinite medium. The line marked Lamb type waves in the region $n^2 < 0$ will be discussed later

4.6. *Fluid motions in acoustic gravity waves*

Having explored the dispersion diagram, let us consider the nature of the fluid motions. We saw from 4.2 that for a propagating wave we have the quantity h given by a sinusoidal function of altitude. However, from 4.1, it is clear that

$$W = \rho^{-\frac{1}{2}} h = \rho_0^{-\frac{1}{2}} \exp(\nu z) \, h \qquad (4.15)$$

is an exponentially growing function of altitude. This does not lead to kinetic energy divergence, since

$$KE_V = \tfrac{1}{2} \rho W^2 = \frac{1}{2} \rho_0 \exp(-2\nu z) \, (\rho_0^{-\frac{1}{2}} \exp(\nu z) \, h))^2 = \frac{h^2}{2} \qquad (4.16)$$

which is bounded.

Now

$$W' = (\mathrm{in} + \nu)W \qquad (4.17)$$

and (2.13) becomes

$$U = \frac{-c^2 \, kn + i\,k\,c^2 \, (\nu - g)}{k^2 c^2 - \omega^2} \, W \qquad (4.18)$$

Again, the horizontal kinetic energy density is obviously bounded.

We can derive the particle orbits from (4.18) without difficulty.

Acoustic wave orbits

As noted above, gravity does not greatly affect the acoustic branch. For simplicity we shall set $g = 0$. Then, with (4.18) and introducing

$$u \sim \frac{\partial \xi}{\partial t} = i\omega\xi$$

$$w \sim \frac{\partial \zeta}{\partial t} = i\omega\zeta$$

(4.19)

$$\xi = \frac{k(n-i\nu)}{n^2 + \nu^2} \zeta$$

(4.20)

Putting

$$\zeta = \cos \omega t; \ \xi = \frac{k\nu}{n^2 + \nu^2} \sin \omega t + \frac{kn}{n^2 + \nu^2} \cos \omega t$$

(4.21)

and the particle orbit is given by

$$\xi^2 + \frac{k^2}{n^2 + \nu^2} \zeta^2 - \frac{2 kn}{n^2 + \nu^2} \xi\zeta = \frac{k^2 \nu^2}{(n^2 + \nu^2)^2},$$

(4.22)

the equation of an ellipse with tilted axes (for $n^2 + \nu^2 > 0$).

For high frequencies, $n^2 \gg \nu^2$, (4.22) reduces to

$$\frac{\xi}{\zeta} = \frac{k}{n}$$

(4.23)

indicating linear motion in the direction of propagating, as with standard acoustic waves. In the particular case of a horizontally propagating wave $(n = 0)$, (4.22) becomes

$$\xi^2 + \frac{k^2}{\nu^2} \zeta^2 = \frac{k^2}{\nu^2},$$

(4.24)

indicating displacement transverse to the direction of propagation, tending toward being completely transverse as $k \to 0$. It is easy to demonstrate that the vorticity $= \frac{\partial u}{\partial z} - \frac{\partial w}{\partial x}$ is not zero. Only in fluids of uniform density are sound waves purely longitudinal and irrotational. From (4.21) it can be seen that the particle traces its orbit in a clockwise direction.

Gravity waves

We may start with (2.13), set $c = \infty$, and make use of (4.19) to find

$$\xi = \frac{-n + i\nu}{k} \zeta$$

(4.25)

and again if

$$\zeta = \cos \omega t$$

$$\xi = - \frac{\nu}{k} \sin \omega t - \frac{n}{k} \cos \omega t$$

then

$$\xi^2 + \zeta^2 \left(\frac{N^2}{\omega^2} + \frac{\omega^2}{c^2 k^2} - 1 \right) + 2 \frac{n}{k} \xi \zeta = \frac{\nu^2}{k^2} \tag{4.26}$$

which is also the equation of a tilted ellipse for $\omega < N$.

Again looking only at horizontal propagation, for $\omega \sim N$,

$$k = \left[\frac{n^2 + \nu^2}{N^2/\omega^2 - 1} \right]^{\frac{1}{2}} \to \infty, \qquad \xi \to 0 \tag{4.27}$$

and the motion is transverse. As $\omega \to 0$

$$\zeta \to 0 \tag{4.28}$$

$\xi \to \nu/k$, and the motion is again longitudinal. This behavior and the intermediate steps are summarized in fig. 4. From (4.26) the trajectory is executed in a counterclockwise direction - opposite to acoustic waves.

Midgley and Liemohn (1966) have given a very interesting discussion of particle orbits and propagation.

4.7. *Polarization relationships*

Taking the form from (4.1), we can write

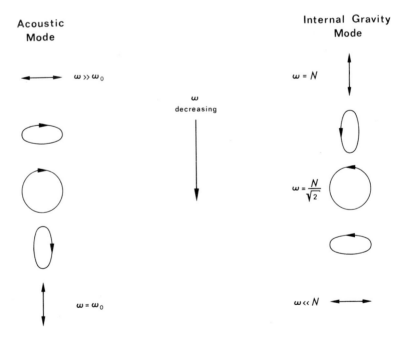

Fig. 4. Particle orbits for a horizontally propagating wave for the two families of solutions. The horizontal orbit size is much less than a wavelength.

$$W/Z = U/X = \frac{P_1}{p_0 P} = \frac{\rho_1}{\rho_0 R} \sim A \; \rho^{-\frac{1}{2}} \exp(\mathrm{i}(kx+nz-\omega t))$$

$$\sim A \, \exp(\nu z)\exp(\mathrm{i}(kx+nz-\omega t)) \tag{4.29}$$

where A is a constant, presumed small.

Substitution in eqs. (2.1), (2.4), and (2.13) leads to the following polarization relations:

$$Z = \omega(\omega^2 - k^2 c^2)$$
$$X = \omega k c^2[n + \mathrm{i}g/c^2(1-\gamma/2)]$$
$$P = \gamma \omega^2 \, [n + \mathrm{i}g/c^2(1-\gamma/2)] \tag{4.30}$$
$$R = n\omega^2 - \mathrm{i}k^2 g(\gamma-1) + \mathrm{i}\frac{\gamma g \omega^2}{2c^2}$$

These relationships may be thought of as representing vectors on a complex diagram, showing the relative amplitudes and phases of the different oscillating components.

Note that these relationships indicate the percentage perturbation of pressure and density increases with height. A height will be reached where our perturbation treatment will not be applicable, and non-linear effects must be considered.

At very low frequencies, we have

$$R/X \simeq \frac{\mathrm{i}(\gamma-1)^{\frac{1}{2}}}{c} \tag{4.31}$$

which relates density perturbations to horizontal velocities.

We can crudely think of the motions in the following qualitative ways. For the acoustic waves, fluid comes together, is compressed, and sinks into a denser region before the compressed fluid elastically expands and is buoyed up on the second half of the cycle.

For gravity waves, fluid comes together too slowly to be greatly compressed. It sinks, is compressionally heated; its density becomes lower than its surroundings and it is buoyed back up, causing the fluid flow direction to reverse.

Midgley and Liemohn (1966) have discussed the physical details much more carefully.

5. PHASE AND GROUP VELOCITIES; PROPAGATION SURFACES AND ENERGY FLOW

The information of section 4.5 can be seen in another way. By picking an ω, as a period $(= 2\pi/\omega)$, for a series of k we may solve for n. The points k, n for a given ω are plotted in fig. 5, taken from Hines (1960). Such surfaces are known as propagation surfaces, and are discussed also by Tolstoy (1963) and Eckart (1960). The family of ellipses represents a sequence of acoustic waves, while the hyperbolas represent internal gravity waves.

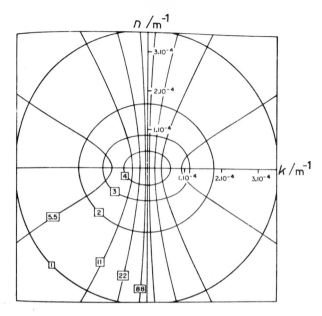

Fig. 5. Propagation surfaces of acoustic gravity waves. The periods in minutes are shown in boxes on the corresponding curves. The cut off periods for acoustic and gravity waves are 4.4 and 4.9 min respectively. (After Hines, 1960.)

An interesting point can also be noted here. Looking at the hyperbola for a particular period, we see that the ratio k/n is nearly constant over all but a small part of the curve. For waves of that period, with horizontal wavelengths somewhat less than the maximum, the wave can only propagate in one direction; alternatively, the frequency depends only on the direction of propagation. This point is also noted by Landau and Lifshitz (1959, pp. 44-46). The longer periods propagate closer to the vertical, but note that these waves cannot propagate vertically. For long period gravity waves, then, we have a family of wave fronts tilted slightly from the horizontal, moving upward or downward.

Remembering that $V_x = \omega/k$; $V_z = \omega/n$, we can form a refractive index vector $\eta_x = ck/\omega$, $\eta_z = cn/\omega$.

This is plotted in fig. 6 (after Hines, 1960). Here the distance from the origin gives the index of refraction - waves with period less than 1 min are seen to propagate isotropically with the speed of sound, while smaller η values represent more rapid propagation. Note that acoustic wave phase may propagate much more rapidly near ω_0 than in the high frequency limit, and more rapidly vertically. Internal gravity wave phase propagates more slowly than sound, and more rapidly horizontally.

The group velocity may be written

$$U_x = \frac{\partial \omega}{\partial k}, \qquad U_z = \frac{\partial \omega}{\partial n}$$

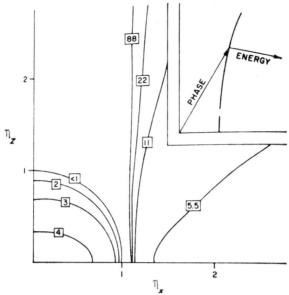

Fig. 6. Contours of constant period in the η_x, η_z domain. The periods (in min) are shown in boxes on the corresponding curves. The basic parameters are as for fig. 5. The relation between phase and energy progression is indicated by the geometric construction in the inset. (After Hines, 1960.)

and is known from general considerations to be the velocity of energy propagation. Since the lines in fig. 6 are lines of constant ω, we see that U is perpendicular to these lines and directed toward shorter periods. This is illustrated in the inset, where it is clear that the vertical direction of energy propagation may be opposite to the direction of phase propagation. Specifically, a downward phase propagation may accompany upward energy propagation, although for longer periods the flow is nearly horizontal. See also Eckart (1960).

6. BOUNDARY CONDITIONS AND BOUNDARY WAVES

At a rigid horizontal surface, the normal velocity must vanish, or

$$W = 0 \tag{6.1}$$

At the surface between two compressible fluids (labeled 1 and 2) of different densities, we require

$$W_1 = W_2 \tag{6.2}$$

and

$$p_1 = p_2 \tag{6.3}$$

However, since the surface separating the fluids also moves, we must express this as

$$\frac{Dp_1}{Dt} = \frac{Dp_2}{Dt} \tag{6.4}$$

Since

$$\frac{Dp}{Dt} = c^2 \frac{D\rho}{Dt} = -c^2 \rho \nabla v \tag{6.5}$$

condition (6.5) may be written (for our 2-dimensional case)

$$c_1^2 \rho_1 [ikU_1 + W_1'] = c_2^2 \rho_2 [ikU_2 + W_2'] \tag{6.6}$$

For the case of a free surface, $\rho_2 = 0$, and (6.6) becomes

$$ikU_1 + W_1' = 0 \tag{6.7}$$

In general, remembering (2.13)

$$U = ik \frac{c^2 W' - gW}{k^2 c^2 - \omega^2}$$

we have

$$\rho_1(k^2 g W_1 - \omega^2 W_1') = \rho_2(k^2 g W_2 - \omega^2 W_2') \frac{c_2^2(k^2 c_1^2 - \omega^2)}{c_1^2(k^2 c_2^2 - \omega^2)} \tag{6.8}$$

The presence of boundaries allows additional wave types to those discussed above. Boundary waves are waves whose energy is concentrated at a boundary of discontinuity of one or more parameters (c, ρ, ρ') and correspond to $n^2 < 0$ on both sides of the boundary - i.e., an exponential variation of amplitude. On physical grounds, we demand that these waves give a vanishing of energy density as $z \to \infty$.

Tolstoy (1963) discusses these waves for several situations. We will mention only two which are of particular interest.

The first of these is the Lamb wave (Lamb, 1945, p. 548). Here we satisfy B. C. (6.1) by setting $W \equiv 0$ everywhere. Then, from (2.12),

$$ikg\rho U + \frac{\partial}{\partial z} (\rho c^2 \, ikU) = 0 \tag{6.9}$$

$$\frac{g}{c^2} (\rho c^2 U) + \frac{\partial}{\partial z} (\rho c^2 U) = 0 \tag{6.10}$$

$$\rho c^2 U = (\rho c^2 U)_{z=0} \exp(-g/c^2 z), \quad z > 0 \tag{6.11}$$

or

$$U = U_{z=0} \exp((2\nu - g/c^2)z), \quad z > 0 \tag{6.12}$$

if $c^2 = $ constant.

Stability of the medium requires $2\nu > g/c^2$, so the amplitude increases with height. However,

$$\rho U^2 \sim \exp(-2\nu z)\exp(2(2\nu - g/c^2)z) = \exp(2(\nu - g/c^2)z) \tag{6.13}$$

which does go to zero.

Another wave in a stratified compressible fluid, at a free surface of medium 2, $z < 0$, is found from (6.8), with $\rho_1 = 0$.

$$k^2 g \, W_2 - \omega^2 W_2' = 0 \qquad (6.14)$$

We are looking for solutions of the form

$$W_2 \sim \exp(-\nu_2 z)\exp(n_2' z) \qquad (6.15)$$

Then we have as a dispersion relation

$$\frac{k^2 g}{\omega^2} = \nu_2 + n_2' \qquad (6.16)$$

where the prime with n_2 does not mean d/dz but

$$n_2' = i n_2 = \left[k^2 - \frac{\omega^2}{c^2} - \frac{k^2}{\omega^2} N^2 + \nu_2^2 \right]^{\frac{1}{2}} \qquad (6.17)$$

which is real.

This has surface waves, and also, substituting

$$\omega = kc \qquad (6.18)$$

into (6.17) one finds

$$n_2' = \left(\frac{g}{c^2} - \nu_2 \right) \qquad (6.19)$$

Putting (6.19) and (6.18) into (6.16) proves that (6.18) is a solution. By (6.15), we have

$$W_2 \sim \exp((g/c^2)z) \quad z < 0$$

This represents a horizontally traveling sound wave, with a small vertical component arising from buoyancy effects in the gravity field. The condition for energy density $\to 0$ as $z \to -\infty$ is the same as for the Lamb wave. These we may term Lamb-type waves.

We can make the following remarks about the Lamb waves and Lamb-type waves. First, they are not true boundary waves, but modified acoustic waves, traveling parallel to the density stratification. Second, they need the presence of a boundary, to prevent the local energy density from becoming infinite in one direction.

The position of these waves has previously been indicated on the diagnostic diagram.

7. REFLECTION AND TRANSMISSION COEFFICIENTS

7.1. *Some general remarks*

The standard procedure for obtaining reflection and transmission coefficients at an interface between layers with constant coefficients is to consider a wave of unit amplitude incident on a boundary, which is partly reflected (with amplitude R) and partly transmitted with amplitude T. The boundary conditions are invoked to solve for R and T. If the incident wave is in medium 1, these are respectively

$$\exp(i(kx+n_1z-\omega t))$$
$$R\ \exp(i(kx-n_1z-\omega t))$$
$$T\ \exp(i(kx+n_2z-\omega t))$$

It is interesting to note that this only specifies the ω, k of the transmitted wave. If the two media are somewhat different, so that the $\omega(k)$ acoustic curves of the first medium intersect the internal wave solutions of the second medium, we have sufficient conditions to allow transformation of an acoustic wave to an internal wave. As we saw before, this will be possible if $c_2 > c_1$. An obvious condition is that

$$N_2 > v_1c_1 = \omega_1 .$$

It is also necessary that the slope of the internal wave solution for 2 near $\omega = 0$ exceed c_1. These conditions are not sufficient, since they do not require the intersection of ω_1 and ω_2 curves.

7.2. *Calculation of the reflection coefficient*

We will illustrate the technique by considering discontinuities in density gradient in the presence of a gravity field. We have two half spaces in contact at $z = 0$.

In half space 1,

$$z < 0 \qquad \rho_1 = \rho_0 \exp(-2v_1z)$$

while in half space 2,

$$z > 0 \qquad \rho_2 = \rho_0 \exp(-2v_2z)$$

while

$$c_1 = c_2$$

Now

$$W_1 = \rho_1^{-\frac{1}{2}}\ h_1 = \rho_1^{-\frac{1}{2}}\ (\exp(i(kx+n_1z-\omega t)) + R\ \exp(i(kx-n_1z-\omega t)))$$
$$W_2 = \rho_2^{-\frac{1}{2}}\ h_2 = \rho_2^{-\frac{1}{2}}\ T\ \exp(i(kx+n_2z-\omega t))$$

Applying the boundary conditions (6.2) and (6.8), at $z = 0$ leads immediately to

$$1 + R = T$$
$$v_1(1+R) + in_1(R-1) = (v_2-in_2)T$$

from whence

$$R = \frac{v_2-v_1+i(n_1-n_2)}{v_1-v_2+i(n_1+n_2)} \qquad\qquad (7.1)$$

If n_2 is imaginary and n_1 real,

$$n_2 = in_2'$$

and

$$R = \exp(-2i\chi)$$

where   (7.2)

$$\chi = \arctan \frac{\nu_2 - \nu_1 + n_2'}{n_1}$$

since $|R| = 1$, this corresponds to total reflection of plane body waves. Recalling

$$n^2 = \frac{\omega^2}{c^2} - k^2 + \frac{k^2 N^2}{\omega^2} - \nu^2$$

$$N^2 = 2\nu g - g^2/c^2$$

we see that if $\nu_1 < \nu_2$, then $N_1 < N_2$, and only acoustic waves will be reflected. On the other hand, if $\nu_2 < \nu_1$, $N_2 < N_1$, then only internal gravity waves would be subject to total reflection.

These results are shown graphically in fig. 7, for $\nu_1 < \nu_2$.

Looking at fig. 7a it is clear that gravity waves in the lined area (in re-

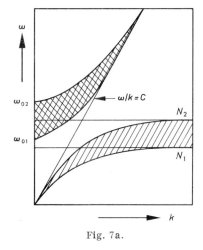

Fig. 7a.

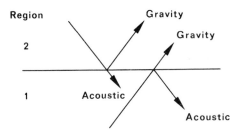

Fig. 7a, b. Differences of characteristic diagrams for two half-space when $\nu_1 < \nu_2$ and resulting reflections.

gion 2) will not propagate in region 1, while acoustic waves in the cross hatched area (in region 1) will not propagate in region 2. This indicates that these waves will be reflected, as shown in fig. 7b. In this case we have total reflection of energy from the interface with a change of phase given by 2χ.

If we have a 3 layer structure, with a region 2 of finite thickness between two semi-infinite spaces of region 1, we would expect that internal gravity wave energy once in the layer, would propagate along it, unable to get out. See fig. 8.

This occurs because region 2 is a region of large N. In the atmosphere, we expect regions of maximum N to act as channels for internal waves.

Similarly, a region of minimum ω_0 acts as a trap for acoustic waves, as does the classical low sound velocity channel.

These processes are counterparts of the optical processes of total internal reflection, and the layers mentioned above are similar to 'light pipes'.

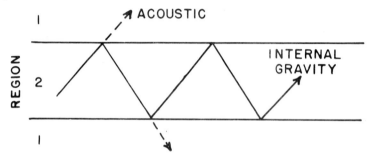

Fig. 8. Schematic indication for ducting by a region of large N.

8. REFLECTION AND DUCTING IN THE ATMOSPHERE

With the general ideas of reflection, let us explore some possible cases. We note first that for an isothermal layer

$$c \sim T^{\frac{1}{2}}, \qquad \nu \sim 1/T; \qquad \omega_0 \sim c\nu \sim T^{-\frac{1}{2}}; \qquad N^2 \sim T^{-1}; \qquad N \sim T^{-\frac{1}{2}}.$$

Thus, for a warm layer 1, cold layer 2, we may draw the diagram (see fig. 9) for waves incident from region 1.

In this case, sound waves below a certain frequency will be reflected by the cold layer, as will some of the gravity waves with $n_1 \approx 0$. However, those with $n_1 \gg 0$ (propagating upward more strongly) will enter region 2.

In this case, the warm layer acts to reflect high frequency sound waves and internal waves, while letting low frequencies pass through. Note that this latter is due to a region of large N values in the region of incidence, while the former is due to the higher sound velocity in region 2 (fig. 10).

In fig. 11, from Tolstoy (1963), we see a plot of c, N and ω_0 for the atmosphere for the lowest 200 km. Looking at the curve for c (which is $\sim T^{\frac{1}{2}}$) we see that very broadly we can categorize the atmosphere by a succession

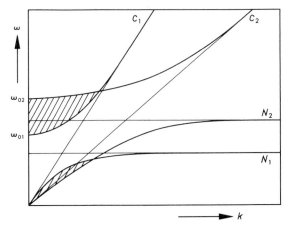

Fig. 9. Differences of characteristic diagrams for warm half-space 1, cold half-space 2. Shaded areas show reflection by region 2.

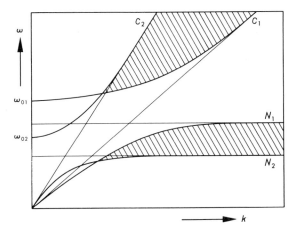

Fig. 10. Differences of characteristic diagrams for cold half-space 1, warm half-space 2. Shaded areas show reflection by region 2.

of regions with warm troposphere, cold stratosphere, warm stratopause region, colder mesopause, and hot thermosphere. Thus qualitatively we could expect a series of reflecting layers, reflecting different types of waves, with the warm thermosphere being the most important. However, when we consider layers rather than half-spaces, we must ask whether the slab is thick enough to act as a half space. Physical insight, from quantum mechanics and optics suggest that an incident wave may penetrate about one wavelength into a region where it has an imaginary wave number. If the thickness of the layer or layers is greater than this, we may expect our half-space insight to hold. If the layer is appreciably less thick than this,

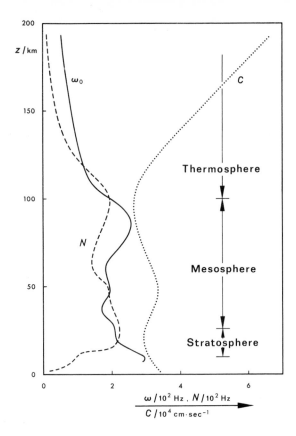

Fig. 11. Structure of the earth's atmosphere. (After Tolstoy, 1963.)

the wavelength will not notice this region very much, and integrate its effect with that of the regions of real wave number on either side.

We note also that regions of ducting are clearly shown:
1) Min ω_0 - most important in thermosphere
2) Max N - Upper mesosphere, stratosphere
3) Min c - Upper mesosphere, stratosphere.

Again, wavelength considerations must be borne in mind - too long a wavelength may not be trapped, and also may not 'fit' in the waveguide.

A final point should be made here, In a non-isothermal atmosphere, $(1/\rho)(d\rho/dz)$ can be large, and $N > \omega_c$. This is shown for two regions of the atmosphere in fig. 11, where dT/dz exceeds about 2.3^o/km. In this case, the gravity and acoustic wave sequences can not be separated. The plot in refractive index space with ω as parameter is shown in fig. 12 (taken from Hines, 1960). The change is not great for $\omega < 0.3\omega_0$ or $\omega > 3N$, but when $\omega_0 < \omega < N$ there is a complete change in the diagram. An internal gravity

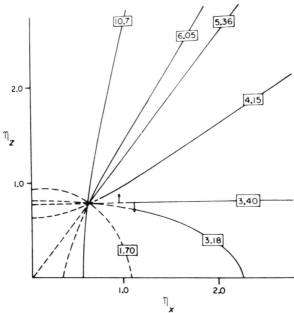

Fig. 12. Contours of constant period in the $\eta_x \cdot \eta_z$ domain, for a region where the acoustic cut off period is 5.36 min, and the gravity wave cut off is 3.40 min. (After Hines, 1960.)

wave with large horizontal and vertical wavelength may propagate much faster than the speed of sound, while sound waves may propagate more slowly. Most distressing, the direction of energy propagation can reverse in a very narrow interval, passing through infinite values.

In the next lecture, we shall consider the propagation of waves in a realistic atmosphere.

ACKNOWLEDGEMENTS

The support of NASA Grant NSG-173 and the Florida State University in the preparation of this review is gratefully acknowledged. I thank Professors Seymour L. Hess and Richard L. Pfeffer for their encouragement.

REFERENCES

Eckart, C., 1960, Hydrodynamics of Oceans and Atmospheres, Pergamon Press, New York, 284.
Eliassen, A. and E. Kleinschmidt, 1957, Handbuch der Physik 48, 1.
Hines, C. O., 1960, Internal atmospheric gravity waves at ionospheric heights, Can. J. Phys. 38, 1441.

Lamb, H., 1945, Hydrodynamics, Dover Publications, New York.

Landau, L.D. and E.M. Lifshitz, 1959, Fluid Mechanics, Pergamon Press, London.

Midgley, J.E. and H.B. Liemohn, 1966, Gravity waves in a realistic atmosphere, J. Geoph. Res. 71, 3729.

Tolstoy, J., 1963, The theory of waves in stratified fluids including the effects of gravity and rotation, Revs. Mod. Phys. 35, 207.

COMMENT

Hines:

Present linear theory allows to understand the existence of waves, their mechanism of propagation and the magnitude of the speed of propagation. For higher altitudes nonlinear terms must be considered because the velocity of motion becomes large there (against the phase velocity). In this context one interesting point are interactions, for example between short and long period gravity waves.

DISCUSSION

Spizzichino:

Que sait-on actuellement sur les effets non-linéaires dans les ondes de gravité? Existe-t-il des publications sur ce sujet?

Gille:

The non-linear effects in gravity waves, and the mode interactions mentioned by Professor Hines have been treated extensively for waves on water. A recent survey is Kinsman Water Waves, 1965. Hasselman (J. Fluid Mech. 15, 1963) has also treated this subject in detail. Wehausen and Laitone (Handbuch der Physik IX, 1960) have also discussed it.

Erkmen:

I think in Dr. Gille's paper (beginning of section 2) the statement of 'we assume that the *motions* and *fluctuations* are small, so that the equations of motion may be linearized.' is not clear.

Related with this statement, I would like to point out one of the well-known features of the perturbation theory that in order to linearize the equations of motion by the perturbation method, we have to assume that perturbation quantities must be smaller in comparison to their basic (undisturbed) quantities.

Of course, in addition to this we have some other assumptions associated with the perturbation method also.

Gille:

Dr. Erkman has correctly noted that the motions must be small compared to something. For wave problems, we may require that the amplitude of the particle motions are small compared to the wave length, or equivalently, that particle velocities are much less than the wave velocity.

Kergastel:

Je voudrais poser quelques questions relatives à la signification physique des ondes de gravité qui peuvent se résumer ainsi: si vous rencon-
trez un homme dans la rue de même que vous pourriez lui expliquer ce
qu'est une onde acoustique, que répondrez vous s'il vous demande ce qu'est
une onde de gravité.

Comment une propagation horizontale est elle possible sans intervention
de la pression?

Explication sur les considérations qualitatives de la fin du section 4.

Quelles sont les dimensions de la particule en mouvement et comment
expliquer les variations du vent en tenant compte de la différence des ordres de grandeur des dimensions de la particule et de la longueur d'onde?

Gille:

We are all acquainted with gravity waves at the surface of a lake. In the
same way, we could imagine surfaces of constant density in the atmosphere
displaced into sinusoidal patterns. The equations of motion tell us that for
a given period, the crests at successive levels have a specific alignment,
so that as the waves at the individual levels propagate horizontally, the
wave front appears to propagate with a vertical component. (As an example,
if the wave crests lie along a line going up the left, as the whole pattern
propagates to the right the line of crests appears to propagate up and to the
right.)

The horizontal motion at a given level depends upon the horizontal variation of pressure, $\nabla p_h \sim dp/dx$, as shown by equation (2.2).

As I said, the qualitative argument is rather crude. However, let us
consider one of our density surfaces, mentioned above. Where it is deformed downward, it is less dense than its surroundings, and is buoyed
back up. This buoyancy compared to its surroundings is for the same reasons that appeared in the derivation of the Väisälä frequency - the density
of the descending material increases because of compression, but because
of compressional heating it does not increase as rapidly as the unperturbed
basic density. When the local kinetic energy is completely converted to potential energy (buoyancy) the process reverses and the buoyant force begins
to push material up. The phenomenon is similar to water waves, with the
added features of stratification and compressibility.

The dimensions of the particle and its motion are much less than the
wave length. On the other hand, the particle must be large enough that it
can be regarded as a continuum - i.e. all dimensions large compared to a
molecular mean free path. Since the particle covers a distance small compared to the wave length in a wave period, its velocity is small compared
to the wave speed.

ACOUSTIC-GRAVITY WAVE DUCTING IN
THE ATMOSPHERE BY
VERTICAL TEMPERATURE STRUCTURE

John C. GILLE

Department of Meteorology, Florida State University,
Tallahassee, Florida

Abstract. Pfeffer's matrix method of calculating wave propagation in non-isothermal atmospheres is described. Both the fundamental (a Lamb wave) and solutions having nodes in the vertical are predicted. The results are discussed; particular attention is given to the requirement that any atmosphere must include the mesopause temperature minimum to yield realistic results. Radiative and photochemical effects are touched briefly.

Résumé. La propagation des ondes dans l'atmosphère non-isothermique est calculée par la méthode matricielle de Pfeffer. On introduit les différentes solutions, la fondamentale (une onde de Lamb) et celles ayant un certain nombre de noeuds le-long de la verticale. Les résultats sont discutés; on tient particulièrement compte de la nécessité que chaque atmosphère doit inclure un minimum de température dans la mésopause afin de donner des résultats réalistes. On parle brièvement des effects photochimiques et du rayonnement.

1. EARLY STUDIES OF ATMOSPHERIC WAVE PROPAGATION

Lamb (1945) and Pekeris (1948) considered the propagation of waves in one layer atmospheres, with both uniform temperatures and constant lapse rates. Pekeris (1948) and Scorer (1950) also considered analytically the propagation in an atmosphere with a troposphere having a constant lapse rate and an isothermal stratosphere. They both found solutions involving confluent hypergeometric functions, and it is clear that an attempt to extend this to many layers would be an involved project.

In addition, both predicted the existence of a cut off frequency, above which waves would not propagate. This may be understood by considering the temperature distribution used by Pekeris (fig. 1). This may be approximated by a two layer atmosphere, with the lower layer warmer, as shown in fig. 2.

The shading represents the regions where propagating stratospheric solutions exist; tropospheric waves in these parts of the diagram will continue on upward, and be absent at the surface far from the source. Conversely, those solutions for the troposphere which cannot propagate in the stratosphere are reflected, channeled in the troposphere, and observable at great distances. Above ω_c we see that no trapping exists, and thus high frequency (short period) waves should be absent from barograms of nuclear explosions

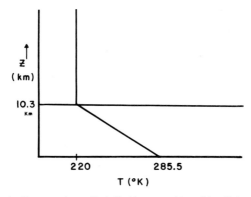

Fig. 1. Temperature distribution considered by Pekeris.

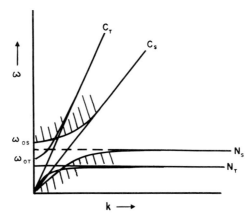

Fig. 2. Characteristic diagram for the two layer atmosphere with warm troposphere, cold stratosphere.

measured several thousand km from the detonation, if the atmosphere has such a structure.

In fact, the solution Pekeris found corresponds to the Lamb type waves, but again the same reasoning holds - those trapped will be seen at large distance, those not trapped will 'leak' upward and no appreciable energy will remain at the surface at great distances.

The observations of these short-period waves led Yamamoto (1957) and Hunt, Palmer and Penney (1960) to consider more complex atmospheres. Rather than consider their results explicitly, let us see how the problem was formulated by Pfeffer (1962) and Press and Harkrider (1962) and see the results for some simple but illustrative atmospheres calculated by Pfeffer and Zarichny (1962).

2. MATRIX FORMULATION OF THE ISOTHERMAL LAYER APPROACH

We shall discuss the formulation due to Pfeffer (1962), (hereafter referred to as P). That of Press and Harkrider (1962) (PH) is very similar. Both of these papers treated the calculation of the disturbance at a large distance from a point explosive source, and so used cylindrical geometry. This is not necessary in a general consideration of free modes; we shall continue to use rectangular coordinates.

The method is to write a soluble equation for one quantity, write a general form of the solution in each layer with undetermined coefficients, then determine the coefficients from the boundary conditions on pressure and vertical velocity. Following the classical treatments, we may write an equation for the divergence, defined as

$$d = \frac{\partial u}{\partial x} + \frac{\partial w}{\partial z} .$$

We assume

$$d = D(x) \, \exp(i(kx - \omega t)) , \qquad p_1 = P(z) \, \exp(i(kx - \omega t)) .$$

Then, remembering eqs. (2.11), (2.12), and (2.10) from the first lecture,

$$\rho \frac{\partial^2 u}{\partial t^2} = -g\rho \frac{\partial w}{\partial x} + \frac{\partial}{\partial x} \left[\rho c^2 \left(\frac{\partial u}{\partial x} + \frac{\partial w}{\partial z} \right) \right] \qquad \text{A}$$

$$\rho \frac{\partial^2 w}{\partial t^2} = g\rho \frac{\partial u}{\partial x} + \frac{\partial}{\partial z} \left[\rho c^2 \left(\frac{\partial u}{\partial x} + \frac{\partial w}{\partial z} \right) \right] \qquad \text{B}$$

$$\frac{\partial p_1}{\partial t} = wg\rho - \rho c^2 \left(\frac{\partial u}{\partial x} + \frac{\partial w}{\partial z} \right) \qquad \text{C}$$

we obtain, by taking $\partial/\partial x$ of A and $\partial/\partial z$ of B

$$D'' + \left(\frac{dc^2}{dz} - g\gamma \right) \frac{1}{c^2} D' + \left[-k^2 + \frac{\omega^2}{c^2} + \frac{k^2}{\omega^2} \left(\frac{g}{c^2} \frac{dc^2}{dz} + N^2 \right) \right] D = 0 \qquad (1)$$

Taking $\partial^2/\partial t^2$ of B and substituting from A

$$(g^2 k^2 - \omega^4) W = \omega^2 c^2 D' + g(c^2 k^2 - \omega^2) D \qquad (2)$$

and from C

$$P = \frac{i\rho}{\omega} (c^2 D - g W) \qquad (3)$$

(see also Lamb, 1945).

Eq. (1) is a second order differential equation with variable coefficients - the one used by Pekeris (1948) which has confluent hypergeometric functions as its solutions. Instead of trying to extend this treatment, P assumed that each layer was isothermal (i.e., c^2 = constant) and used a large number of layers to express the temperature variation.

For the nth layer, we have

$$D'' - \frac{g\gamma}{c_n^2} D' + \left[-k^2 + \frac{\omega^2}{c_n^2} + \frac{k^2}{\omega^2} N_n^2 \right] D = 0 .$$

Solutions may be expressed as

$$D(z) = \exp(\nu_n z)\left[a_n \exp(n'_n z) + b_n \exp(-n'_n z)\right] \tag{4}$$

where z is measured from the base of the layer, and

$$n' = in = + i\left[\frac{\omega^2}{c^2} - k^2 + \frac{k^2}{\omega^2} N^2 - \nu^2\right]^{\frac{1}{2}}$$

Putting (4) into (2) gives

$$[g^2 k^2 - \omega^4]W = a_n[g\, c_n^2\, k^2 - \tfrac{1}{2}g\gamma\, \omega^2 + \omega^2\, c_n^2\, n'_n]\exp(\nu_n z)\exp(n'_n z)$$
$$+ b_n[g\, c_n^2\, k^2 - \tfrac{1}{2}g\gamma\, \omega^2 - \omega^2\, c_n^2\, n'_n]\exp(\nu_n z)\exp(-n'_n z) \tag{5}$$

Putting (4) and (5) into (3) results in

$$-\frac{i}{\rho_n\omega}[g^2 k^2 - \omega^4]P = a_n[\tfrac{1}{2}g^2\, \gamma - \omega^2\, c_n^2 - g\, c_n^2\, n'_n]\exp(\nu_n z)\exp(n'_n z)$$
$$+ b_n[\tfrac{1}{2}g^2\, \gamma - \omega^2\, c_n^2 + g\, c_n^2\, n'_n]\exp(\nu_n z)\exp(-n'_n z) \tag{6}$$

Now P and W are expressed in terms of the a's and b's. We could have begun by writing a general form of the solution for W, then expressing P in terms of this, and applying the boundary conditions. This results in a slightly more cumbersome set of equations (Pfeffer, private communication) although the results would be equivalent.

To eliminate the $2N$ constants, we must apply $2N$ boundary conditions. These are

1) At the surface, $W = 0$.
2) In the top layer (a half space) the total kinetic energy is finite, i.e., $a_N = 0$. Also, Pfeffer required that n'_N be real, since the interest was in propagating, not attenuating waves.

At each of the $N - 1$ interfaces between layers, we require that

1) Vertical velocities on both sides of the interface be equal;
2) The total pressure be continuous across the interface and put in the form $p_m(z) - g\rho_{0m}\, \zeta = p_{m+1}(z) - g\rho_{0m+1}\, \zeta$ where ζ is the height of the interface above its equilibrium value, and p_m is the perturbation pressure in the mth layer.

Since

$$\frac{\partial \zeta}{\partial t} = i\,\omega\,\zeta = w$$

these boundary conditions can be formulated

$$\begin{bmatrix} W_B \\ P_B \end{bmatrix}_{n+1} = \begin{bmatrix} 1 & 0 \\ \dfrac{ig\Delta\rho_n}{\omega} & 1 \end{bmatrix}\begin{bmatrix} W_H \\ P_H \end{bmatrix}_n = [F_n]\begin{bmatrix} W_H \\ P_H \end{bmatrix}_n \tag{7}$$

where B, H denote the bottom and the top of the layers, and

$$\Delta\rho_n = \rho_{H,\,n} - \rho_{B,\,n+1}$$

We can now write

$$\begin{bmatrix} W_H \\ P_H \end{bmatrix}_n = [H_n] \begin{bmatrix} a \\ b \end{bmatrix}_n$$

$$\begin{bmatrix} W_B \\ P_B \end{bmatrix}_n = [B_n] \begin{bmatrix} a \\ b \end{bmatrix}_n .$$

Then

$$\begin{bmatrix} W_H \\ P_H \end{bmatrix}_n = [H_n] [B_n]^{-1} \begin{bmatrix} W_B \\ P_B \end{bmatrix}_n$$

and from (7)

$$\begin{bmatrix} W_B \\ P_B \end{bmatrix}_{n+1} = [F_n] [H_n] [B_n]^{-1} \begin{bmatrix} W_B \\ P_B \end{bmatrix}_n = [M_n] \begin{bmatrix} W_B \\ P_B \end{bmatrix}_n .$$

By induction we write

$$\begin{bmatrix} W_B \\ P_B \end{bmatrix}_N = \prod_{N-1} [M_N] \begin{bmatrix} W_B \\ P_B \end{bmatrix}_1$$

or

$$\begin{bmatrix} W_{BN} \\ P_{BN} \end{bmatrix} = \begin{bmatrix} \theta_1 & \theta_2 \\ \theta_3 & \theta_4 \end{bmatrix} \begin{bmatrix} 0 \\ P_{B1} \end{bmatrix} \tag{8}$$

which may be written

$$\theta_4 \, W_{BN} - \theta_2 \, P_{BN} = 0 , \tag{9}$$

where

$$W_{BN} = \frac{g \, c_N^2 \, k^2 - \dfrac{g \gamma \omega^2}{2} - \omega^2 \, c_N^2 \, n_N'}{g^2 \, k^2 - \omega^4} \, b_N$$

$$P_{BN} = \frac{\rho \, i \, \omega \left[\frac{1}{2} g^2 \gamma - \omega^2 \, c_N^2 + g \, c_N^2 \, n_N' \right]}{g^2 \, k^2 - \omega^4} \, b_N$$

This is the dispersion relationship. By specifying c^2 and thickness of each layer, we can solve for $\omega(k)$ or $V = \omega/k$ or $U = d\omega/dk$. In practice, this is done by a trial and error method, in the following manner:

1) select k;
2) guess an ω as a solution;
3) evaluate the $[M_N]$, multiply together and get the θ's;
4) calculate W_{BN}, P_{BN};
5) substitute in (9).

In general, this will not be a solution. One must guess another ω, and try again. From the size of the remainder one can soon close in on the proper value.

6) Do for enough values of k to get a family of $\omega(k)$ or equivalent curves.

Since all the numerical results to be presented are either group or phase velocity as a function of period, fig. 3 shows the results for an isothermal atmosphere in this new plot, as a point of reference.

In fig. 4 (from Pfeffer, 1962), results are shown for Pekeris' atmosphere, comparing his analytic solution with a numerical calculation in which the constant lapse rate has been approximated by 20 isothermal layers. The agreement can be seen to be very good, indicating we have not introduced any serious errors by our approximation method.

This was the only justification given by Pfeffer (1962). Hines (1965) expressed doubts about the validity of the isothermal layer approximation procedure, primarily because terms involving vertical derivatives of scale height (or c^2) were neglected. Recently Pierce (1966) has shown that the procedure can be rigorously justified. He remarks that the formulation by P or PH is equivalent to the expression he derives, and is accurate so long as c^2 does not change too greatly over a layer height. As he presents no criteria for accuracy, increasing the number of layers is probably still the best method of assessing accuracy.

3. HUERISTIC RESULTS FOR SIMPLE ATMOSPHERES

3.1. *Pekeris' model atmosphere*

Turning now to the results themselves, we see that, as implied by fig. 2, we have a short period cut off. We also see that for long periods, the group and phase velocities approach a speed ~ 0.91 that of the sound speed at the ground - corresponding to a temperature of 235°K. These long waves 'feel' both stratosphere and troposphere, and perform an averaging (fig. 4).

3.2. *Yamamoto's model atmosphere*

The observation of waves with period below the cut off suggested that the high temperature region of ozone absorption should be included. In fig. 5 we see the temperature altitude curve used by Yamamoto (1957). In fig. 6, taken from Pfeffer and Zarichny (1962) (PZI), we see the calculated U and V curves plotted against period. The short period cut off has vanished, as we expect.

Also interesting is how closely the velocity-period curve is given by the

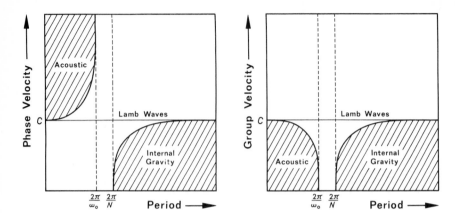

Fig. 3. Group velocity and phase velocity as a function of period for an isothermal
atmosphere.

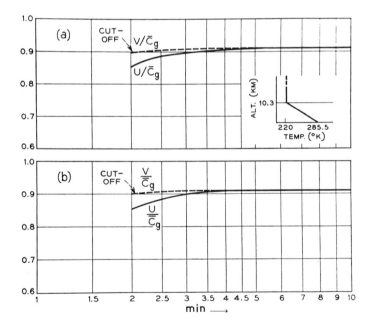

Fig. 4. a) Variation of $U/\bar{c}_g$ and $V/\bar{c}_g$ with period for Pekeris' two-layer model atmosphere, calculated by the matrix procedure using 20 isothermal layers to represent the vertical variation of temperature in the tropopause. $\bar{c}_g$ is the sound speed at
the ground. The model is shown in the insert. b) Variation of $\bar{U}/\bar{c}_g$ and $V/\bar{c}_g$ calculated analytically by Pekeris. 1948. (After Pfeffer. 1962.)

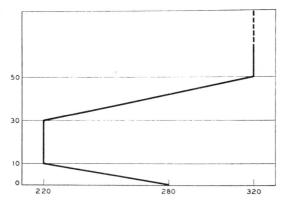

Fig. 5. Yamamoto's model atmosphere. (After Pfeffer and Zarichny. 1962.)

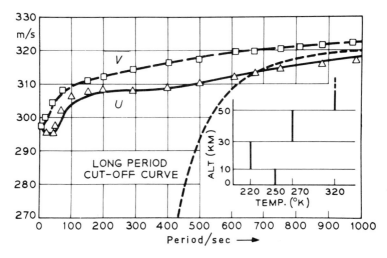

Fig. 6. Variation of group velocity (U) and phase velocity (V) with period for the fundamental mode for each of two four layer models. The curves are for the atmosphere shown in fig. 5. Squares and triangles are for the four isothermal layers shown in the inset. The temperature of each layer is the mean of the corresponding layer in fig. 5. The dashed cut off curve represents the boundary between cellular and non-cellular solutions in the infinite layer. (After Pfeffer and Zarichny. 1962.)

crude calculations based on the 4 thick isothermal layers. We can understand this by considering that for short period (short wavelengths) the waves are mainly confined to a single layer, while the longest ones sample large distances, and the details of the structure do not affect them. The discrepancies are largest near $\lambda \approx 20$ km which is of the order of the layer thicknesses.

Figs. 7 and 8, also from PZI, illustrate the effect of a warm thermosphere. There are three interesting features:

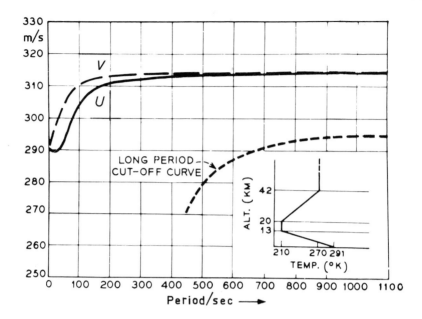

Fig. 7. Variation of group velocity (*U*) and phase velocity (*V*) with period for the fundamental mode for the 'four-layer' model atmosphere shown in the inset. (After Pfeffer and Zarichny. 1962.)

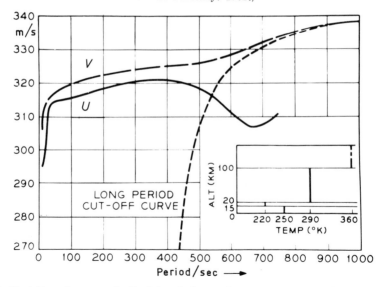

Fig. 8. Variation of group velocity (*U*) and phase velocity (*V*) with period for the fundamental mode for the four layer atmosphere shown in the inset. (Same source as fig. 7.)

1) The thermosphere affects primarily the longest period waves. This is to be expected - the longest wavelengths penetrate furthest into the thermosphere.

2) Inverse dispersion may occur - i.e. speed decreasing with increasing period.

3) A long period cut off may occur. This is illustrated graphically in fig. 9.

Fig. 9 shows the region of propagating ('cellular') solutions in the hot thermosphere by shading. Solutions in the lower atmosphere which lie in these regions would not be trapped. The formation of modes (see next section) means only certain solutions are propagated in the lower atmosphere. These are illustrated by the lines labeled n = 1, 2, 3, etc. Each of these and the fundamental has a long period cut off.

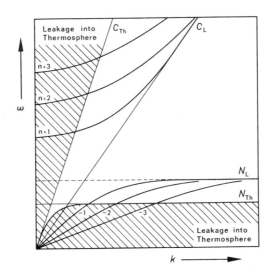

Fig. 9. Schematic illustration of long period cut off by a hot thermosphere. Shaded areas represent cellular solutions in the thermosphere, and absence of trapping. Lines are mode solutions described in next section.

4. A BRIEF DIGRESSION ON WAVE GUIDE THEORY

The rigid lower boundary will act to reflect a wave front incident obliquely upon it, and we have seen that an upper structure that reflects or refracts waves incident obliquely on it back to the surface also exists. The possibility of forming a wave guide mode of crossing wave fronts exists. In addition, we can have waves for which both reflections take place above the surface. A very lucid treatment of this subject, developing electro-magnetic and acoustic theory together, is given by Budden (1961). We will follow his treatment in the first part of this section.

Consider a wave guide whose boundaries are the planes $z = 0$ and $z = h$, with reflection coefficients

$$R_g(\theta) = \exp(-2i\chi\!\downarrow) \qquad z = 0$$

$$R(\theta) = \exp(-2i\chi\!\uparrow) \qquad z = h \tag{1}$$

for a plane wave whose normal makes an angle θ with either boundary.

If some quantity obeying the wave equation is given by

$$F_1 = F_0 \exp(-i(kx + nz))$$

After reflection at $z = h$, and return to the lower boundary

$$F_2 = R(\theta) \, F_0 \exp(-i(kx - nz))\exp(-2inh)$$

(the last factor takes account of phase change of the wave in traveling up to and back from the upper boundary). After F_2 is reflected from the bottom,

$$F_3 = R_g(\theta) \, R(\theta) \exp(-2inh)F_1$$

The condition that a wave guide exists is that F_1 and F_3 must be identical. This requires

$$R(\theta) \, R_g(\theta) \exp(-2inh) = 1 \tag{2}$$

For a plane of perfect reflection, $R = 1$. Thus, if upper and lower surfaces are rigid boundaries,

$$\exp(-2inh) = 1$$

or

$$nh = m\pi \tag{3}$$

where m is an integer, the mode number.

Those modes are similar to TM electromagnetic modes, and are shown in fig. 10 (after Budden, 1961). Note that an $m = 0$ mode is possible here.

A free surface is one which cannot sustain any change of pressure. For displacements, $R = -1$. Again we find $nh = m\pi$, but a detailed study of the equations indicate that they are like TE electromagnetic modes. Their prop-

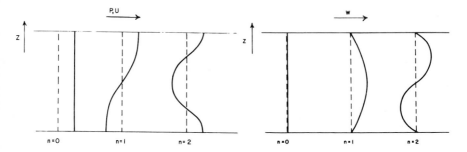

Fig. 10. The dependence of fluctuating pressure and velocities across a guide with perfectly reflecting rigid boundaries. for the first few modes. (After Budden. 1961.)

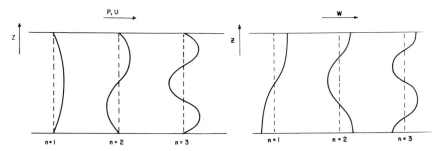

P, U

W

z

z

n = 1   n = 2   n = 3   n = 1   n = 2   n = 3

Fig. 11. The dependence of perturbation pressure and velocities across a guide with perfectly reflecting free boundaries, for the first few modes. (After Budden, 1961.)

erties are shown in fig. 11 (after Budden, 1961). Here no $m = 0$ mode is possible.

The more usual geophysical case is given by one rigid and one free boundary. Here we find

$$nh = (m - \tfrac{1}{2}) \pi \tag{4}$$

and again no $m = 0$ mode is possible. Here u and w are shown in fig. 12 (from Budden, 1961). The particle motions are shown in fig. 13.

We can write

$$K \sin \theta = n \tag{5}$$

where K is the wave number along the direction of a wave normal. Then

$$Kh \sin \theta = (m - \tfrac{1}{2}) \pi$$

has a minimum frequency of propagation, corresponding to $\sin \theta = 1$, and, with $K_c = \omega_c/c$

$$\omega_c(m) = \frac{(m - \tfrac{1}{2}) \pi c}{h} \tag{7}$$

In general $\omega_c/\omega = \sin \theta$,

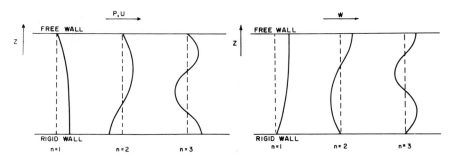

P, U

W

FREE WALL

FREE WALL

z

z

RIGID WALL

RIGID WALL

n = 1   n = 2   n = 3   n = 1   n = 2   n = 3

Fig. 12. The dependence of perturbation pressure and velocities across a guide with one rigid, one free boundary, for the first few modes. (After Budden, 1961.)

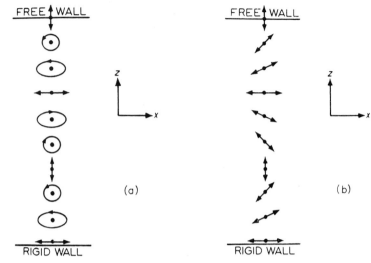

Fig. 13. Particle orbits for a sound wave of mode 2 in a guide with one rigid, one free boundary. Fig. (a) is for mode with frequency greater than cut off (propagation) fig. (b) for frequency below cut off (evanescent).

and noting that the wave fronts move in the x direction so that $kx - \omega t = K \cos \theta x - \omega t = $ const., the phase velocity is given by

$$V = \frac{\omega}{k} = \frac{\omega}{K \cos \theta} = \frac{c}{\cos \theta} = c(1 - \omega_c^2/\omega^2)^{-\frac{1}{2}} \tag{9}$$

The group velocity is

$$U = c\left(1 - \frac{\omega_c^2}{\omega^2}\right)^{\frac{1}{2}} \tag{10}$$

This behavior is shown in fig. 14.
In the general case, from (1) and (2)

$$nh = \chi(\theta)\uparrow + \chi(\theta)\downarrow + m\pi \tag{11}$$

For stratified media, Tolstoy (1955) shows how reflection coefficients may be calculated for a layered medium, and how this formulation may be generalized to a medium with continuously varying parameters. In general, χ depends on ω and k. For thick layers (approximating half spaces) the method of calculating reflection coefficients has been discussed in the first lecture.

Eq. (11) makes very clear that there are two sources of dispersion:
1) Dispersion appearing in the equations for n. This depends on internal fluid resonances, and appears in unbounded fluids. Tolstoy (1963) has termed this structural dispersion.
2) The interference between upward and downward traveling waves leads to dispersion. This has been termed geometric dispersion by Tolstoy (1963).

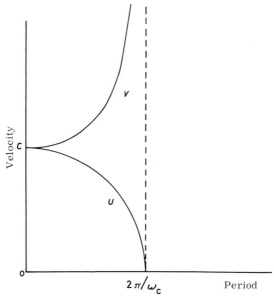

Fig. 14. Phase velocity V and group velocity U as a function of period for any mode in a wave guide with perfectly reflecting walls. Here ω_c is the cut off frequency.

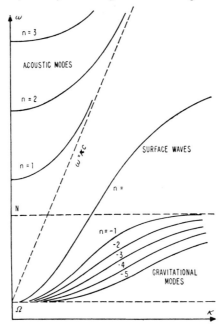

Fig. 15. ω versus k diagram for the general case of an ocean of constant depth and constant N, ω_0 and c. Low frequency region near the earth's rotation frequency Ω is not considered here. (After Eckart, 1960.)

Tolstoy also shows that for exponential modes $(n^2 < 0)$, $m = 0$. There is then no vertical phase variation; the wave fronts are normal to the planes of stratification. These are the Lamb type waves, which thus play the role of the zeroth acoustical mode. This is the wave which has been discussed until this point. Following PZI, we shall refer to this as the fundamental.

The effect of the boundaries is to 'quantize' the vertical wave number n, forcing it to assume (non-zero) integer values. This is shown for the case of the ocean in fig. 15 (from Eckart, 1960). Although this is simpler than the atmosphere, it illustrates the general behavior.

5. HIGHER MODES IN SIMPLE ATMOSPHERES

We see in fig. 15 that there are several discrete ω's corresponding to a single k, which are all solutions. These have been calculated by PZI, for Yamamoto's atmosphere. Since the warmest layer is the upper half-space, there are long period cut-offs for these modes.

It is more instructive however to consider in greater detail the series of calculations by Pfeffer and Zarichny (1963) and Pfeffer (1964) on the COSPAR atmosphere, which is shown in fig. 16. In this section we shall consider the

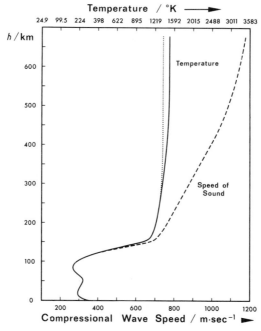

Fig. 16. Average vertical variation of absolute temperature in the atmosphere estimated by the Committee on Space Research (solid curve) and related compressional wave speed (solid curve up to 74 km and broken curve above this level) in m sec^{-1}. (After Pfeffer and Zarichny, 1963.)

higher modes for the COSPAR atmosphere terminated at 52 km by an isothermal half space. Later we will consider the effects of termination at
110, 300 and 700 km.

In the case of 52 km termination there is just one temperature minimum,
or conventional sound channel. The fundamental and higher modes are presented by Pfeffer (1964) and shown in fig. 17. Note that we again have long

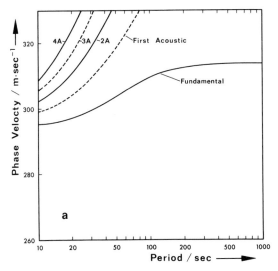

Fig. 17a.

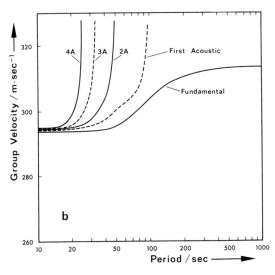

Fig. 17b.

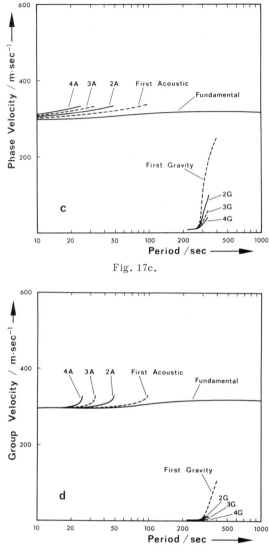

Fig. 17c.

Fig. 17a-d. Phase velocity and group velocity for the 52 km COSPAR atmosphere.
(After Pfeffer, 1964.)

period cut-offs in both acoustic and gravity modes. This is due to longer
wavelengths in the duct becoming incident at higher angles on the half space,
until they are no longer returned. The fundamental is not cut off because the
upper half space is slightly cooler than the surface. The longer periods for
the fundamental have higher velocities than the shorter periods.

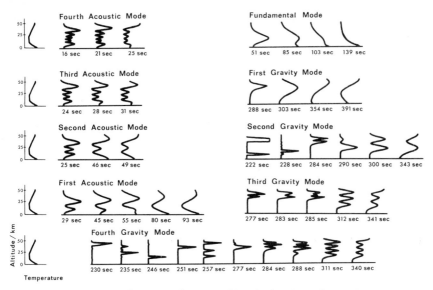

Fig. 18. Kinetic energy density as function of height for the 52 km COSPAR atmosphere. (After Pfeffer, 1964.)

Fig. 18, also from Pfeffer (1964) shows the location of the kinetic energy for the various modes at various periods. (The temperature profile is to the left.)

Taking the fourth acoustic (4A) mode as an example, we note the four nodal planes at 16 and 21 sec periods, and the limited energy along the temperature incline. At 25 sec, the energy curve is not coming back to zero at the top. Energy is penetrating on into the half space, and not being returned. This is the cut-off period for this mode. Here the ducting seems to be between the two regions of high temperature.

On the other hand, the fourth gravity mode has only 3 nodes. Again mode cut off is signalled by the sudden increase in half space energy - here at 340 sec period.

The behavior of the gravity modes is less easily understood than the acoustic modes. However, we note the tendency to concentrate in the region of large N (along the temperature incline). This region appears to be the duct for the first gravity mode at 288 sec.

At 303 sec, where the wavelength is greater, the lower reflecting region seems at the top of the region of negative temperature gradient, and eventually at the ground.

The fundamental energy, at short periods, is concentrated in the low speed channel - where we saw the acoustic energy was. Note the similarity between the 85 sec fundamental and 1A at 80 sec, and the difference at 103 and 93, respectively. At long periods its exponential character becomes very clear with energy concentrated at the surface. It is the higher speed at the warm surface than in the cold channel which increases the fundamental velocity with increasing period.

The real atmosphere possesses two temperature minima, of course, but the modes of the lower channel are very helpful in understanding the modes of the whole atmosphere.

6. DUCTING IN AN ATMOSPHERE WITH TWO SOUND CHANNELS

PZI noted that important characteristics of waves recorded at the earth's surface due to explosions in the lower atmosphere might be strongly influenced by the mesospheric temperature minimum, and that firm conclusions about wave propagation in the atmosphere required theoretical calculations based on models with two sound channels. Velocity-period relationships for atmospheres with two minima have been obtained by Gazaryan (1961), Weston (1962), Press and Harkrider (1962) and Pfeffer and Zarichny (1963) (hereafter denoted as PZ II).

6.1. *Effect of termination height on the fundamental mode*
PZ II calculated the properties of the fundamental and compared the results when the atmosphere was terminated by an isothermal half space at 52, 110 and 130 km. The results are shown in fig. 19. An immediately comprehensible effect is the lower short period velocity for the 110 and 130 km atmospheres, due to the concentration of short period acoustic-like waves in the upper (slow) sound channel. We also note the high velocity of long-period waves, due to the influence of the high temperature, high speed region, between 110 and 130 km.

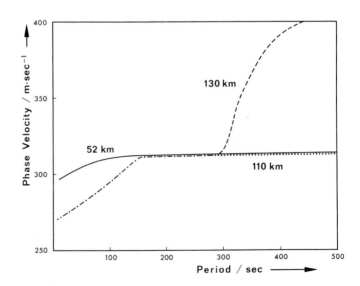

Fig. 19a.

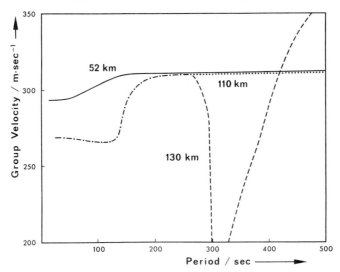

Fig. 19a,b. Theoretical velocity-period curves for the fundamental mode of the COSPAR atmosphere for three termination heights. (After Pfeffer and Zarichny, 1963.)

In the upper portion of fig. 20 is a plot of kinetic energy density against altitude. It shows that, for short periods, the kinetic energy density of the waves is concentrated in the stratospheric sound channel for the **52 km** model, and in the mesopause channel for the **110 and 130 km models.**

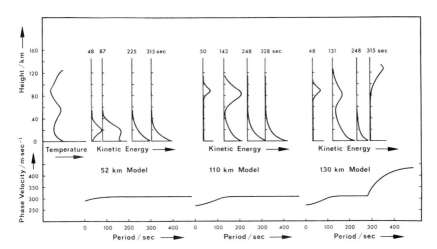

Fig. 20. Vertical profiles of the kinetic energy of the waves per unit volume at selected periods. The vertical scale and the temperature profile are shown on the left hand side of the figure. The phase velocity curves are shown at the bottom for the three models. (After Pfeffer and Zarichny, 1963.)

The intermediate period waves (150-290 sec), which have horizontal
wavelengths from 46-94 km, will not fit in either channel. These are bound
to the rigid surface of the earth, with kinetic energy decreasing exponentially with height. These wave speeds are not influenced significantly by
temperature distribution above the stratopause. The previous figure showed
that the group and phase velocities nearly coincide over this range of periods.

For periods > 290 sec, the waves are sensitive only to major differences
between the lower and upper atmospheres. The kinetic energy per unit volume decreases exponentially with altitude in the 52 and 110 km models, but
is confined to the upper atmosphere in the 130 km model. The exponential
decrease with height in the first two cases is characteristic of all models
in which the temperature maximum is at the surface.

6.2. *Modes in the* 300 *km COSPAR atmosphere*

Proceeding as before to find all ω's associated with a particular k, PZ II
shows, for the 300 km COSPAR atmosphere, the velocity-period curves
shown in fig. 21.

Here we see the great complexity of 5 acoustic and 5 gravity modes,
(see fig. 23 for greater detail). Not shown, the fundamental has a cut-off
for period > 1000 sec, due to the warm thermosphere and all other modes
cut off before this. This, of course, refers to the surface, and only means
that energy is leaking up from the lowest layers. The cut-offs are shown
more clearly in fig. 22 for a similar atmosphere, calculated by *PH*, although their fundamental does not cut off. Note that S_0 is what we have
called the fundamental, S_1 is the first acoustic, etc., while GR_0 is what we
have called the first gravity mode.

In fig. 23 we see the same calculation on an expanded velocity scale, and
compared to the 52 km 'fundamental' and first acoustic mode.

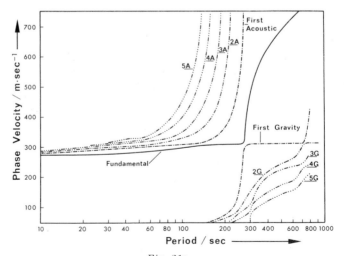

Fig. 21a.

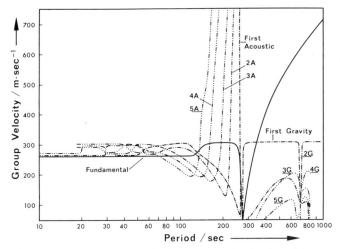

Fig. 21a.b. Dispersion curves for the fundamental mode, the first five acoustic modes, and the first five gravity modes. a) Phase velocity versus period; b) group velocity versus period. (After Pfeffer and Zarichny, 1963.)

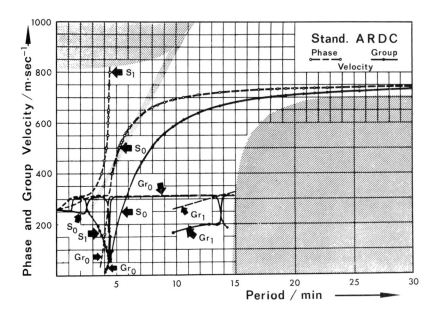

Fig. 22. Phase and group velocity for the ARDC standard atmosphere. Shaded regions correspond to cellular solution in the thermosphere. (After Press and Harkrider, 1962.)

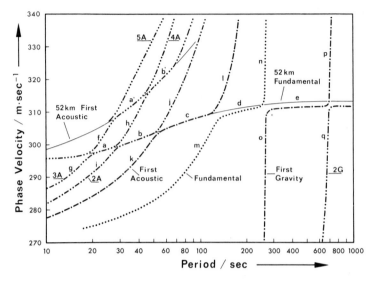

Fig. 23a.

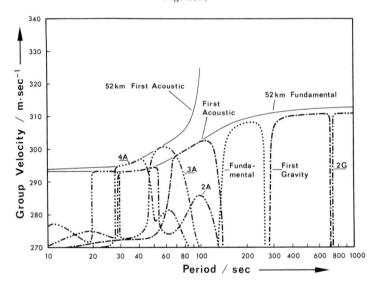

Fig. 23a,b. Comparison between dispersion curves for the 52 km and 300 km models, showing the quasing-horizontal portions of the phase and group-velocity curves for the 300 km model coincide with the solutions for the 52 km model. a) phase velocity versus period; b) group velocity versus period. The small letters in the upper figure refer to points at which vertical profiles of kinetic energy were calculated and are shown in fig. 26. (After Pfeffer and Zarichny. 1963.)

Note that the phase velocity curves for the fundamental mode, first gravity mode and the first three acoustic modes are step-like functions, with rather steep short and long period branches, separated from one another by nearly horizontal intermediate period branches.

The group velocity curves have broad maxima, separated from one another by small but distinct intervals of period. The most surprising point is that selected horizontal portions of the phase velocity curves coincide with the phase velocity curve of the 52 km model atmosphere, while other horizontal portions coincide with the first acoustic. The plateaus of the group velocity curves coincide with the 52 km group velocity curves. Not only do the horizontal portions lie along common lines, but the vertical portions of the curves for different mode numbers are seen to be very closely aligned. PZ II agrees with the conclusion of PH that 'the character of the propagating disturbance at any time is perhaps better represented by pseudo-dispersion curves formed by segments of several modes'. These horizontal portions are clearly strongly dependent on the lower channel and the warmer regions around it. PH present all the properties of their dispersion curves which are unaffected by what happens above 100 km, and these are, in agreement with PZ II, the horizontal portions. The vertically rising portions of the curves depend on the atmosphere above 110 km, and therefore we would not expect them to be strongly excited by near surface disturbances, whether of the lee-wave or point impulse type. In addition, amplitudes are proportional to $(dU/dP)^{-\frac{1}{2}}$ (where P is the period); again, we expect little surface amplitude at these periods.

This suggests that one might look for these holes in the spectrum on observed barograms. PZ II does this in a very ingenious manner, and presents evidence from recorded barograms that narrow intervals of period are missing for periods where these vertical curve segments are.

The effect of latitudinal and seasonal variations have been calculated by PZ II and PH. However, these affect mainly the lower atmosphere, and thus say little about the wave spectrum above the second sound channel. Variations in this region have been incorporated by PZ II, whose results are shown in fig. 24. Note that the COSPAR atmosphere appears to allow higher frequency (shorter period) waves to leak upward in both the fundamental and first gravity modes. It would be interesting to look for a variation in wave spectra at ionospheric heights with sunspot cycle, to see if there is this tendency for high solar index to go with longer period waves.

6.3. *Mode interaction*

Let us take a moment to try to understand this phenomenon of mode segments corresponding to portions of larger curves. Tolstoy (1956) has discussed the technique of separating a complex layered waveguide into two partial waveguides along a nodal surface. Then free boundary conditions are applied along this surface, the two guides are solved separately, and then overlaid. For values of ω having the same k's as solutions, this ω, k is applicable to the complete wave guide. If the mode number of the lower guide is l, the upper u, and of the complete guide m, then

$$l + u = m \qquad (1)$$

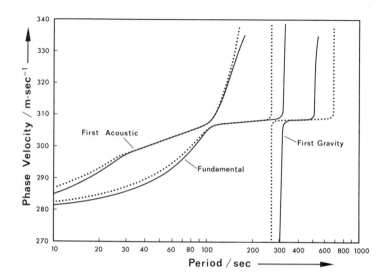

Fig. 24a.

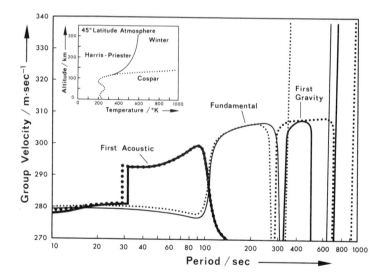

Fig. 24a,b. Dispersion curves for model atmospheres consisting of the temperature structure at 45ºN in winter up to 90 km merged with a nighttime atmosphere for a period of minimum solar activity due to Harris and Priester (solid curve) and with the mean COSPAR atmosphere (dotted curves). a) phase velocity versus period. b) group velocity versus period. The atmospheres are shown in the inset. (After Pfeffer and Zarichny, 1963.)

Considering a temperature structure like that in fig. 16, let us imagine a boundary surface through the stratopause region at 52 km. Now considering separately the ω, k solutions of the upper and lower guides, we find that the vertical curves corrspond to sections of acoustic modes of the upper channel, while as noted, the horizontal portions are similar to the fundamental and first acoustic of the lower channel. We can transform the PZ results into the ω-k plane as indicated in fig. 25.

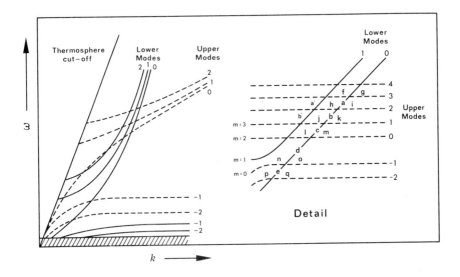

Fig. 25. Schematic diagram of mode interaction in an atmosphere with two sound channels. Lower and upper modes are for the portion of a COSPAR atmosphere below and above a fictitious free surface at about 52 km.

Letters have been put in, corresponding to the appropriate portion of the PZ II curves. The curves have also been labeled with mode numbers u and l for the two half-wave guides. Where intersections occur, solutions for the whole wave guide are possible, with m given by (1).

In common with Tolstoy's (1955, 1956) findings about elastic wave propagation, the modes of the complete wave guide follow a path made up approximately of segments of upper modes alternating with segments of lower guide modes. Consider, for example, the path beginning on $u = 2$. This is a solution to the whole wave guide, with $m = 2$, with both nodes (and we expect, the energy) in the upper channel. At the intersection (2,0) with the lower fundamental, the complete mode switches to follow the lower mode line. We anticipate energy in the lower channel now, in common with an atmosphere with no upper channel. The upper guide, with little energy concentration, is altering its solution. At the next intersection, (1,0), the complete mode again switches to the upper mode - energy is in the upper channel, and the lower channel solution is in transition to one with one mode - the lower first acoustic.

As implied above, when the complete guide mode is following an upper mode line, its characteristics are those of the upper guide, and it is strongly coupled to the upper modes; similarly, on the lower mode segments it looks like a lower mode.

This is completely corroborated by the energy density curve of PZ II (fig. 26). Looking first at the horizontal portions of the velocity-period curves, we note the close correspondence between the energy density of the modes (written in the form $m(u, l)$), 3(3,0), 2(2,0), 1(1,0) and the $l = 0$ mode of the lower channel alone. Also 4(3,1) and 3(2,1) follow the $l = 1$ line. Similarly, looking at the vertical portions, we see g, f and r are 3(3,0), 4(3,1) 5(3,2) all have $u = 3$, and i, h, s are 2(2,0), 3(2,1) 4(2,2) have $u = 2$. Note also that $l = 1$ corresponds to one energy minimum in the lower channel, and $u = 2$ or 3 correspond to 2 or 3 energy minima in the upper channel. In the vertical branches, there is so little energy in the lower channel that the number of nodes cannot be seen on this scale.

Another interesting sequence is to follow the course of $m = 3$ and $m = 2$.

$m = 3$				$m = 2$			
Curve section	u	l	P	Curve section	u	l	P
g	3		14 sec	i	2		34 sec
a		0	27 sec	b		0	36 sec
h	2		39 sec	j		1	46 sec
b'		1	56 sec				

A further corroboration of the nature of the vertical portions of the curves in seen in fig. 27, which is for an atmosphere with a rigid top and isothermal half-space at the surface. Since the fundamental depends upon the lower boundary for its existence, it should disappear. On the other hand, since all but the longest period waves are located below 300 km, the presence of the lid should have little effect. This is seen to be the case. The gravity modes are identified by their approach to a long period high velocity asymptote, while the acoustic modes approach infinite velocities or cut off at long periods.

One can ask for further physical insight into these points of sudden change. It appears from the formulation of Eckart (1960) that they are related to the relative positions of the points where $\omega = N(z)$ and $\omega/k = C(z)$. In his formulation of the problem, the relative positions of these points on a phase diagram determine the character of the solution. After a qualitative examination of the solutions for an atmosphere with one temperature minimum, and constant lapse rate thermosphere he remarks that when the vertical description of the solution '... contains two oscillatory segments separated by a non-oscillatory one, small changes in k and ω may produce large quantitative changes in the phase path'. These changes include switching the maximum amplitude between upper and lower channels.

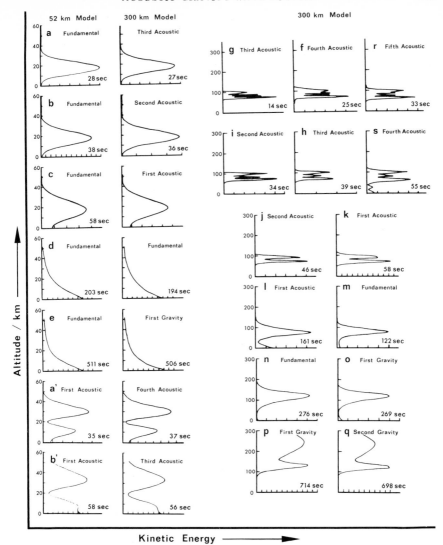

Fig. 26. Vertical profiles of the kinetic energy of the waves per unit volume. a) comparison between profiles for the 52 km and 300 km models at the points a, b, c, d, e, a', and b' of fig. 23; b) comparisons among the profiles at points g, f, and r; i, h and s; j and k; l and m; n and o; and p and q of fig. 23. Curves are normalized to have same maximum amplitude. (After Pfeffer and Zarichny, 1963.)

The phase diagrams also explain the appearance of extra nodes in the numerical calculations of a given mode, since it is possible to add any number of pairs of cancelling nodes without affecting the net mode number. The application of an Eckart-type analysis of the modes of an atmosphere

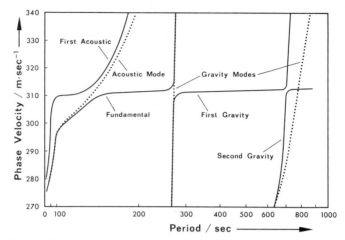

Fig. 27. Phase velocity versus period for the COSPAR atmosphere bounded by a rigid surface at the ground and a half space above 300 km (solid curves) and for the same atmosphere with the boundary conditions reversed (dotted curves). (After Pfeffer and Zarichny. 1963.)

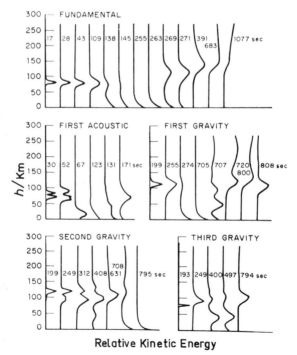

Relative Kinetic Energy

Fig. 28. Vertical profiles of relative kinetic energy in some of the lowest modes. (After Pfeffer. 1964.)

with two temperature minima should provide further understanding of the relevant mode interactions taking place.

6.4. *Energy density*

Energy density diagrams (figs. 26 and 28) provide quite useful information, since neither pressure oscillations nor wave motions can be observed where there is no energy.

The interesting case of surface pressure oscillations and simultaneous ionospheric disturbances is seen to be rare, but we quickly note possibilities at about 270 sec (F, 1G), 707 sec (1G, 2G) 400 to 497 sec (3G). These are also the periods we would expect to see excited by broad band sources in the lower atmosphere, like volcanic activity, earthquakes and atmospheric motions.

Similarly, the periods for which large amounts of energy are leaked into the ionosphere can be picked out - 1077 sec (F) and 720 to 800 sec (1G). These might be observable at great heights.

7. SOME DIABATIC EFFECTS

7.1. *Radiative damping of acoustic gravity waves*

Golitsyn (1965) calculates that in the troposhere, the damping of waves by radiative heat transfer will be 6 orders of magnitude greater than the viscous damping, although he finds at 100 km the radiation damping will be less than viscous damping, as the viscous damping increases while radiation damping decreases somewhat with height (Golitsyn, 1963).

This numerical result is based on a simple model of gray or frequency independent absorption. Unfortunately, this model may lead to qualitatively misleading results as well as numerical inaccuracy. The expression for radiative dissipation of a temperature disturbance in a gray has been transformed by Goody (1964) into a form applicable to a non-gray gas. The validity of this technique for the calculation of radiative stabilization of a fluid against cellular convection has been demonstrated by Gille and Goody (1964). Quantitative studies of radiative damping in the real atmosphere should be made. Laboratory testing may also be possible.

One particularly interesting possibility is that very low frequency waves may propagate with the isothermal sound velocity, $C_T = \sqrt{RT}$ rather than the adiabatic velocity $C_S = \sqrt{\gamma RT}$.

7.2. *Photochemical destabilization of gravity waves near the mesopause*

A number of recent studies, notably Leovy (1964) and Lindzen and Goody (1965), have developed linearized forms of the equations of motion in which photochemical and radiative heat sources are included. Naturally enough these involve a considerable number of drastic simplifications. Leovy (1966) has applied these ideas to gravity waves near the mesopause. If an amplification mechanism can be found, i.e., mechanism giving the waves in the mesosphere a positive growth rate, it would be nearly equivalent to putting a source in this region. A strongly attenuated wave coming up from below could have energy fed into it and amplify to observable size. If the amplification mechanism is frequency dependent, it has implications for the expected resulting spectrum.

We can see the physical basis for an amplification if we consider a column of the atmosphere displaced from its equilibrium position. If it is warmed by diabatic processes when displaced upward, it will be at a higher temperature when it comes down, and have less negative buoyancy than on the way up. Clearly, the restoring force has been reduced, and the wave amplitude will be attenuated. Here, we have a negative correlation between temperature and vertical velocity - a circumstance known in theoretical meteorology to be associated with the destruction of kinetic energy.

Conversely, if the column cools on upward displacement, its negative buoyancy is reduced, and it comes down with greater velocity through the equilibrium position than it possessed going up.

What diabatic processes might be involved? Leovy's (1966) treatment included the photochemistry of oxygen and ozone, and led to perturbation terms representing the following effects:

1) Absorption of solar radiation by fluctuating amounts of molecular oxygen;
2) Absorption of solar radiation by fluctuating amounts of ozone;
3) Chemical energy released by formation of molecular oxygen and ozone from atomic oxygen.
4) Infrared radiation.

I will merely state here the results he found, which apply to gravity waves with period 10^3 sec $< P < 10^6$ sec. First, since infrared radiation acts to destroy the temperature difference between the displaced column and its surroundings, destroying buoyancy, this always destroys wave energy. Second, the recombination heating and absorption of solar energy by ozone is a destabilizing effect, when the atomic mixing ratio increases with height. However, absorption by molecular oxygen is stabilizing under these circumstances.

In a numerical calculation, he finds an exponential growth rate (omitting infrared radiative effects) greater than 3×10^{-6} sec^{-1} near 90 km, for $\omega > 2.10^{-4}$ $(P \sim 1\frac{1}{2}$ hr). This indicates a doubling of amplitude in $2\frac{1}{2}$ days. The radiative damping is roughly calculated to be 10^{-6} sec, and eddy losses about the same for $\lambda \sim 30$ km. Damping thus will still remove all but the longest waves.

These results apply to mean conditions, and growth rates vary as the square of the atomic oxygen concentration. Since it appears that the upper winter mesosphere may be oxygen rich, this mechanism could be given a qualitative test by looking for seasonal variation of wave amplitudes and spectra in the upper mesosphere.

Certainly there are a number of very interesting ideas in this paper, and further work on these lines should be undertaken.

8. FUTURE PROBLEMS IN WAVE THEORY

As is certainly clear, at present only a beginning has been made in the study of acoustic-gravity wave propagation in the atmosphere. Some important problems remaining have been discussed elsewhere - notably the effects of winds, electromagnetic forces, and non-linear interactions. The diabatic effects of radiative heating and photochemistry have been mentioned above.

There are still important problems connected with the ducting effects of temperature structure. Eckart (1960) and Weston (1961, 1962) and Pitteway and Hines (1965) have deduced general results for continuous distributions of atmospheric parameters. A number of theoretical difficulties have been lucidly set forth by Hines (1965), and although some have been answered by Pierce (1966), it appears that more work will be necessary before the nature of ducting and mode formation is fully clarified.

The effect of horizontal variation also remains for future consideration. Although velocity period curves have been calculated for different latitudes by PZ II and PH, no one has considered propagation along a path in which there are horizontal variations of temperature, heights of thermal features, topography, or wind. This is relevant to the upper atmosphere observer as well as the constructor of synthetic barograms, since energy not confined in a duct may be available to excite disturbances at E region heights. (This problem has been suggested by Pfeffer.)

In all our discussion of wave propagation, we have said very little about sources of wave energy. Until we have a clear picture of the reflection and dissipation processes in an atmosphere with winds, it will be difficult to know whether the source of energy lies in the lower atmosphere or not. It is clear that nuclear explosions, volcanic eruptions and earthquakes do create wave trains at great heights. Under what conditional meteorological disturbances in the troposphere are able to propagate energy to these heights is not clear.

A final question might be whether, by observation at the surface or with ionospheric sounding, we can obtain an atmospheric seismogram, which could then be inverted to yield information about the atmosphere or the source. J. V. Dave of the U.S. National Center for Atmospheric Research has remarked that the Umkehr method of obtaining height distribution of ozone is like unscrambling an egg. If so, we have the omlet of source, wind, and temperature to unscramble and properly reconstitute. A real start on this would not appear possible until we have better solutions to the forward problem.

Looking back at these rather large holes in our knowledge, it seems fair to say that the development of theory enabling us to handle the complexity we see in nature, and the observational search for confirmation of these theories promise to keep us supplied with challenging problems for the foreseeable future.

ACKNOWLEDGEMENTS

The preparation of this paper was supported by NASA under grant NSG-173 and by the Florida State University. The previously unpublished diagrams of Pfeffer resulted from studies supported in part by the National Science Foundation grant NSF GP 2371 and in part by the Office of Naval Research under contract Nonr 266(70). I thank Professor Seymour Hess for his encouragement. It is a pleasure to acknowledge my debt to Professor Richard Pfeffer, who first interested me in this problem, allowed me to use unpublished material and gave me the benefit of may insights.

REFERENCES

Budden, K.G., 1961, The Wave Guide Mode Theory of Wave Propagation. Prentice Hall. Inc., Englewood Cliffs, N.J., 325.

Eckart, C., 1960, Hydrodynamics of Oceans and Atmospheres. Pergamon Press. New York, 290.

Gazaryan, Yu.L., 1961. Infrasonic normal modes in the atmosphere. Soviet Physics-Acoustics 7, 17.

Gille, J.C. and R.M.Goody. 1964. Convection in a radiating gas. J. Fluid Mech. 20, 47.

Golitsyn, G.S., 1963. The influence of radiative transfer on the propagation of sound in the atmosphere, Izv. Geophys. Ser., 589.

Golitsyn, G.S., 1965. Damping of small oscillations in the atmosphere due to viscosity and thermal conductivity. Izv. Atmospheric and Oceanic Physics Series 1, 82.

Goody, R.M., 1964, Atmospheric Radiation; I, Theoretical Basis, Oxford University Press. 436.

Hines, C.O., 1965, Atmospheric gravity waves: A new toy for the wave theorist. Radio Science 69D, 375.

Hunt, J.N., R.Palmer and W.Penney. 1960. Atmospheric waves caused by large explosions, Phil. Trans. Roy. Soc. A252, 275.

Lamb, H., 1945, Hydrodynamics. Dover Publications, New York, 738.

Leovy, C.B., 1964, Simple models of thermally driven mesospheric circulation. J. Atmos. Sci. 21, 327.

Leovy, C.B., 1966. Photochemical destabilization of gravity waves near the mesopause. J. Atmos. Sci. 23, 223.

Lindzen, R.S. and R.M.Goody. 1965. The radiative-photochemical processes in mesospheric dynamics. Part I. models for radiative and photochemical processes. J. Atmos. Sci. 22, 341.

Pekeris, C.L., 1948, The propagation of a pulse in the atmosphere. Part II. Phys. Rev. 73, 145.

Pfeffer, R.L., 1962. A multi-layer model for the study of acoustic-gravity wave propagation in the earth's atmosphere. J. Atmos. Sci. 19, 251.

Pfeffer, R.L., 1964, unpublished report.

Pfeffer, R.L. and J.Zarichny. 1962. Acoustic-gravity wave propagation from nuclear explosions in the earth's atmosphere, J. Atmos. Sci. 19, 256.

Pfeffer, R.L. and J.Zarichny, 1963. Acoustic-gravity wave propagation in an atmosphere with the two sound channels. Geofisica Pura e Applicata 55, 175.

Pitteway, M.L.V. and C.O.Hines. 1965. The reflection and ducting of atmospheric acoustic-gravity waves. Can. J. Phys. 43, 2222.

Pierce, A.D., 1966. Justification of the use of multiple isothermal layers as an approximation to the real atmosphere for acoustic-gravity wave propagation, Radio Science 1, 265.

Press, F. and D.Harkrider. 1962. Propagation of acoustic-gravity waves in the atmosphere, J. Geophys. Res. 67, 3889.

Scorer, R.S., 1950. The dispersion of a pressure pulse in the atmosphere. Proc. Roy. Soc. A201, 137.

Tolstoy. I.. 1955a, Note on the propagation of normal modes in inhomogeneous media. J. Acoust. Soc. Am. 27. 274.

Tolstoy. I.. 1955b. Dispersion and simple harmonic point sources in wave ducts, J. Acoust. Soc. Am. 27. 897.

Tolstoy. I.. 1956. Resonant frequencies and high modes in layered wave guides. J. Acoust. Soc. Am. 28. 1182.

Tolstoy. I.. 1963. The theory of waves in stratified fluids including the effects of gravity and rotation. Revs. Mod. Phys. 35. 207.

Weston. V. H.. 1961. The pressure pulse produced by a large explosion in the atmosphere. Can. J. Phys. 39. 993.

Weston. V. H., 1962. Gravity and acoustical waves. Can. J. Phys. 40. 446.

DISCUSSION

Hines:

Requirement for the calculations presented is an evanescent wave in the upper half-space. For example in fig. 22 the cut-off range has been indicated. In this region there is no full ducting, but eventually a leaky wave guide with partial reflection only at the upper limit of the duct. It is an open question of what importance partial ducting can be under these conditions (see J. P. Friedman, J. Geophys. Res., 1966).

Such partially ducted gravity waves must of course be described by a complex wave number in the duct; the range of horizontal propagation depends then on the attenuation coefficient.

If for gravity waves ducted in the mesospheric duct the leakage is rather small propagation could be obtained over large horizontal distances.

Houll:

The nonlinearity in the equations of motion occurs in the convective terms: u_i $(\partial u_i / \partial \kappa_i)$. For amplitude expansions to be valid, the first approximation to u_i must be given by a linearized theory, and these can only be a finite number of modes.

For fully nonlinear cases, one can resort to techniques which average over many periods. When properly carried out, one gets equations which describe the propagation of wave numbers and energy of the waves. Such methods do not work for dissipative problems (Witham, J. Fluid Mech., 1966).

I fail to see how the amplification of waves by a chemical mechanism can have any geophysical importance. The reaction rates in a realistic atmosphere are simply too slow to any appreciable chemical effect.

Gille:

Leovy remarks 'Evidently the destabilizing mechanisms discussed here are at best marginal for the atomic oxygen concentration used here'. However, he points out that small descending motions are sufficient to produce a three-fold increase of atomic oxygen and ten-fold increase in growth rate. I would think that a doubling of amplitude in 6 hr (or less than one wave cycle) would be geophysically important. In support of this, it should be noted that it has been independently suggested that there is a connection between the disturbed upper winter mesosphere and the large scale descending motions expected to be present.

GRAVITY WAVES IN THE PRESENCE OF WIND SHEARS AND DISSIPATIVE PROCESSES

C. O. HINES
University of Chicago, USA *

Abstract. The propagation of gravity waves through the mesosphere is seriously affected by anisotropic filtering due to the wind profile. A second filtering influence is imposed by dissipative processes.

Résumé. La propagation d'ondes de gravité à travers la mésosphère est sérieusement affectée par filtrage anisotrope dû au profile de vent. Une seconde influence de filtrage est imposée par des procès dissipatifs.

The propagation of gravity-wave energy in the real atmosphere is affected by the presence of wind shears. The effect can be thought of as a consequence of the Doppler-shifting of wave frequency that follows upon propagation to different levels in turn, the frequency being reckoned in a succession of coordinate systems each of which moves with the background wind at the level in question. The horizontal wave number remains constant from one level to another, but the vertical wave number alters in response to the alteration of frequency. A process which may be viewed as one of successive partial reflections occurs as a consequence.

Calculations for circumstances representative of the real atmosphere indicate that the transmission of gravity-wave energy is essentially unaffected if the horizontal speed of propagation is sufficiently large in comparison to the (horizontal) wind component in the direction of horizontal propagation. Transmission can be seriously suppressed, however, in two circumstances: 1) if the wind component is positive and equal to the horizontal phase speed at any height, thus Doppler-shifting the wave frequency to zero, or 2) if the wind component is negative and sufficiently large in magnitude to Doppler-shift the wave period down to values near the Brunt-Väisälä period (of 5-8 min, below the ionosphere).

For application to ionospheric studies, these considerations seem most important when coupled with the known winds of the mesosphere and lower thermosphere. The mesospheric wind system is primarily zonal, being directed toward the west in summer and toward the east in winter, and it contains wind speeds up to 100 m/sec. Waves traveling to the west in sum-

---

* Now: University of Toronto, Canada.

mer and to the east in winter, with any smaller horizontal phase speeds, will then be unable to penetrate efficiently from stratospheric to thermospheric heights, because of Doppler-shifting to zero frequency. Waves oppositely directed will achieve good penetration unless they propagate very slowly or have wave periods (as measured in a ground-based coordinate system) already fairly near to the Brunt-Väisälä period. Northward and southward propagating waves will be unaffected by the mesospheric winds - since the projected wind speed vanishes for them - although they can be partially reflected by the vertical variations of temperature they encounter.

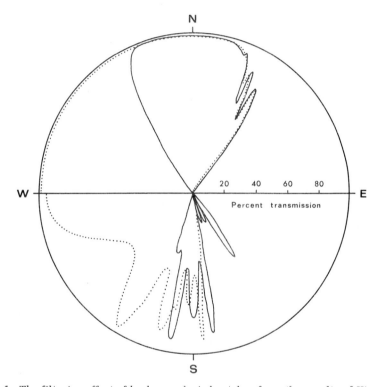

Fig. 1. The filtering effect of background winds, taken from the results of Hines and Reddy (1967). The curves show percentage energy transmission, measured radially from the center of the circle, as a function of azimuth of wave propagation. They illustrate the behavior for a wave period of 10 min (continuous curve) and of 60 min (dotted curve), in both cases for a horizontal phase speed of 50 m/sec. The wind profile in this case is one representative of the middle atmosphere in winter, rising from small values at 25 km height to a maximum speed of 80 m/sec, directed toward the east, near 65 km height, and decreasing to small values once again at 85 km. The upper half of the circle represents the effects of winds alone, and the bottom half the effects of winds combined with the temperature profile of the standard atmosphere. (The curves for these cases are in fact symmetrical about the east-west axis, since the background wind lies in the east-west plane, and so only half of the diagram is given for each.)

The background winds of the lower thermosphere contain strong tidal components, and may be directed toward any azimuth; they can then inhibit the
vertical transmission of gravity waves traveling in any direction, provided
only that the phase speed of the waves is not much greater than the wind
speeds (which are again of the order 100 m/sec).

If a spectrum of waves is incident on the mesosphere from below, with
intensities distributed uniformly in azimuth, then the spectrum that passes
through and ultimately reaches ionospheric heights should have intensities
distributed nonuniformly, as a consequence of the filtering action just out-
lined. The spectrum available in the ionosphere should, moreover, reveal
seasonal and diurnal changes, as the winds of the mesosphere and lower
thermosphere undergo their seasonal and diurnal changes. Further changes
may of course be anticipated as a consequence of changes in the generating
processes, but they lie beyond the scope of the present comments.

The foregoing discussion is derived primarily from the analysis of
Hines and Reddy (1967), which may be consulted for additional details and
references. Fig. 1 is taken from this reference.

A spectrum of gravity waves, propagating upward, undergoes a further
filtering imposed by dissipative processes, see fig. 2. The effects of molecular viscosity and thermal conduction are particularly important in this connection, as they necessarily increase with height. Ohmic losses can be important within the ionosphere, for waves of sufficiently long period.

The effect of viscosity and thermal conduction can be indicated in part
by establishing the height at which, for a given wave period and wave num-

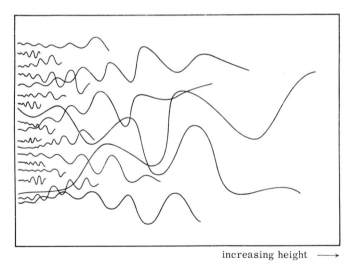

increasing height ⟶

Fig. 2. The viscous filtering of the gravity-wave spectrum. A broad spectrum, com-
prising waves of a number of different wavelengths, is incident from below. Viscosity
and thermal conduction act to remove those of shorter wavelength at lower levels,
leaving only those of longer wavelength at higher levels. The amplitude of each wave
increases with height, until dissipation becomes severe and the oscillation is quenched.

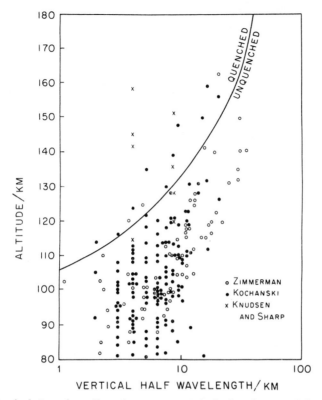

Fig. 3. The depletion of small-scale structure at high altitudes. Wind data of Zimmerman (1964) and Kochanski (1964) reveal that the smallest vertical scale sizes, plotted here against the height at which they were found, increase in scale with increasing height. The very smallest scales closely match the quenching cut-off for internal gravity waves (Hines, 1964), shown here by the continuous curve. Vertical scale sizes in temperature structure reported for one ocassion by Knudsen and Sharp (1965) are somewhat smaller than anticipated theoretically at the higher levels, but not by an inexplicable margin (because of interference and possible non-linear effects).

ber, viscous effects become important. A simple criterion of this sort, introduced by Hines (1960), has been employed (Hines, 1964) to evaluate as a function of height the smallest vertical wave length which can escape severe viscous effects, see fig. 3. A more detailed examination by Pitteway and Hines (1963) yields formulae from which vertical variations of vertical wave number may be evaluated, as a consequence of viscosity and thermal conduction. Examination of these formulae reveals that the real part of the vertical wave number tends to decrease with increasing altitude - the vertical wavelength tends to increase (in such a fashion as to nearly escape the 'serious' effects contemplated in the simpler criterion) - while the imaginary part is such as to impose an energy fall-off in the direction of energy progression as one

would expect on physical grounds. Despite the upward decrease of energy
(for wave energy progression upward), the amplitude may continue to increase with height over very great ranges of height as a consequence of the
decrease of gas density, before finally succumbing to the overwhelming
effect of energy loss. Detailed waveforms in which these qualitative behav-
iors may be identified have been presented by Midgley and Liemohn (1966).

REFERENCES

Hines, C.O., 1960, Can. J. Phys. 38, 1441.
Hines, C.O., 1964, J. Geophys. Res. 69, 2847.
Hines, C.O. and C.A. Reddy, 1967, J. Geophys. Res. 72, 1015.
Knudsen, W.C. and G.W. Sharp, 1965, J. Geophys. Res. 70, 143.
Kochanski, A., 1964, J. Geophys. Res. 69, 3651.
Midgley, J.E. and H.B. Liemohn, 1966, J. Geophys. Res. 71, 3729.
Pitteway, M.L.V. and C.O. Hines, 1963.
Rawer, K., 1939. Ann. Physik 35, 385.
Zimmerman, S.P., 1964, J. Geophys. Res. 69, 784.

COMMENT

Rawer:
    When discussing the range of validity of the multi-slice method it might
be interesting to know the results of a full wave method when applied to the
problem of radio wave propagation through a medium with continuously
variable refraction index. I did this (Rawer, 1939) in order to study
the occurrence of partial reflection. The result was that (in the absence of
absorption) partial transmission and reflection occur under two conditions:
1) for thin layers (thinner than one vacuum-wavelength) over the whole frequency range;
2) for thick layers in a small frequency range around the critical case
where the refraction index just gets to zero at the peak of the layer.
    In all other cases thick layers give either almost perfect reflection (on
freqencies below the critical case), or almost perfect transmission (on frequencies above), even if, in principle, wave solutions always admit a reflected and a transmitted wave.

DISCUSSION

Spizzichino:
    Pour étudier l'influence d'un vent sur une onde de gravité vous rempla-
cez un profil de vent sans discontinuité par un 'modèle' simplifié de profil
discontinu (fig. 4).
    A-t-on le droit d'introduire ces discontinuités? Ne crée-t-on pas ainsi

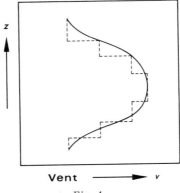

Fig. 4.

artificiellement de réflexions partielles qui n'existeraient pas si le profil était continu?

Hines:

A continuously varying medium will lead to partial reflection, just as a discontinuously varying one will. In the limit of small steps with small discontinuities, it can be shown that the two calculations of reflection are equivalent (with an exception in the case of Doppler-shifted frequency vanishing at some level, which requires special consideration). We have as yet no criteria for the smallness of the steps required for equivalence, and it is for this reason that I hesitate to ascribe any significance to the fine structure in the transmission coefficient that the computations reveal. I have no doubts about the over-all form and level of the computed coefficients, however.

Spizzichino:

Si j'ai bien compris, votre méthode de traitement consiste à remplacer les variables p, ρ, V par les développements

$$p = p_0 + p_1 + \dots$$

$$\rho = \rho_0 + \rho_1 + \dots$$

$$V = v_0 + v_1 + \dots .$$

La différence avec la théorie classique des ondes de gravité exposée ce matin par M. Gille réside donc dans l'introduction du terme V_0. Une conséquence de l'introduction de ce terme est que vous devez remplacer le symbole $\partial/\partial t$ de la théorie classique par:

$$\frac{\partial}{\partial t} + v_0 \cdot \nabla .$$

Ce qui explique que vous devez remplacer ω par

$$\omega - v_0 \cdot k .$$

Mais l'introduction du terme v_0 peut avoir d'autres conséquences. En particulier, il s'introduit dans l'équation du moment un terme

$$2\rho_1 \, \omega_0 \times v_0 \, ,$$

qui représente une modulation de la force de Coriolis par les fluctuations de densité du milieu causées par l'onde de gravité. Ce terme est-il réellement négligeable, ou l'avez vous seulement négligé dans un but de simplicité?

Hines:

The earth's rotation has been ignored throughout, although of course it is relevant in principle and should be included for long-period oscillations. In most waves of interest, the term to which you direct attention would be smaller than the Coriolis force that arises from $\omega_0 \times v_1$, by a factor of the order v_0/c where c is the speed of sound. Any full analysis of the effects of the earth's rotation should include this additional term, but with typical values of v_0 it is not likely to alter the results in any severe fashion.

Spizzichino:

A-t-on déjà étudié l'attenuation d'une onde de gravité traversant un milieu turbulent?

Hines:

No, except to the extent that the effect of turbulence can be treated formally by the same equations as those that include viscous and thermal conductivity effects.

Revah:

Peut-on déduire la gamme des vitesses de phase verticales que l'on devrait observer dans la basse ionosphère, du modèle de 'filtrage' des vitesses de phase horizontales au niveau de la mésosphère?

Hines:

It would certainly be possible to convert from period and horizontal phase speed, which are the independent parameters selected for the Hines-Reddy analysis, to period and vertical phase speed, and so deduce the transmission coefficients as a function of vertical phase speed at a given period (and azimuth of propagation). This is not quite what you ask for, however, since it will only yield preferred vertical phase speeds. The actual range of vertical phase speeds would depend on additional factors such as generation and dissipation.

Hoult:

The Tollmein-Schlichting singularity in hydrodynamic stability theory is logarithmic near the critical layer. Do you think that turbulence may occur here because of the algebraic nature of the singularity?

Hines:
I have not gone into the nature of the singularity, nor of the instability that would be produced. I call attention to the critical layers as a source of turbulence only because some source is required, they appear to be possible candidates, and a number of observed features would fall into place if they are the source.

Stilke:
I would like to ask, by what means it has been shown that the preponderance of the 12-h period of solar tide (wind measurements in about 80 km height) in comparison with the 24-h period might be explained (reflection of tidal waves, giving rise to standing waves). This explanation I think was given in the lecture of Spizzichino.

Hines:
I am sorry, but I missed Dr. Spizzichino's discussion. I can only say that there are mechanisms which could strongly reflect the tidal waves in the E-region, and could give rise to a standing wave. These mechanisms include not only the effect of wind shears and temperature structure, but also that of Hall current systems.

Question:
Under what conditions is it necessary to include the Coriolis force?

Hines:
The answer to this depends on the errors you are willing to tolerate. At a period τ, measured in hours, errors due to the neglect of the Coriolis force can be as large as $\tau/12$ in order of magnitude, though some of the errors are only of order $(\tau/12)^2$. These errors are likely to become significant, then, at periods in the range 2-4 h, say, and cannot be ignored at longer periods. In applying these comments, τ is to be taken as the period measured in a coordinate system which moves with the background wind (if any), and so Coriolis effects become important for all waves near 'critical levels' where the Doppler-shifted wave frequency vanishes. I might add that, in the daytime F-region, hydromagnetic effects tend to be of order 2τ, and so are more important than the Coriolis effect.

Question:
Are tidal waves to be considered as gravity waves too?

Hines:
The tidal oscillations that have been considered in greatest detail are indeed of the same general family as the gravity waves I have been discussing, the only differences being in the approximations that are made for convenience. A second type of tidal oscillation, inherently evanescent in the vertical direction, has recently come into prominence; it is usually thought of as a different class of wave, though the nomenclature is to some extent arbitrary.

APPLICATIONS OF GRAVITY-WAVE THEORY TO UPPER ATMOSPHERIC STUDIES

C. O. HINES
University of Chicago, USA *

Abstract. Arguments are given that filtered gravity waves may explain the wind structure near the base of the thermosphere, ionospheric drifts and travelling ionospheric disturbances.

Résumé. Des ondes de gravité filtrées expliqueraient la structure du vent près de la base de la thermosphère, les 'drifts' ionosphériques et les perturbations itinérantes dans l'ionosphère.

It would seem to be fruitful to examine the application of gravity-wave concepts to a wide variety of upper atmospheric studies, including: wave forms in noctilucent clouds; irregular structure in wind systems near the base of the thermosphere; similar structure in vertical temperature profiles; the creation of turbulence and the termination of turbulence at the turbopause; moving cells of enhanced airglow emission; ionospheric 'drifts'; traveling ionospheric disturbances; cellular structure in the distribution of ionization in the mesosphere. In same cases, inclusion in this list is quite speculative. In three cases, however, fairly strong arguments exist for a gravity-wave interpretation of the observations: the wind structure near the base of the thermosphere, traveling ionospheric disturbances, and ionospheric drifts. These cases will be discussed in turn.

The primary arguments concerned with the wind structure have been presented by Hines (1960). He notes that the observed time scales for the irregular wind structure ($\sim$ 2 h) lie in the gravity-wave range; that the nearly horizontal layering of the structure is theoretically consistent with such time scales, as is the nearly horizontal orientation of the winds themselves; and that theory would predict the upward increase of amplitude in the larger-scale components and the upward decrease of amplitude in the smaller-scale structures that is observed, the one being a consequence of the upward decrease of the gas density that supports the energy propaga-

* Now: University of Toronto. Canada.

tion, and the other being the consequence of an overriding dissipation of energy through viscous losses. The viscous cut-off of the smaller-scale structures has subsequently been confirmed for higher elevations (Hines, 1964a) with the aid of data derived from rocket-released vapor trails.

Traveling ionospheric disturbances (TID's) likewise have characteristics which closely match those of gravity waves (Hines, 1960, 1964b). Their periods, typically 10 min -3 h, are of course in the gravity-wave range. The fact that they frequently do not extend upward in height to the F_2-layer (Heisler, 1958) indicates that their energy does not come from above, despite the observed characteristically downward progression of their structure, while both of these observational aspects can be accounted for by the gravity-wave interpretation: the energy rises from lower levels, and may de dissipated by viscosity and thermal conduction before reaching the F_2-layer, while the phase structure internal to a wave group necessarily moves downward. An observed propagation over great distances on occasion, without appreciable loss of amplitude, may be explained as a consequence of a strong ducting of wave energy lower in the atmosphere, which results from an effect of vertical temperature variations (Friedman, 1966). A vertical up-turning of the frontal surface in TID's which penetrate to great heights (Thome, 1964) can be explained qualitatively and semi-quantitatively as a consequence of dissipative processes.

The case in favor of a gravity-wave interpretation of ionospheric drifts is only indirect, and carries weight only above the turbopause. Below that level, turbulence may give rise to the ionization structure that produces the observed diffraction patterns. But above, turbulence is absent and another mechanism must be found. If the case for a gravity-wave interpretation for TID's is accepted, then it is natural to extrapolate the interpretation downward: the waves are believed to be propagating to the F-region TID's from below, and so must be passing through the region of drift observations, and indeed the wave spectrum must be broader at the lower levels since dissipation is less severe there. Moreover, there is observed to be a close connection on occasion between the passage of TID's and the occurrence of sporadic-E sheets, with the latter often descending from the F-layer as a downward continuation of the motion of structure within the TID. If the gravity waves that produce TID's are on occasion intense enough to produce sporadic-E, then surely they are on more frequent occasions - perhaps invariably - intense enough to produce the irregularities that are detected in drift observations. The filtering action of dissipative processes (Hines, 1960) and of wind shears (Hines and Reddy, 1967) can then account for the upward increase of horizontal speed that is observed (e.g. Heisler, 1963). The directional filtering imposed by winds can also be operative in producing seasonal and diurnal variations of mean drift direction; for example, the winds of the mesosphere preferentially transmit waves moving to the west in winter and to the east in summer, in agreement with observed seasonal changes in the drift velocities (e.g. Rao and Rao, 1963). The singular levels that can occur in the presence of background wind shears can give an observational enhancement, at any given level, to the waves that are singular at that level, and the diffraction pattern caused by these waves would move with the wind velocity; this behavior can account for the observation (Wright and Fedor, 1966) that, on about half the occasions considered, there was a close correlation between the drift velocity and the true wind velocity at a level of observation believed to be above the turbopause.

REFERENCES

Faynot. J. M.. 1964. C. R. Acad. Sci. Paris 258. 5692: 1965. Space Research V. 229.
Friedman. J. P.. 1966. J. Geophys. Res. 71. 1033.
Heisler. J. H.. 1958. Australian J. Phys. 11. 79.
Heisler. L. H.. 1963. J. Atmosph. Terr. Phys. 25. 71.
Hines. C. O.. 1960. Can. J. Phys. 38. 1441.
Hines. C. O.. 1964a. J. Geophys. Res. 69. 2847.
Hines. C. O.. 1964b. in: Research in Geophysics: 1. Sun. Upper Atmosphere and Space. Hugh Odishaw ed.. M. I. T. Press. ch. 12.
Hines. C. O. and C. A. Reddy. 1967. J. Geophys. Res. 72. 1015 ·
Kotadia. K. M.. 1967. Ann. Géophys. 23. 1.
Rao, P. B. and B. R. Rao. 1963. Proc. Internat. Conf. Ionosphere. A. C. Stickland ed.. Institute of Physics and Physical Soc. (London) 363.
Thome. G. D.. 1964. J. Geophys. Res. 69. 4047.
Wright, J. W. and L. S. Fedor. 1967. in: Space Research VII. R. L. Smith-Rose. ed. (North-Holland. Amsterdam) p. 67.

COMMENTS

Rawer:

A lot of experimental evidence has been obtained with the technique of direct recording of ionospheric characteristics, mainly h' and MUF. In Europe there is now existing a network of five stations which apply this technique regularly (Athens, Darmstadt, Dourbes, Freiburg and Istanbul) and since a short time there is one tropical station (Dapango in Togo). Freiburg has the longest series of continuous recordings, by now 10 years. The disturbances are clearly seen on these records mostly as descending traces in the h'/t diagram as well as in the MUF$/t$ diagram. The inclination of these traces corresponds to the apparent speed. However, when reducing to real heights, an apparent vertical velocity of 115 m/s has been found in the average, with rather large dispersion. Thus the subsequent traces are not really parallel, even ascending traces or pieces of such appear occasionally. (In movie projection of 30 sec ionograms one normally sees the appearance of the deformation first at the high frequency end of the trace from where it descends along the trace disappearing normally at the transition from F- to E-region traces. However, sometimes an E_s of 'sequential type', i.e. developping from an E_2 or high E_s, appears several minutes after a strong transitorial perturbation in F.)

The main results can be summarized as follows: Transitoria are a daytime phenomenon, appearing each day shortly after sunrise and disappearing after sunset. In the night only very few cases have been observed. (There are smooth, long period (1 h or more) height variations but which have not at all the shape of the transitoria.) The number of occurrences at the peak of F_2 is of the order of 5-10 per h. The lowest altitude where they can be seen regularly is the bottom of the F-region (near 160 km in day, 200 km and more during night). In the $h'(t)$ record, for every day, the lower border of the F-trace is seriously deformed by the transitoria, but not at night. The seasonal statistics at Freiburg show a small difference of the occurrence in summer and winter time (but in summer rather often the lower border of the F-region is invisible because of blanketing by E_s).

As to the height range it extends certainly to the F_2 peak. But there are French observations (Faynot, 1964, 1965) with the Alouette satellite from which it appears that many of the disturbances observed at Garchy when Alouette was passing above, were first observed on the satellite (thus at 1000 km), then went down the topside trace and then only disappeared on the bottom-side ionogram.

To my feeling a comparison of nuclear explosion phenomena on these records with transitoria showed that the first give rather similar but stronger effects (Kotadia, 1967). This observation is in favour of an explanation by gravity waves, because the explosion waves are certainly of this type. However, theoreticians should reconsider the attenuation estimations because quite large heights are observed. Also the very clear statistics of diurnal appearance has to be explained eventually by a consideration of the excitation mechanism.

Lalonde:

I would like to comment on Prof. Rawer's data showing large scale traveling disturbances at large heights during the night and smaller scale disturbances descending from the F-region in the E-region during the day.

In Puerto Rico we observe typical night time profiles to show an E-region peak of a few thousand electrons per cm^3 centered at about 110 km, and perhaps 20 km thick. Above this is a valley which is about an order of magnitude lower in electron density, and which extends to heights as high as 250 km, where the underside of the F-layer appears. This may mean, at least for some of your observing stations, that there is not sufficient density at the lower heights at night for you to detect these traveling disturbances, whereas there is sufficient density during the day to enable detection from F- way down to E-region heights. Moreover, if the smaller scale disturbances were typical of only lower heights, that is E-region heights, this may explain why sounder techniques do not detect these at night - since the mechanism required for detection has disappeared.

Hines: (Reply to Prof. Rawer)

The first place I would look for an explanation of the daytime maximum of occurrence of TID-like ripples on ionograms would be in an observational selection. This could result, for example, from the reflection characteristics of the daytime layer in which the electron density changes only slowly with height, and in which minor perturbations of the profile can give rise to substantial changes of apparent height (as in the formation of an F_1 trace on ionograms, even when no true F_1-peak exists).

Failing a solution to the problem there, I would look for a day-night change in the response of the ionization to the perturbing neutral-gas gravity wave. Such a change might be brought about by the change in the role of the ionization profile, or of the ion production rate (acting on the perturbations of neutral gas density), in producing measurable ionization perturba-tions. Next I would look to consequences of the filtering action that can be imposed by tides lower down, as discussed in my first lecture, and finally to day-night variations in the generation process.

Rawer: (gives some evidence about results of ionospheric drift observa-tions, see contribution Harnischmacher-Rawer)
It is felt that the total amount of information is by far greater than that used by theorists for comparing with their ideas and computations. Theo-rists are invited to look more closely into experimental data, in particular Vol. XXXIII of Annals of the IGY, where many data are assembled.

DISCUSSION

Misme:
Est-il possible d'évaluer le plus fort pourcentage de transport d'énergie dans le sens de bas (près du sol) en haut jusque vers 50 km ?

Hines:
In the paper by Dr. Reddy and me, more than 90% energy transmission was found in some circumstances.

Ilias:
I would ask Prof. Hines if some ionospheric results concerning the virtual height variation of the F-layer and observed by the continuous recording technique, can be interpreted as gravity-wave influences on the upper at-mosphere. I would like to state that from 1-year statistic of the Athens station data came out that a) the period of such h' disturbances is of the or-der of 1 h during winter, but it becomes much shorter in summer (5 to 10 min); b) the occurrence distribution of 500 cases during 1964-1965 indi-cates that the above virtual height variation is a day time phenomenon with a mean maximum occurring at approximately 10 to 11 L.T.

Hines:
I see no reason why these variations could not be caused by gravity waves, though I have no immediate suggestions to make as to the source of changes in the spectrum; too many possible causes can be introduced, to make a choice.

Spizzichino:
Peut-on expliquer par des effets non-linéaires les forts cisaillements de vents qui apparaissent lors de la propagation d'une onde de gravité ? (phé-nomène bien connu des expérimentalistes). (fig. 1.)

Hines:
A nonlinear effect might operate to steepen wave fronts, and might then act to produce the strong shears you discuss, but the problem has not yet

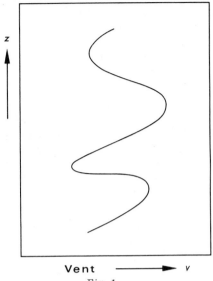

Vent ———▶ *v*

Fig. 1.

been analyzed adequately to know. Alternatively, interference between two or more waves of considerably greater scale can give the appearance of small-scale structure, and hence strong shears. This would occur even as a linear process, but it could give rise to nonlinear effects.

Eisemann:

If the small scale irregularities above the E-region may be explained by internal gravity waves, then at least a part of the observed E-region irregularities must also be produced by these waves.

But then it seems doubtful to me to derive the neutral wind in the E-region from the motion of these irregularities.

Hines:

I agree entirely, and have in fact been advocating extreme caution on this point for many years. There is some hope, however, that even the waves will tend to pick out the wind as a result of a selective enhancement of waves which are stationary in a wind-borne coordinate system, or as a result of other processes in a statistical compilation. Again, below the turbopause, there is the distinct possibility that turbulence is the main source of drift irregularities, and hence that the irregularities will be borne by the wind at those levels. The statistical properties of the inferred drifts at the lower levels exhibit good agreement with winds detected by meteor trails, I understand.

Ranzi:

The F_2-perturbation discussed by Prof. Rawer have a period of 10 min; is it not too low (according to the gravity wave theory) to be found in the high ionosphere?

Hines:

The filter action in the lower duct is not well known and it is now impossible to establish the cut-off frequency. The period you mention is about at the lower limit of periods for *internal* gravity waves locally, but not for *evanescent* gravity waves.

Ranzi:

From a comparison I have performed some years ago, between the backscatter sounding data of Roma and the vertical sounding data of Breisach, it was shown that days of more important irregularities revealed by the two methods were coincident. No direct correlation was found in the details, that is between the passage of a large scale moving irregularity over Breisach (as revealed by backscatter sounding) and the perturbations appearing in the Breisach vertical sounding.

I would like to point out that backscatter sounding shows that the period of the large scale moving F_2 irregularities gradually increases after sunrise until noon.

Hines: (Final remarks)

There undoubtedly remain many observational aspects of TID's, drifts and irregular winds which have not yet been explained by the gravity-wave thesis. But surely it is too soon to expect such explanations, particularly when it is recognized that many of the answers are likely to depend on processes and parameters not under observation. I would claim that the gravity-wave theory provides the only available defensible theory for TID's, and that it is pre-eminent for drifts above the turbopause and for irregular winds as well. I would also claim that the small number of theorists who are directing their attention to gravity waves cannot properly be charged with the task of explaining all the observations; they have theoretical problems enough, as it is. It would seem to me that the time has now come when observers, who wish detailed interpretations of their observations, ought to establish (through students, perhaps) programs of theoretical interpretation which will help to carry the burden.

THE GENERAL THEORY OF TURBULENCE *
TURBULENCE IN THE ATMOSPHERE

R. BOLGIANO Jr.
School of Electrical Engineering
and
Center for Radiophysics and Space Research,
Cornell University

Part I. THE GENERAL THEORY OF TURBULENCE

Abstract. These lectures develop the theory of turbulence, including spectral representation thereof, both in an incompressible fluid and in the stably stratified atmosphere. They consider particularly the roles of mean shear and of density (temperature) stratification in modifying structure, not only of the turbulence itself but also of inhomogeneities of the radio refractive index. It is concluded that the first order effect of shear is to produce a highly anisotropic spectrum in which the high wavenumber components are aligned closely with the direction of shear. It is further determined that, if a buoyancy subrange occurs, the refractivity spectrum within this subrange will most probably be inversely proportional to the first power of wave number magnitude.

Résumé. Ces conférences developpent la théorie de turbulence y compris la représentation spectrale de cette dernière, dans les deux cas d'un liquide incompressible et d'une atmosphère contenant des couches stables. Nous considérons particulièrement les rôles du cisaillement moyen et de stratifications de densité (ou de température); ces influences peuvent modifier non seulement la structure de la turbulence elle-même, mais aussi celle des inhomogénéités de l'indice de réfraction des ondes radioélectriques. Nous concluons que c'est l'effet de premier ordre du cisaillement de transformer considérablement le spectre qui devient ainsi très anisotrope. Dans le spectre déformé les componentes correspondant à des nombres d'ondes élevés dépendent étroitement de la direction du cisaillement. En outre au cas où une partie du spectre est influencée par une force ascensionelle nous trouvons dans cette sousgamme un spectre de réfraction qui est très probablement inversement proportionnel à la première puissance du nombre d'onde absolu.

1. INTRODUCTION

A study of movements and structure in the atmosphere, below 120 km, without any consideration of turbulence could, yield at best, only partial understanding of the problems of this region. The deformative and diffusive effects of turbulence play vital roles in the production of irregularities and in the establishment of the equilibrium (or lack thereof) of many of the pro-

* This work was supported in part by the Advanced Research Projects Agency under a research contract with the Air Force Office of Scientific Research.

cesses occurring at these levels. For example, the chemical reactions, the transport of heat, and the attachment of electrons to neutral particles are all influenced by turbulent diffusion. Similarly, the fine-scale structure that appears so often to be present is a direct consequence of the action of turbulence on larger inhomogeneities produced by linear motions or by other means.

To illuminate these roles and thus gain deeper insight into the problems at hand, it is necessary to have a detailed picture of the flow processes as they occur in the atmosphere. Consequently, it seems worthwhile, at this time, to examine the nature of atmospheric turbulence.

Because of the exceedingly large Reynolds Nos. that characterize the atmosphere, the flow is always potentially turbulent. In fact, evidence indicates that, below the turbopause (105-110 km), it is invariably turbulent, in greater or lesser degree. In spite of this uniformity of occurrence, atmospheric turbulence is more variable and, in many respects, more complicated than that with which the aerodynamicist must deal in his consideration of boundary layers, jets, and wakes.

The compressibility of the medium and the usually stable stratification associated therewith must be taken into account. The dynamic effects of gravity (buoyancy), of shear, and of non-coupled, larger-scale irregular motions must be recognized. Anisotropy is the rule, not the exception. Many fluctuating, non-uniform motions occur that do not meet all the requirements of laboratory turbulence but that nevertheless play important roles in the production and subsequent distortion of irregularities. All of these factors must be considered.

In order to approach this formidable task by relatively easy stages we shall first consider turbulence in an incompressible, homogeneous medium and attempt to grasp the processes of energy exchange and irregularity production in these relatively simple circumstances. We shall then show that in the atmosphere, under conditions pertinent to most instances as regards turbulence, the flow may be treated as incompressible if the analysis is carried out in terms of potential quantities (potential temperature and densities). The stratification implicit in the typically non-uniform profile of potential temperature is then the principal remaining characteristic the effects of which must be incorporated into out analysis. These aspects of the problem will be considered at length in the second lecture.

2. TURBULENCE IN AN INCOMPRESSIBLE HOMOGENEOUS MEDIUM

To commence our analysis we require the equations of motion in an incompressible, homogeneous medium. They reduce, in these circumstances, to the continuity equation *

$$\frac{\partial U_i}{\partial x_i} = 0 \tag{1}$$

---

* The summation rule is used throughout this paper. Thus read $\sum_i \frac{\partial U_i}{\partial x_i}$ for $\frac{\partial U_i}{\partial x_i}$, for example.

and the expression for the conservation of momentum

$$\rho\left[\frac{\partial U_i}{\partial t} + U_l\frac{\partial U_i}{\partial x_i}\right] = \frac{\partial}{\partial x_\gamma}\left[-P\,\delta_{i\gamma} + \mu\left(\frac{\partial U_i}{\partial x_\gamma} + \frac{\partial U_\gamma}{\partial x_i}\right)\right],\tag{2}$$

where U_i is the total velocity vector, ρ is the constant density of the medium, P is the total pressure, μ is the dynamic viscosity of the medium, δ_{ij} is the Kronecker delta ($= 1$, $i=j$; $= 0$, $i\neq j$), and cartesian tensor notation is employed in which a repeated index indicates summation over the three cartesian components.

Since we shall be interested primarily in (randomly) fluctuating terms, let us follow Reynolds in decomposing the motion into mean and fluctuating parts. Thus,

$$\begin{aligned}U_i &= \overline{U}_i + u_i \\ P &= \overline{P} + p,\end{aligned}\tag{3}$$

with $\overline{u}_i \equiv \overline{p} \equiv 0$. By this method it is possible to analyze separately the mean and 'turbulent' motions and to identify the mechanisms by which they are coupled together.

2.1. *The mean motion*

If we substitute (3) in (1) and (2) and average, we have for the statement of continuity

$$\frac{\partial\overline{U}_i}{\partial x_i} = 0.\tag{4}$$

The expression for the conservation of mean momentum may then be written, taking note of the fact that (2) and (4) imply a divergence-free fluctuating velocity field as well,

$$\frac{\partial\overline{U}_i}{\partial t} = -\overline{U}_l\frac{\partial\overline{U}_i}{\partial x_l} + \frac{1}{\rho}\frac{\partial}{\partial x_\gamma}\left[-\overline{P}\,\delta_{i\gamma} + \mu\left(\frac{\partial\overline{U}_i}{\partial x_\gamma} + \frac{\partial\overline{U}_\gamma}{\partial x_i}\right) - \rho\,\overline{u_i u_\gamma}\right].\tag{5}$$

Here $\rho\,\overline{u_i u_\gamma}$ is the Reynolds stress by which it is possible to describe the force that arises in the divergence of momentum flux, i.e., the average transport of turbulent momentum by the turbulence.

A whole field of study has grown up around the determination of the mean velocity distribution $\overline{U}_i$. This has often involved the assumption of a phenomenological relation between $\overline{u_i u_\gamma}$ and $\partial\overline{U}_i/\partial x_\gamma$, e.g., the introduction of austausch coefficients, eddy viscosity and diffusivity, the 'mixing-length theory', etc. Application of any such diffusion model presumes that the characteristic length scale l of the irregular motion is small compared to the length scale associated with the mean profile, $(\partial\overline{U}_i/\partial x_l)/(\partial^2\overline{U}_i/\partial x_\gamma\partial x_\gamma)$. In the atmosphere, and in boundary layer flow in general, this is not typically the case. Consequently, this type approach to the problem, while providing some insight, has failed to yield fully satisfactory results.

More recently, in connection with atmospheric application, Monin and Obouhov (1954) have proposed a similarity solution based on the observation that turbulent stress and heat flux are nearly independent of altitude near the surface (up to 50-100 m). These 'constants', together with the buoyancy parameter, $g/\overline{T}$, are used to defined scales of velocity, length, and temperature in terms of which the problem may be non-dimensionalized and universal solutions sought. Efforts along these lines by a number of workers have resulted in considerable success. For further details reference should be made to Chapter 3 of the recent book by Lumley and Panofsky (1964).

2.2. *The fluctuation quantities and their energy budget*

The equations governing the fluctuating parts of the dependent variables may be generated by subtracting (4) and (5) from (1) and (2), respectively. As noted above, u_i is divergence-free; i.e., $\partial u_i/\partial x_i = 0$. From consideration of momentum we have

$$\frac{\partial u_i}{\partial t} = -u_l \frac{\partial \overline{U}_i}{\partial x_l} - \overline{U}_l \frac{\partial u_i}{\partial x_l} - u_l \frac{\partial u_i}{\partial x_l} + \frac{\partial \overline{u_i u_l}}{\partial x_l} - \frac{1}{\rho}\frac{\partial p}{\partial x_i} + \nu \frac{\partial^2 u_i}{\partial x_r \partial x_r} \tag{6}$$

This expression indicates interaction between the mean and fluctuating motions through the first and second terms on the right-hand-side. The first term exhibits a force arising in the turbulent transport of meanflow momentum down the gradient of $\overline{U}_i$. The second term represents the advection of turbulent momentum by the mean flow. The third and fourth terms describe the turbulent transport of turbulent momentum while the fifth gives the force of turbulent pressure fluctuations; the last term, finally, accounts for the molecular transport of turbulent momentum. It is worthy of note that, if the turbulence itself is (locally) homogeneous, the fourth term makes (nearly) zero contribution and may usually be neglected in comparison with the other processes.

In order to study the budget of turbulent energy (i.e., the production, redistribution, and dissipation of turbulent k.e.) it is helpful to form an expression for the time-rate-of-change of the quantity $\overline{e}_\alpha \equiv \frac{1}{2}\overline{u_\alpha^2}$, which gives the average kinetic energy per unit mass associated with the α-direction. Such an equation may be derived by writing (6) in terms of u_α, multiplying by u_α, and averaging. This results in

$$\frac{\partial \overline{e}_\alpha}{\partial t} = \underbrace{-\overline{u_\alpha u_l}\frac{\partial \overline{U}_\alpha}{\partial x_l}}_{(i)} + \underbrace{\frac{\partial}{\partial x_l}\left[-\overline{e}_\alpha\,\overline{U}_l - \tfrac{1}{2}\overline{u_\alpha u_\alpha u_l} + \nu\frac{\partial \overline{e}_\alpha}{\partial x_l}\right.}_{(ii)}$$

$$\underbrace{\left.+\nu\frac{\partial \overline{u_\alpha u_l}}{\partial x_\alpha}\right]}_{} - \underbrace{\frac{1}{\rho}\frac{\partial \overline{u_\alpha p}}{\partial x_\alpha}}_{(iii)} \tag{7}$$

$$\underbrace{-\overline{\frac{\partial u_\alpha}{\partial x_l}\,\nu\left(\frac{\partial u_\alpha}{\partial x_l} + \frac{\partial u_l}{\partial x_\alpha}\right)}}_{(iv)}$$

Let us examine the terms on the right-hand-side of (7).

(i) is commonly referred to as the 'production' term in that it describes the mechanism by which mean-flow energy is converted into turbulent energy. However, the process is more correctly thought of as 'energy feeding' since it couples energy from $\overline{U}_\alpha$ to an already existant u_α. That this term

does describe the conversion of energy from the mean flow to the turbulence can be clearly understood if one also examines an expression for the
budget of mean-flow k.e., $\frac{1}{2}\overline{U}_\alpha^2$. In such an equation there appears a term
$-\overline{U}_\alpha\ \partial\overline{u_\alpha u_l}/\partial x_l$, which is identifiable as the rate of working of the mean
flow against the Reynolds stress. The sum of this term and (i) is just the
divergence of $\overline{u_\alpha u_l}\ \overline{U}_\alpha$ and therefore makes no contribution to the whole
flow field, provided the fluctuation velocities are confined to a finite region
in space. Hence, (i) is the negative of the rate at which kinetic energy is
abstracted from the mean flow as a consequence of the turbulence and is
the rate at which energy is fed to the turbulence.

Term (ii) is the divergence of flux of turbulent energy (by mean-flow and
turbulent advection and by molecular diffusion). As such it makes no contribution to the whole turbulence field, simply describing the transfer of
energy from one part of space to another, or from one eddy to another.

Term (iii) when summed over the three coordinate components (i.e.,
$\partial\overline{u_i p}/\rho\ \partial x_i$), is the divergence of the working of turbulent velocities against
turbulent pressure fluctuations. It also makes no contribution to the whole
turbulence field, although it may account for the exchange of turbulent energy among the various coordinate components.

Term (iv) describes the rate of working of the turbulent velocity field
against the viscous forces in the α-direction. It is always non-negative
when integrated over the turbulent region and also, at a point, when
summed over all coordinate components. Thus, in total it represents contributions to the viscous dissipation ϵ, although locally it may describe
transfer of energy.

2.3. *Spectral representation*

Since we are primarily interested in structure, it is often helpful to re-
solve the fluctuating quantities into sinusoidal components in space (at an
instant), i.e., to make a Fourier analysis of the flow field. Therefore, we
introduce the velocity and pressure spectra by

$$u_i(x,t) \equiv \int_{k\text{-space}} e^{i k \cdot x}\ Z_i(k,t)\mathrm{d}k$$

and   (8)

$$p(x,t) \equiv \int_{k\text{-space}} e^{i k \cdot x}\ W(k,t)\mathrm{d}k.$$

($\mathrm{d}k$ means the volume element in the 'wave-number space', briefly k-space.)
It is then possible to express (6), the statement of conservation of momentum, in spectral terms.

However, before proceeding it is helpful to note that, if $\overline{U}_i$ is not constant (there is mean shear), the structure of the fluctuations will be
strained and thus altered. This effect can be illuminated by expressing $\overline{U}_i$
in a Maclaurin series,

$$\overline{U}_i = \overline{U}_{i_0} + x_k\ \frac{\partial \overline{U}_i}{\partial x_k} + \dots ,$$

and performing the analysis in a coordinate system that moves with the reference velocity $\overline{U}_{i_0}$. Then, to a first approximation, the second term on the right-hand-side of (6) may be written

$$-\frac{\partial \overline{U}_l}{\partial x_k} x_k \frac{\partial u_i}{\partial x_l} \quad .$$

Note that in the Fourier analysis

$$x_k \frac{\partial u_i(x,t)}{\partial x_l} = \int\limits_{k\text{-space}} e^{i k \cdot x}\left[-\frac{\partial}{\partial k_k}\{k_l Z_i(k,t)\}\right]dk \quad . \tag{9}$$

Then, assuming local homogeneity and expressing pressure fluctuations in terms of velocity fluctuations and gradients, (6) becomes

$$\frac{\partial Z_i(k,t)}{\partial t} = -\frac{\partial \overline{U}_i}{\partial x_l} Z_l(k,t) + \frac{\partial \overline{U}_l}{\partial x_k}\left[\frac{\partial}{\partial k_k}\{k_l Z_i(k,t)\} - 2\frac{k_i k_l}{k^2} Z_k(k,t)\right]$$

$$-i \int\limits_{k\text{-space}} k_l Z_l(k-k',t)\left[Z_i(k',t) - \frac{k_i k_k}{k^2} Z_k(k',t)\right]dk' \tag{10}$$

$$-\nu k^2 Z_i(k,t) \quad .$$

Both linear and non-linear (integral) exchange mechanisms are depicted in this expression, as well as dissipation. It is apparent that the non-linear processes transfer momentum from one sinusoidal (wave number) component to another. It is not so clear that some of the linear processes do also.

To help visualize the manner in which contributions are made to the Reynolds stresses at the various scales we introduce the energy spectrum tensor $\Phi_{ij}(k)$ for locally homogeneous turbulence. This latter qualifying phrase is meant to imply independence of the functional form of statistical quantities on location, so that the velocity covariance (at an instant) may be expressed as a tensor

$$\overline{u_i(x,t)u_j(x+r,t)} \equiv R_{ij}(r)a(x) \qquad 0 \le a \le 1 \quad . \tag{11}$$

Under these circumstance we may write

$$\overline{Z_i^*(k+\sigma,t)Z_j(k,t)} \equiv \Phi_{ij}(k)v(\sigma) \quad , \tag{12}$$

where the * denotes the complex conjugate of the quantity and $v(\sigma)$ is a measure of the correlation in the velocity spectra as a function of wave number. (For strictly homogeneous turbulence v is the Dirac delta function, indicating no correlation except among velocity components of the same vector wave number.) We thus have

$$\overline{u_i(x,t)u_j(x+r,t)} = \int\limits_{k\text{-space}} \int\limits_{\sigma\text{-space}} e^{i(k \cdot r - \sigma \cdot x)}\Phi_{ij}(k)v(\sigma)d\sigma dk \tag{13}$$

and

$$\Phi_{ij}(k) = \frac{1}{8\pi^3} \int_{r\text{-space}} e^{-i\boldsymbol{k}\cdot\boldsymbol{r}} R_{ij}(\boldsymbol{r})\mathrm{d}\boldsymbol{r}$$

$$v(\sigma) = \frac{1}{8\pi^3} \int_{x\text{-space}} e^{i\boldsymbol{\sigma}\cdot\boldsymbol{x}} a(\boldsymbol{x})\mathrm{d}\boldsymbol{x} \tag{14}$$

From these relations we see that

$$v(0) = \frac{1}{8\pi^3} \int a(\boldsymbol{x})\mathrm{d}\boldsymbol{x} \equiv V_0$$

is a measure of the volume of turbulent fluid and that

$$\Phi_{ij}(k) = \frac{\overline{Z_i^*(k,t)Z_j(k,t)}}{V_0} . \tag{15}$$

It is now possible to calculate the time-rate-of-change of $\Phi_{ij}(k)$, starting from (10) and employing the above definitions. The result is

$$\frac{\partial \Phi_{ij}(k)}{\partial t} = -\left[\frac{\partial \overline{U_j}}{\partial x_l} \Phi_{il}(k) + \frac{\partial \overline{U_i}}{\partial x_l} \Phi_{lj}(k)\right]$$

$$+ \frac{\partial \overline{U_l}}{\partial x_m} \left[\Phi_{ij}(k)\delta_{ml} + \frac{\partial}{\partial k_m}\{k_l \Phi_{ij}(k)\} + 2\{\frac{k_j k_l}{k^2} \Phi_{im}(k) + \frac{k_i k_l}{k^2} \Phi_{mj}(k)\}\right]$$

$$+ \int_{k\text{-space}} Q_{ij}(k,k')\mathrm{d}k' + \int_{k\text{-space}} V_{ij}(k,k')\mathrm{d}k' - 2\nu k^2 \Phi_{ij}(k) . \tag{16}$$

In order to study the budget of energy in wave number space let us examine $\Phi_{\alpha\alpha}(k)$. This term represents the contributions to $\bar{e}_\alpha$ in the sense

$$\bar{e}_\alpha = \tfrac{1}{2}\overline{|u_\alpha(x,t)|^2} = \tfrac{1}{2}a(x) \int_{k\text{-space}} \Phi_{\alpha\alpha}(k)\mathrm{d}k . \tag{17}$$

Thus,

$$\frac{\partial \Phi_{\alpha\alpha}}{\partial t} = -2\underset{\text{(i)}}{\frac{\partial \overline{U_\alpha}}{\partial x_l} \mathcal{R}\{\Phi_{\alpha l}\}} + \frac{\partial \overline{U_l}}{\partial x_m}\left[\underset{\text{(ii)}}{\frac{\partial}{\partial k_m}(k_l \Phi_{\alpha\alpha})} + \underset{\text{(iii)}}{4\frac{k_\alpha k_l}{k^2} \mathcal{R}\{\Phi_{\alpha m}\}}\right]$$

$$+ \underset{\substack{k\text{-space}\\ \text{(iv)}}}{\int Q_{\alpha\alpha}(k,k')\mathrm{d}k'} + \underset{\substack{k\text{-space}\\ \text{(v)}}}{\int V_{\alpha\alpha}(k,k')\mathrm{d}k'} \underset{\text{(vi)}}{-2\nu k^2 \Phi_{\alpha\alpha}} , \tag{18}$$

where $\mathcal{R}\{\ \}$ stands for the real part of the enclosed expression.

2.4. *Interpretation of spectral transfer*

We now wish to consider the roles of the various terms in (18). First let us look at (i) and (vi) since these are straight forward.

The quantity in term (i) describes the feeding of the turbulence by the mean shear at wave number $\boldsymbol{k}$. While it may be positive for one direction of $\boldsymbol{k}$ and negative for another, its net contribution over all wave number components is invariably positive. This requires anisotropic structure over at least a part of wave number space; but, as we shall see, the shear insures this condition.

Term (vi) is always negative and thus represents the removal of energy by viscous effects. In fact,

$$2\nu \int_{\boldsymbol{k}\text{-space}} k^2 \Phi_{ii}(\boldsymbol{k}) \, d\boldsymbol{k} = \epsilon \; ,$$

the viscous dissipation rate.

Consider now terms (iii) and (v), which describe the energy exchange effected by the pressure fluctuations. For both of these the sum over all directional components is zero. That is,

$$V_{ii}(\boldsymbol{k}, \boldsymbol{k}') = \frac{k_i k_l}{k^2} \, \mathcal{R}\{\Phi_{im}\} = 0 \; ,$$

a consequence of the incompressibility of the medium. Hence, terms (iii) and (v) make no net contribution to $\Phi_{ii}(\boldsymbol{k})$, the total kinetic energy at wave number $\boldsymbol{k}$. They simply transfer energy associated with a given $\boldsymbol{k}$ from one directional component to another. Usually it is agreed that (v) serves to promote isotropy, tending to build up the weaker components at the expense of the stronger. Deissler (1961) has shown, however, that in intense shear (iii) may tend to produce anisotropy.

Finally let us look at terms (ii) and (iv). They represent inertial transfer that arises in the non-linear term in the Navier-Stokes equation. Note that $Q_{ij}(\boldsymbol{k}', \boldsymbol{k}) = -Q_{ij}(\boldsymbol{k}, \boldsymbol{k}')$. Hence, the integral of (iv) over all wave number space is identically zero. Similarly, the integral of (ii) over all wave number space is (see (9))

$$\lim_{\boldsymbol{r} \to 0} (-r_m) \frac{\partial R_{\alpha\alpha}(\boldsymbol{r})}{\partial r_l} \; ,$$

which is also identically zero. Hence, neither of these terms makes any net contribution to $\bar{e}_\alpha$. They simply transfer energy identified with a given direction from one vector wave number to another. This average flux of energy must be from smaller to larger wave numbers since the dissipation peaks at the high end of the spectrum.

In the absence of shear term (iv) represents the sole mechanism transferring energy through wave number space. It embodies the classical inertial transfer process that is at the heart of the universal equilibrium theory of turbulence. The manner in which term (ii) effects a transfer of energy across $\boldsymbol{k}$-space is less clear, though the fact that it does is well established.

To gain a better understanding of this process let us sum (18) over the three directional components so as to yield a similar relation pertaining to the total kinetic energy spectrum $\Phi_{ii}(\boldsymbol{k})$. Then let us examine more closely the term corresponding to (ii) in (18), which may be written

$$\frac{\partial \overline{U}_l}{\partial x_m} \, k_l \, \frac{\partial \Phi_{ii}}{\partial k_m} .$$

We shall wish to explore the nature of $k_l \ \partial \Phi_{ii}/\partial k_m$ as a function of $\boldsymbol{k}$.

If the structure is isotropic, so that contours of constant Φ_{ii} are circles in the $k_l - k_m$ plane, $k_l \ \partial \Phi_{ii}/\partial k_m$ will be negative in the first and third quadrants and symmetrically positive in the second and fourth. Energy will be transferred from the first and third to the second and fourth quadrants in wave number space, thus producing anisotropy. This is depicted in fig. 1.

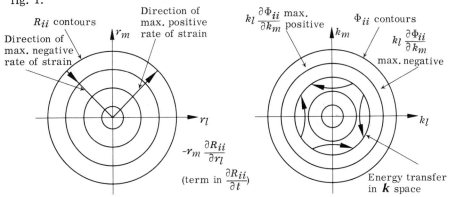

Fig. 1. The effect of shear strain on isotropic structure.

Another way of visualizing this effect is to consider the deformation caused by the shear $\partial \overline{U}_l / \partial x_m$. This may be expressed as a rate-of-strain

$$\tfrac{1}{2}\left(\frac{\partial \overline{U}_l}{\partial x_m} + \frac{\partial \overline{U}_m}{\partial x_l}\right)$$

and a rate-of-rotation

$$\tfrac{1}{2}\left(\frac{\partial \overline{U}_l}{\partial x_m} - \frac{\partial \overline{U}_m}{\partial x_l}\right) .$$

Then a small separation $s\lambda_i^0$ will be deformed (stretched and rotated) at the rates

$$\frac{1}{s}\frac{ds}{dt} = \tfrac{1}{2}\left(\frac{\partial \overline{U}_l}{\partial x_m} + \frac{\partial \overline{U}_m}{\partial x_l}\right)\lambda_l^0\lambda_m^0$$

and

$$\frac{d\varphi_{lm}}{dt} = \tfrac{1}{2}\left(\frac{\partial \overline{U}_l}{\partial x_m}\lambda_m^{02} - \frac{\partial \overline{U}_m}{\partial x_l}\lambda_l^{02}\right) ,$$

where φ_{lm} is the angle of the projection on the l-m plane of the unit vector λ^0, measured from an arbitrary reference axis. Thus, in the presence of simple shear, say $\partial \bar{U}_1/\partial x_3$, a given structure element not only will be stretched along the 45° direction and compressed along the 135° direction (taking the 1- and 3-directions as 0° and 90°, respectively) but also will be subject to rotation in the clockwise direction. Fig. 2 illustrates the nature of such deformation.

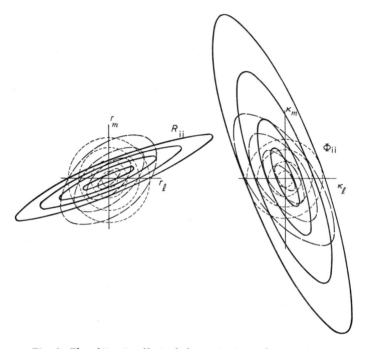

Fig. 2. The ultimate effect of shear strain on the structure.

Structure that has been exposed to such deformation for a considerable time will be distorted so that its energy is associated primarily with wave numbers in the second and fourth quadrants, close to the 3-axis, over an ever increasing range of k_3. For large wave number magnitude most of the contribution to $\partial \Phi_{ii}/\partial k_3$ will be made by such highly deformed structure, whereas at smaller values of k the more intense, more nearly isotropic structure will make the major contributions to $\partial \Phi_{ii}/\partial k_3$. In the latter circumstances the integral of $k_1 \, \partial \Phi_{ii}/\partial k_3$ over all directions in wave number space will tend to be negative; in the former, the major contributions to the integral will come from those parts of the second and fourth quadrants in which $\left| \partial \Phi_{ii}/\partial k_3 \right|$ is large and $k_1 \, \partial \Phi_{ii}/\partial k_3$ is positive. Hence, the term

$$\frac{\partial \bar{U}_i}{\partial x_3} \, k_1 \, \frac{\partial \Phi_{ii}}{\partial k_3}$$

will operate to abstract energy from the inner part of wave number space, transferring it to larger wave number components that are closely aligned along the 3-axis.

3. TURBULENT MIXING

Inasmuch as our underlying concern in these studies is with the scattering and reflection of electromagnetic waves by non-homogeneities of atmospheric properties, we are much interested in processes by which such inhomogeneities may be produced and in the structure that results. Since the radio refractive index at these altitudes is determined primarily by electron density, it is fluctuations of this parameter that we wish to examine. These fluctuations may arise, for example, in variations of the ionization, recombination, and attachment rates; but they will then, typically, be of very large scale. Smaller scale irregularities may be produced by the stirring and mixing action of the flow field operating on large scale inhomogeneities already present. For this reason we must look into the fluid dynamical development of structure of a conserved, passive, scalar property of the atmosphere.

3.1. *Analysis of irregularities*

Let us call the passive, scalar quantity to be analyzed Ψ. Since it is conserved (in the actual atmosphere potential electron density, for example, will be conserved under the usually valid assumption of isentropic flow), Ψ satisfies the equation

$$\frac{\partial \Psi}{\partial t} + \frac{\partial}{\partial x_l}(U_l \Psi) = D \frac{\partial^2 \Psi}{\partial x_\gamma \partial x_\gamma}, \tag{19}$$

in which D is the molecular diffusivity for Ψ. If Ψ is represented as the sum of mean and fluctuating terms

$$\Psi = \overline{\Psi} + \psi$$

and if the analysis is carried out in coordinates moving with the mean velocity $\overline{U}_{l_0}$, the fluctuating part of Ψ satisfies the equation

$$\frac{\partial \psi}{\partial t} = -u_l \frac{\partial \overline{\Psi}}{\partial x_l} - \frac{\partial \overline{U}_l}{\partial x_m} x_m \frac{\partial \psi}{\partial x_l} - \frac{\partial}{\partial x_l}(u_l \psi - \overline{u_l \psi}) + D \frac{\partial^2 \psi}{\partial x_\gamma \partial x_\gamma}. \tag{20}$$

Now, if as in the earlier treatment of turbulence we introduce spectral quantities $A_\psi(\mathbf{k}, t)$, $\Phi_\psi(\mathbf{k})$, and $\Phi_{\psi i}(\mathbf{k})$ defined by

$$\psi(\mathbf{x}, t) \equiv \int_{\mathbf{k}\text{-space}} e^{i\mathbf{k}\cdot\mathbf{x}} A_\psi(\mathbf{k}, t) d\mathbf{k} \tag{21}$$

and

$$\Phi_\psi(\mathbf{k}) = \frac{\overline{|A_\psi(\mathbf{k}, t)|^2}}{V_0}; \qquad \Phi_{\psi i}(\mathbf{k}) = \frac{\overline{A_\psi^*(\mathbf{k}, t) Z_i(\mathbf{k}, t)}}{V_0}, \tag{22}$$

an expression for the time-rate-of-change of contributions to the mean-square fluctuations of Ψ, $\overline{\psi^2}$, may be developed by straight forward procedures. The result, similar to (18), is

$$\frac{\partial \Phi_\psi}{\partial t} = -2 \frac{\partial \overline{\Psi}}{\partial x_l} \, \mathcal{R}\{\Phi_{\psi l}\} + \frac{\partial \overline{U}_l}{\partial x_m} \left[\Phi_\psi \, \delta_{ml} + \frac{\partial}{\partial k_m} (k_l \Phi_\psi) \right]$$

(i)   (ii)   (23)

$$+ \int_{k\text{-space}} Q_\psi(\boldsymbol{k}, \boldsymbol{k}') \mathrm{d}\boldsymbol{k}' - 2 D k^2 \Phi_\psi \,.$$

$\boldsymbol{k}$-space
(iii)   (iv)

For a statistically steady state, such that Φ_ψ is constant, independent of time, the terms on the right-hand-side of (23) express the balance of the processes of production, redistribution, and dissipation of the spectral content of ψ. In order to gain further insight as to the structure of ψ it is necessary to look at these terms and the roles they play in some detail.

3.2. *Interpretation of spectral exchange*
The terms in (23) correspond almost identically to similar terms in (18). (i) represents the production, or feeding, of Ψ fluctuations via disturbance of the mean gradient of Ψ by the irregular velocity field. Note it is essential that the velocity have a non-zero component in the direction of the gradient of Ψ and further that this velocity component be correlated with the Ψ deviation over a part of wave number space at least. Under these circumstances, which are often satisfied, the integral of (i) over all $\boldsymbol{k}$-space will be positive, giving the rate of production of $\overline{\psi^2}$.

Term (iv) describes the dissipation (i.e., the smoothing out and elimination by molecular diffusion) of Ψ fluctuations. It is always negative and, as a consequence of the k^2 factor, peaks at the high wave number end of the spectrum. The total dissipation rate of Ψ fluctuation, χ_ψ, is given by

$$\chi_\psi = 2D \int_{k\text{-space}} k^2 \Phi_\psi(\boldsymbol{k}) \mathrm{d}\boldsymbol{k}.$$

(24)

The coherence in $\Phi_{\psi i}(\boldsymbol{k})$ occurs primarily at the lower wave numbers (larger scales) so that the production and dissipation spectra tend not to overlap appreciably. This is possible only if there exists a mechanism whereby large-scale irregularities may be converted into ones of smaller scale. This, of course, is the role of terms (ii) and (iii) in (23). For each the integral over all wave number space is identically zero $(Q_\psi(\boldsymbol{k}, \boldsymbol{k}) =$ $= -Q_\psi(\boldsymbol{k}, \boldsymbol{k}'))$, indicating that it makes no net contribution to $\overline{\psi^2}$. They simply transfer contributions to $\overline{\psi^2}$ from one wave number $\boldsymbol{k}$ to another.

Term (iii) depicts the usual turbulent (internal) mixing, which is the dominant transfer process in a field of strong (fully developed) turbulence. Under these circumstances and provided the production and dissipation ranges are widely separated (invariably the case in the atmosphere), there will be a range of wave numbers in which the flux of $\overline{\psi^2}$ across wave number space is equal to the dissipation rate χ_ψ. Then, on dimensional grounds

$$\Phi_\psi(k) = c_1 \chi_\psi \, \epsilon^{-\frac{1}{3}} \, k^{-\frac{11}{3}} \,, \tag{25}$$

where c_1 is a constant of order unity. This spectrum should be applicable in the inertial subrange $k_0 \ll k \ll k_d$. k_0 is a measure of the large-scale anisotropic eddies that are primarily responsible for the production of Ψ fluctuations whereas k_d^{-1} is the Kolmogoroff microscale $(\nu^3/\epsilon)^{\frac{1}{4}}$.

If turbulence is weak and the energy cascade implicit in term (iv) of (18) is only slightly developed, at best, yet there is considerable shear of larger-scale velocity components, term (ii) in (23) may describe the dominant transfer process. As was found in the case of turbulence, this transfer is essentially a consequence of the straining and rotation of existing irregularities. The resulting structure is highly anisotropic with contributions to $\overline{\psi^2}$ coming from a wide range of wave numbers, all closely aligned with the direction of the large-scale shear.

If, under these circumstances, production and dissipation of $\overline{\psi^2}$ are widely separated in wave number magnitude, as is likely in the atmosphere, an equilibrium range may exist in which the structure will depend on χ_ψ, $\partial \overline{U}_l/\partial x_m$, and k. Then the spectrum, averaged over all directions in wave number space, should be of the form

$$\frac{1}{4\pi} \int_{4\pi} \Phi_\psi(k) d\Omega(k) = c_2 \, \chi_\psi \left[\left(\frac{\partial \overline{U}_l}{\partial x_m}\right)^2 \right]^{-\frac{1}{2}} k^{-3} \,. \tag{26}$$

Because of the inherent anisotropy it is not possible to make a simple prediction for $\Phi_\psi(k')$ directly.

On the other hand, when the large-scale shear is highly oriented, say $\partial \overline{U}_m/\partial x_m = \partial \overline{U}_1/\partial x_3$ (as might be expected in the upper atmosphere), the magnitude of $\Phi_\psi(k)$ will be significant, in the equilibrium range, only when the vector wave number lies essentially along the 3-axis. The integral in (26) will then be proportional to $\Phi_\psi(0,0,k_3)$. We thus expect

$$\Phi_\psi(0,0,k_3) = c_3 \chi_\psi \left[\left(\frac{\partial \overline{U}_1}{\partial x_3}\right)^2 \right]^{-\frac{1}{2}} k_3^{-3} \,, \tag{27}$$

in which c_3 is a coefficient that depends on the degree of anisotropy. This form of the spectrum will be expected to persist until the diffusion cut-off is reached at k_d, the order of magnitude of which can be calculated on this assumption: $k_d \sim D^{-\frac{1}{2}} |\partial \overline{U}_1/\partial x_3|^{\frac{1}{2}}$.

Part II. TURBULENCE IN THE ATMOSPHERE

4. THE EFFECTS OF ATMOSPHERIC COMPRESSIBILITY

We have considered the nature of turbulence in a homogeneous medium and have looked into the question of the irregularity structure that may be produced, both by intense turbulence and by weak turbulence in the presence of shear. In order to extend our analysis so that we may treat atmospheric problems we must now take cognizance of the principal remaining feature of the atmosphere: that it is compressible and subject to the force of gravity. This, of course, accounts for the fact that, on the average, the atmosphere is horizontally stratified with pressure and density decreasing approximately exponentially with altitude. The exact profiles depend upon the temperature distribution which, in turn, is a function of many processes, including the velocity field within the medium. Nonetheless, some degree of stable stratification characterizes almost all portions of the atmosphere and its effect must be taken into account in analyzing the motions that occur, in particular, turbulence.

It is immediately evident that in a density-stratified medium a particle of fluid displaced vertically from its equilibrium level will be subject to a vertical force (either buoyant or gravitational), which will have a direct effect on its motion. However, whether this force decelerates or accelerates the particle is not so readily discerned. The particle will be moving through a non-uniform pressure field and, being a gas, will expand or be compressed. Consequently, its own density will be altered. The direction of the force exerted will thus depend upon the thermodynamic process according to which the flow takes place as well as upon the stratification of the environment. In any case, since density is now a variable, we shall require at least one additional equation if we are to solve the system. In view of what has been said above it is logical to take for this the First Law of Thermodynamics. This, however, introduces temperature as a variable and it is necessary to add an equation of state to close the system.

Compressibility of the atmosphere results in a considerably more complicated situation than we faced in treating turbulence in a homogeneous medium. In order to reduce the problem to manageable size we shall make a number of simplifying assumptions.

a) The atmosphere will be treated as a perfect gas with pressure, density, and temperature related by $P = (c_P - c_V)\rho T$, in which c_P and c_V are the specific heats at constant pressure and constant volume, respectively. They may be taken to be constant over the scales and temperature variations that will be considered.

b) The velocity of flow will be taken to be small everywhere relative to the local speed of sound, c_0, a wholly realistic approximation for atmospheric turbulence.

c) The Coriolis force will be considered negligible, also a valid approximation for the scales to be considered.

d) Molecular effects will be included only to the extent that they are responsible for the dissipation of energy and of mean-square density and temperature fluctuations. Their dynamic effects will be omitted, which corresponds to the usually valid assumptions of large Reynolds and Peclet numbers.

e) Flow will be assumed to take place isentropically. This requires, in addition to the above, that there be no net liberation of heat by absorption, condensation, or chemical reaction, or that if such processes are important, they occur on scales, both in time and space, large compared to the turbulence we shall investigate.

f) The static distributions of temperature (T_0), pressure (P_0), and density (ρ_0) will be taken to be horizontally and stably stratified. Furthermore, fractional deviations of these quantities from their static values will be assumed small and will therefore be neglected where they appear as perturbation terms.

4.1. *The equations governing atmospheric motions*

In these circumstances the continuity equation must be employed in its full form

$$\frac{\partial \rho}{\partial t} + U \cdot \nabla \rho + \rho \nabla \cdot U = 0 \quad \text{or} \quad \frac{\partial \rho}{\partial t} + U_l \frac{\partial \rho}{\partial x_l} + \rho \frac{\partial U_l}{\partial x_l} = 0 . \qquad (28)$$

On the other hand, on the basis of assumptions (c) and (d), conservation of momentum may be expressed in the abbreviated form

$$\rho\left(\frac{\partial U}{\partial t} + U \cdot \nabla U\right) = g\rho - \nabla P \quad \text{or} \quad \rho\left[\frac{\partial U_i}{\partial t} + U_l \frac{\partial U_i}{\partial x_l}\right] = g_i\rho - \frac{\partial P}{\partial x_i} . \qquad (29)$$

Again, on the basis of the assumptions, the First Law of Thermodynamics may be simply stated,

$$\rho c_V\left[\frac{\partial T}{\partial t} + U \cdot \nabla T\right] + P\nabla \cdot U = 0 \quad \text{or} \quad \rho c_V\left[\frac{\partial T}{\partial t} + U_l \frac{\partial T}{\partial x_l}\right] + P \frac{\partial U_l}{\partial x_l} = 0 . \qquad (30)$$

These, together with the equation of state given in assumption (a), constitute a closed system of equations that our idealized atmosphere must obey.

It is clear that the variability of density has compounded the problem. In (29), for example, the effect of the buoyancy force $g_i(\rho-\rho_0)$ ($g_i\rho_0$ is balanced by the hydrostatic pressure $\partial P_0/\partial x_i$) depends not only on the change in density of the particle of fluid but also on whether this change is greater or less than the variation of density in the environment through which the particle has passed.

The analysis may be simplified appreciably if, at this point, the notion of potential density is introduced. Potential density is, by definition, the density a particle of the (compressible) fluid would have if its pressure were reduced adiabatically to (arbitrary) reference pressure P_∞. Since we have assumed all flow to take place isentropically, it follows that potential density is conserved. That is, the potential density of each individual particle is constant, although the static distribution in the environment will generally decrease with altitude. Hence our problem, stated in terms of potential density, will resemble very closely that of the flow of an incompressible, stratified fluid.

By expressing P in (30) in terms of ρ and T, via the equation of state, and substituting for $\partial U_l/\partial x_l$ from (28), one finds, following a particle, the relations between temperature, density, and pressure for an adiabatic process, which serve to define potential temperature Θ and potential density $\hat{\rho}$:

$$\frac{\Theta}{T} = \left(\frac{\hat{\rho}}{\rho}\right)^{\gamma-1} = \left(\frac{P_\infty}{P}\right)^{(\gamma-1)/\gamma} \quad , \qquad \gamma \equiv c_P/c_V \ . \tag{31}$$

A number of quantities that are conserved may be deduced from these equations. In addition to $\hat{\rho}$ and Θ there is, for example, $P/\rho^\gamma = P_\infty/\hat{\rho}^\gamma$, which is constant for each particle, although it may, and generally does, vary from one particle to the next.

If the statement of conservation of momentum is expressed in terms of potential density, we may, by taking advantage of the assumption of small Mach number (i.e., $(P-P_0)/\gamma P_0 = U^2/c_0{}^2 = M_0^2 \ll 1$) and by cancelling the hydrostatic terms, write (29) as

$$\left(1+\frac{\hat{\rho}-\hat{\rho}_0}{\hat{\rho}_0}\right)\left[\frac{\partial U_i}{\partial t} + U_l \frac{\partial U_i}{\partial x_l}\right] = \frac{g_i}{\hat{\rho}_0}(\hat{\rho}-\hat{\rho}_0) - \frac{\partial}{\partial x_i}\left(\frac{P-P_0}{P_0}\right) - \frac{P-P_0}{P_0}\frac{1}{\hat{\rho}_0}\frac{\partial \hat{\rho}_0}{\partial x_i} \ .$$

Furthermore, if $-\hat{\rho}_0/(\partial\hat{\rho}_0/\partial x_i)$ (the scale height of the potential density distribution) is much greater than the largest motion-scale to be considered, the perturbation term on the left and the last term on the right will make negligible contribution and may be omitted.

Through the equations of state and continuity T and ρ may be eliminated from (30), yielding, to terms of first order,

$$\frac{\partial U_l}{\partial x_l} = -\frac{U_l}{\gamma P_0}\frac{\partial P_0}{\partial x_l} - \frac{\partial}{\partial t}\left(\frac{P-P_0}{\gamma P_0}\right) - U_l\frac{\partial}{\partial x_l}\left(\frac{P-P_0}{\gamma P_0}\right) \ .$$

Here again, on the basis of assumption (b), the last two terms will be of negligible magnitude and may be dropped.

Finally, therefore, we have the system of equations

$$\frac{\partial(\hat{\rho}-\hat{\rho}_0)}{\partial t} + U_l\frac{\partial(\hat{\rho}-\hat{\rho}_0)}{\partial x_l} + U_l\frac{\partial\hat{\rho}_0}{\partial x_l} = 0 \tag{32}$$

$$\frac{\partial U_i}{\partial t} + U_l\frac{\partial U_i}{\partial x_l} = \frac{g_i}{\hat{\rho}_0}(\hat{\rho}-\hat{\rho}_0) - \frac{\partial}{\partial x_i}\left(\frac{P-P_0}{P_0}\right) \tag{33}$$

$$\frac{\partial U_i}{\partial x_i} = -\frac{U_l}{\gamma P_0}\frac{\partial P_0}{\partial x_l} \ , \tag{34}$$

which relate the five variables $(\hat{\rho}-\hat{\rho}_0)$, U_i, $(P-P_0)/P_0$. (32), (33), and (34) may, in principle, be solved for these quantities, given initial and boundary conditions, by treating static pressure and potential density as parameters. Various approaches may be followed.

The steady flow induced by irregular boundaries may be investigated, which leads to certain types of lee waves exhibiting locally intensified shear zones. The nonlinear interactions may be assumed to be of secondary importance and the resulting linear equations solved for the natural modes. This yields internal gravity-type waves at the low frequencies. Thirdly, (turbulent) velocity and density fluctuation fields may be assumed to be superposed on some steady flow. Then both linear and nonlinear interactions may be studied in an attempt to discern the mechanisms by which energy is transferred and structure develops. Considerable attention has been paid earlier to the first two of these approaches. We shall therefore concentrate on the latter approach.

In what follows all reference to density will be to potential density, unless specifically noted to the contrary. Consequently, the carat over the symbol ρ will be omitted and it should be understood that ρ stands for potential density.

If now pressure, density, and velocity are decomposed into static, average, and fluctuating components according to

$$P = P_0 + (\overline{P}-P_0) + p, \qquad \hat{\rho} = \rho_0 + (\overline{\rho}-\rho_0) + \rho, \qquad U_i = \overline{U}_i + u_i,$$

then, by subtracting the average of each equation from (32), (33), and (34), respectively, we may find the equations that the fluctuation terms are required to satisfy. They are

$$\frac{\partial \rho}{\partial t} = -u_l \frac{\partial \overline{\rho}}{\partial x_l} + \overline{U}_l \frac{\partial \rho}{\partial x_l} + u_l \frac{\partial \rho}{\partial x_l} - \overline{u_l \frac{\partial \rho}{\partial x_l}} \tag{35}$$

$$\frac{\partial u_i}{\partial t} = -u_l \frac{\partial \overline{U}_i}{\partial x_l} + \overline{U}_l \frac{\partial u_i}{\partial x_l} + u_l \frac{\partial u_i}{\partial x_l} - \overline{u_l \frac{\partial u_i}{\partial x_l}} + \frac{g_i}{\rho_0} \rho - \frac{\partial}{\partial x_i} \left(\frac{p}{\rho_0} \right) \tag{36}$$

$$\frac{\partial u_i}{\partial x_i} = -\frac{u_l}{\gamma P_0} \frac{\partial P_0}{\partial x_l} \approx \frac{u_3}{\gamma H} = o(1) . \tag{37}$$

Use has been made in (37) of the fact that for the types of motion we shall consider, the (vertical) scale of the turbulent velocities is usually small compared to the scale height, $H \equiv -P_0/(dP_0/dx_3)$, of the atmosphere.

4.2. *The role of buoyancy*

These equations resemble very closely those for the fluctuating velocity and passive scalar quantity ψ derived earlier (the viscous and molecular diffusion terms having been omitted here on the grounds that the Reynolds and Peclet numbers are always very large in the atmosphere). The primary difference resides in the dynamic nature of the density fluctuations, indicated by the presence of ρ in the buoyancy term in (36). In a non-uniform density distribution fluctuations of density will occur as a consequence of turbulence, which fluctuations will, in turn, accelerate or decelerate the very motions that give rise to them. It is this dynamic interaction of the density and velocity fluctuations that distinguishes atmospheric turbulence from the usual laboratory variety, that is responsible for the inherently anisotropic structure characteristic of irregular wind fields, and that must

be understood more fully if we are to have any hope of making useful predictions regarding refractive index structure.

One step is this direction is to consider the role of the buoyancy force in
the budget of turbulent energy. The downward vertical direction of the
gravity force g in the buoyancy term in (36) gives rise to an additional term
$-g\overline{u_3\rho}/\rho_0$ in eq. (7) for $\partial \overline{e}_3/\partial t$. When there is positive (negative) correlation
between the vertical velocity and density fluctuations, as there will tend to
be in the presence of a negative (positive) density gradient, this term will
operate to subtract from (add to) the kinetic energy associated with the
vertical direction. In the usual stably stratified situation buoyancy thus
acts as a sink, abstracting kinetic energy from the turbulence but doing
this selectively in that it directly removes energy only from u_3^2. This, of
course, tends to suppress vertical velocities and leads to anisotropy, which
in the absence of other non-isotropic effects will be axisymmetric about the
direction of gravity.

If, for the moment, we assume a steady state, with k.e. supplied to the
turbulence by, for example, large-scale shear or mean-flow advection at
the same rate that it is abstracted by buoyancy and dissipated by viscosity,
there arise immediately questions as to how the energy of the velocity field
is transferred from one directional component to another and whether there
is an equilibrium degree of non-isotropy of the structure. The latter would
depend upon the stability of the medium and the nature of the source mechanism. Conceivably there is an anisotropic structure such that the energy
transferred from the horizontal to the vertical and from the larger scales
to the smaller is just that required to maintain the assumed equilibrium.
As we have seen, investigation of such questions is aided considerably by
examining the budgets of turbulent kinetic energy and of mean-square density fluctuations, ρ^2, in wave number space. However, before proceeding
to this stage of our study it will be helpful to note two additional points
about buoyancy.

First, let us develop an expression for the budget of mean-square density fluctuations. This may be got from (35) in the same manner that the
expression for $\partial \overline{e}_\alpha/\partial t$ was derived from (6). It is, assuming as usual a
vertical gradient of mean density $\partial \overline{\rho}/\partial x_3$,

$$\frac{\partial \overline{\rho^2}}{\partial t} = -2 \, \overline{u_3\rho} \, \frac{\partial \overline{\rho}}{\partial x_3} - \frac{\partial}{\partial x_l} \left[\overline{\rho^2} \, \overline{U}_l + \overline{\rho^2 u_l} \right] - \chi_\rho \, , \tag{38}$$

where χ_ρ, the rate at which density deviations are smeared-out (dissipated)
by molecular diffusion, reflects the primary role of random molecular motions in this process. The point on which to focus attention is the fact that
the vertical velocity-density covariance, $\overline{u_3\rho}$, which with the buoyancy factor g/ρ_0 accounts for the abstraction of kinetic energy from the turbulence,
also accounts for the production of density deviations in (38). In fact, inasmuch as density deviations represent stored energy (potential energy),
given (per unit mass) by

$$\phi = -\tfrac{1}{2} \frac{g}{\rho_0} \frac{\rho^2}{\partial \overline{\rho}/\partial x_3} \, ,$$

the rate at which such potential energy is produced is $g^{\overline{u_3 \rho}}/\rho_0$. Hence, this term simply describes the manner in which energy associated with the fluctuation components is exchanged between kinetic and potential forms but makes no net contribution to the total fluctuation energy. Moreover, this total fluctuation energy is ultimately 'destroyed', i.e., converted to incoherent thermal motion, by molecular dissipation regardless of whether it reaches this state via the kinetic or potential energy route.

The second point pertains to the relation between potential density and potential temperature. From the equation of state and the definitions of potential temperature and density it is clear that the product of these two potential quantities is constant,

$$\rho\Theta = P_\infty/(c_p - c_V) . \tag{39}$$

It follows, to first order terms (assuming the potential temperature gradient is not too steep), if we write $\Theta = \Theta_0 + (\overline{\Theta} - \Theta_0) + \theta$, that

$$\rho = -\frac{\overline{\rho}}{\overline{\Theta}} \theta = -\frac{\rho_0}{\Theta_0} \theta \tag{40}$$

and

$$\frac{\partial \overline{\rho}}{\partial x_l} = -\frac{\overline{\rho}}{\overline{\Theta}} \frac{\partial \overline{\Theta}}{\partial x_l} = -\frac{\rho_0}{\Theta_0} \frac{\partial \overline{\Theta}}{\partial x_l} . \tag{41}$$

Moreover, since potential temperature is conserved in the assumed isentropic flow, the expression for the budget of mean-square potential temperature fluctuations is

$$\frac{\rho \overline{\theta^2}}{\rho t} = -2 \overline{u_3 \theta} \frac{\partial \overline{\Theta}}{\partial x_3} - \frac{\partial}{\partial x_l} \left[\overline{\theta^2} \, \overline{U}_l + \overline{\theta^2 \, u_l} \right] - \chi_\theta . \tag{42}$$

Thus, the buoyancy term in the kinetic energy budget can be expressed in terms of potential temperature, by $-g^{\overline{u_3 \theta}}/\Theta_0$, and the whole question of the interaction of turbulence with the stratified medium may be discussed in terms of potential temperature rather than density.

4.3. *Spectral representation*

We can, making use of the same spectral notation introduced in Sections 2 and 3, show that the effect of buoyancy is to add a seventh term, $-2(g/\rho_0) \, \mathcal{R}\{\Phi_{\rho 3}(k)\}$, to the right-hand-side of expression (18) for the budget of vertical kinetic energy in wave number space. This represents a sink or source of k.e. at wave number k, depending on the sign of the cospectrum. For the·axisymmetric-type structure suggested earlier this cospectrum must take the form

$$\mathcal{R}\{\Phi_{\rho 3}(k)\} = \left(1 - \frac{k_3^2}{k^2}\right) \mathcal{R}\{F_\rho(k^2, k_3)\} , \tag{43}$$

in which $\mathcal{R}\{F_\rho\}$ can be shown to be an even function of k_3 as a consequence of the mathematically real nature of the velocity and density fluctuations. On the basis of this additional symmetry it seems likely that this cospectrum is either non-negative for all k, or non-positive, and that its integral over all directions of k is either greater than zero, or less than zero, for any k in the range such that the magnitude F_ρ is non-negligible. Thus, we can anticipate that the interaction of vertical velocity-density fluctuations takes place throughout a considerable portion of wave number space and that, for this axisymmetric case, it becomes unimportant in the budget of $\Phi_{ii}(k)$ only at such large wave numbers that F_ρ is negligible, i.e., that the structure is isotropic.

On the other hand, if vertical shear $\partial \overline{U}_1/\partial x_3$ is a dominant feature of the flow field, serving as the principle transfer mechanism in the manner described earlier, then, as we have seen, the structure of $\overline{\rho^2}$ will be associated to a large extent with vector wave numbers in the near vertical direction only. However, continuity requires that $Z_3(k_3, t)$ be essentially zero. As a consequence, one can predict that

$$\Phi_{\rho 3}(k) = \frac{\overline{A_\rho^*(k, t) Z_3(k, t)}}{V_0}$$

will be small, at best, and probably negligible under these circumstances. We would not, therefore, anticipate buoyancy playing an important role in the fluctuation energy budget in the presence of intense vertical shear.

There are many other facets of this matter that need to be explored; but it will be more informative to examine these in the consideration of specific models for the flow and irregularity fields appropriate to those portions of the atmosphere in which we are primarily interested. It is worthy of note at this point, however, that the budgets of mean-square density and temperature fluctuations, in wave number space, are given by expressions exactly analogous to (23) for $\overline{\psi^2}$. The same production and transfer processes will operate to feed $\overline{\rho^2}$ and $\overline{\theta^2}$, and to redistribute contributions to these quantities within k-space, altered only to the extent attributable to those changes in the turbulent velocity structure that are a consequence of the dynamic influence of the density perturbations.

5. TYPES OF STRUCTURE IN THE MIDDLE ATMOSPHERE

From the point of view of concern here the atmosphere between 30 and 120 km divides into zones of three types: (i) the highly stable regions from 30 to 50 km and from 90 to 120 km, characterized by temperature inversions of $3^{\circ}C/km$ and $7^{\circ}C/km$, respectively; (ii) the much less stably stratified layer between 60 and 80 km in which there is a temperature lapse of $4^{\circ}C/km$; and (iii) the nearly isothermal transition zones between. You have considered in other sessions many larger-scale motions that are observed or believed to occur in these regions, such as tides, general circulation patterns, jet streams, and internal waves, and have looked into the mechanisms that give rise to these flows and into the structures they produce. It is our objective here to look at much smaller-scale velocity fields, to predict the refractive index structure that will accompany them, when and if they occur, and to attempt to understand how such 'turbulence' might come about in the regions identified above. Let us consider two broad types of ir-

regular flow: isotropic, as might be expected to occur in nearly homogeneous regions or in relatively small patches in which high intensity, 'fully-
developed' turbulence exists; and anisotropic, of the nature one would anticipate in highly stratified layers.

5.1. *Isotropic turbulence*

This type of structure will be most likely to occur in the presence of a
weak density gradient, say, between 60 and 80 km, where the dynamic effect of density deviations will be relatively unimportant. In fact, under
these circumstances density acts very much as a passive, scalar property
of the atmosphere, which is thus convected and mixed in accordance with
the analysis of Section 3. We would therefore anticipate a $k^{-\frac{5}{3}}$ isotropic
form for the spectrum of both the velocity and density fields, if the turbulence is intense. If the turbulence is weak, but there is strong vertical
shear, we would expect to find highly anisotropic density structure associated for the most part with vertical wavenumbers and proportional to k_3^{-1}.
The driving mechanisms from which such homogeneous turbulence could
draw its kinetic energy are not well identified nor thoroughly understood.
Nonetheless, evidence from diffusion studies is strongly suggestive of the
occurrence of this type of turbulent flow at these levels.

Another type of situation in which isotropic turbulence is likely to be
found is the case of highly localized, intense turbulence such as that which
may occur in jets or narrow shear zones or may be induced in small regions by the breaking of internal waves. These means of turbulence production are more probable in the transition zones, at the stratopause and
mesopause; but the wavebreaking process may also take place in the highly
stratified regions. Regardless of the specific nature of production, such
fully-developed, high intensity turbulence will tend, within the turbulent
zone, to mix the medium thoroughly. The density gradient will be largely if
not totally eliminated here. On the other hand, there will be large near-
discontinuities in density at the top and bottom surfaces of the turbulent
patch, much as indicated in fig. 3.

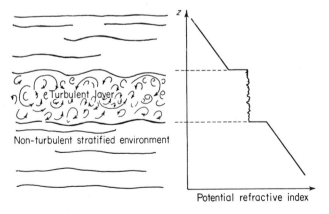

Fig. 3. A turbulent layer in stably stratified surroundings.

Under these circumstances the density (and refractive index) irregularities within the patch, while exhibiting structure of the $k^{-\frac{5}{3}}$ form, usually
will be of very low intensity and probably of little importance to radio
propagation. However, the abrupt changes in density (and refractive index)
at the top and bottom of the patch will often be sufficiently great to have a
marked effect. Let us suppose, for example, that the mean gradient of
electron density, $d\overline{N}/dz$, is 10^9/km and that the turbulence exists in a layer 300 m deep. The ΔN at each surface would then be 1.5×10^8, the associated change in refractive index, approximately 3×10^{-3} $(f_m/\text{MHz})^{-2}$.
f_m is the operating frequency in MHz.

The amount of electromagnetic radiation 'reflected' by such a transition
will, of course, depend also on the shape of the 'discontinuity', both the
profile of its cross section and the altitude variations of its surface. Un-
fortunely, there is as yet little that can be said on theoretical grounds
about these features. However, wind tunnel observations of the boundary
between a turbulent wake and the irrotational surrounding fluid indicate that
the transition from turbulent to non-turbulent flow typically occurs in a
distance comparable to the Kolmogorov inner scale of turbulence $((\nu^3/\epsilon)^{\frac{1}{4}} \sim$
~ 1 m at 100 km) where as the undulating structure of the surface reflects
principally the scale of the energy containing eddies. Since these two scales
are normally widely separated in high intensity turbulence, we can anticipate a discontinuity structure in which the irregular, wave-like variations
in surface altitude have wavelength very much larger than the thickness of
the transition. Moreover, when the surrounding non-turbulent medium is
stably stratified, one would expect this two-dimensional nature of the transition to be even more pronounced.

Calculation of the reflected and scattered power from such refractive
index structure requires detailed (statistical) knowledge of surface shape.
We are in a position now to make some reasonably intelligent estimates
about this shape and may thus proceed to compute the effect on the propagation of electromagnetic waves.

5.2. *Stratified turbulence*

If, by one mechanism or another, an irregular velocity field is produced
in a stably stratified medium, one is tempted to postulate an equilibrium
structure in the small scale (high wave number) portion of the spectrum
that will reflect in some appropriate way the effects of the stratification.
Several such proposals have been made. In this section we shall look at the
basis for these, much of which is common, at the differences in their
premises, and at various predictions that arise out of these theories.

In our study, in Section 4, of the effects of buoyancy we found an expression for the budget of kinetic energy in wave number space (eq. (18)
plus the buoyancy term $-2\,(g/\rho_0)\,\mathcal{R}\{\Phi_{\rho 3}\}$). This contains a production (or
feeding) term, an abstraction term (buoyancy), a dissipation term, and a
number of transfer terms all of which make no net contribution, positive or
negative, to the total kinetic energy. Similarly, we noted that the budget
for mean-square density fluctuations takes the form (23) in wave number
space and, moreover, that by multiplying each term in this equation by

$-\frac{1}{2}g/(\rho_0\,\partial\bar{\rho}/\partial x_3)$ it may be converted to an expression for the budget of the potential energy fluctuations associated with the density deviations. In this form this equation also contains a production term (the same as the buoyance abstraction term in the kinetic energy relation), a dissipation term, and transfer terms. If now, in each case, the transfer terms are integrated over all that portion of wave number space outside a spherical shell of radius k, the resulting quantities

$$S_{\text{k.e.}}(k) \equiv \frac{\partial\bar{U}_1}{\partial x_3}\int_{|\boldsymbol{l}|>k}\mathcal{R}\{\Phi_{13}\}\mathrm{d}^3l + \frac{g}{\rho_0}\int_{|\boldsymbol{l}|>k}\mathcal{R}\{\Phi_{\rho3}\}\mathrm{d}^3l + \nu\int_{|\boldsymbol{l}|>k}l^2\,\Phi_{ii}\,\mathrm{d}^3l \quad (44)$$

and

$$S_{\text{p.e.}}(k) \equiv -\frac{g}{\rho_0}\int_{|\boldsymbol{l}|>k}\mathcal{R}\{\Phi_{\rho3}\}\mathrm{d}^3l + \frac{gD\rho}{\rho_0\left|\frac{\partial\bar{\rho}}{\partial\rho_3}\right|}\int_{|\boldsymbol{l}|>k}l^2\Phi_\rho\,\mathrm{d}^3l \quad (45)$$

describe the flux through wave number space of contributions to the fluctuation energy.

The basis of the equilibrium theories is that, in the tail of the spectrum, there exists a structure of a universal form that is independent of the energy containing eddies. A further premise of the (inertial and buoyancy) subrange theories is that all types of dissipation occur principally at high wave numbers, beyond the subrange under consideration. Thus in (44) and (45) the last terms may be replaced by ϵ and $\chi_{\text{p.e.}}$, respectively. Moreover, production, which is associated primarily with the energy containing eddies, can be said to make insignificantly little or no contribution to $S_{\text{k.e.}}$ or $S_{\text{p.e.}}$, when k lies in the equilibrium range. For the axisymmetric structure suggested earlier the first term in (44) is identically zero. It follows that $S_{\text{p.e.}}(k) \approx \chi_{\text{p.e.}}$, a constant in the subranges. On the other hand, if the gravity force is to have any influence at all (i.e., if a buoyancy subrange is to exist), the buoyancy term in (44) must play a non-trivial role and $S_{\text{k.e.}}$ must decrease with increasing k.

However, the flux of total fluctuation energy, in the subranges,

$$S_{\text{k.e.}}(k) + S_{\text{p.e.}}(k) = \epsilon + \chi_{\text{p.e.}} = \text{const.} \quad (46)$$

We thus appear to have a contradiction as regards $S_{\text{k.e.}}$ in the buoyancy subrange (if one exists): $S_{\text{k.e.}}$ must decrease, yet it must equal

$$\epsilon + \chi_{\text{p.e.}} - S_{\text{p.e.}}(k) \approx \epsilon\,,$$

a constant. This conflict can be resolved only if $S_{\text{k.e.}}(k) \ll S_{\text{p.e.}}(k)$, so that a negligible increase in $S_{\text{p.e.}}(k)$, arising in the spectral tail of the potential energy production term, constitutes a significant decrease in $S_{\text{k.e.}}(k)$. Note that this inequality is a necessary but not sufficient condition for the existence of a buoyancy subrange. Hence, it will be of some interest to examine the ratio of $S_{\text{p.e.}}$ to $S_{\text{k.e.}}$.

$$S_{\text{p.e.}}(k) \sim \frac{g}{\rho_0\left|\partial\bar{\rho}/\partial x_3\right|}\frac{kE_\rho(k)}{\tau(k)}\,,$$

where

$$E_\rho(k) \equiv \int_{4\pi} \Phi_\rho(I)\mathrm{d}\Omega(I),$$

where $\mathrm{d}\Omega$ is an elemental solid angle, and $\tau(k)$ is the time scale of eddies of size $1/k$.

$$S_{\text{k.e.}}(k) \sim \frac{kE(k)}{\tau(k)}.$$

Thus

$$R_{\text{b}} \equiv \frac{S_{\text{p.e.}}(k)}{S_{\text{k.e.}}(k)} = \frac{g}{\rho_0 |\partial\bar\rho/\partial x_3|} \frac{E_\rho(k)}{E(k)} = \frac{g}{\rho_0} \left| \frac{\partial\bar\rho}{\partial x_3} \right| \frac{E_\rho(k)/ |\partial\bar\rho/\partial x_3|}{E(k)}^2. \qquad (47)$$

The first of the buoyancy subrange proposals (Bolgiano, 1959, 1962) suggests that the equilibrium structure in the subrange should depend upon g/ρ_0, χ_ρ (to reflect the essentially constant $\chi_{\text{p.e.}}$), and k only. On dimensional grounds this yields

$$E(k) \sim \chi_\rho^{\frac{2}{5}} \left(\frac{g}{\rho_0}\right)^{\frac{4}{5}} k^{-\frac{11}{5}}$$

and   (48)

$$E_\rho(k) \sim \chi_\rho^{\frac{4}{5}} \left(\frac{g}{\rho_0}\right)^{-\frac{2}{5}} k^{-\frac{7}{5}}.$$

If we presume the

$$\chi_\rho = \left| l_1 \frac{\partial\bar\rho}{\partial x_3} \right|^2 \left[\frac{g}{\rho_0} \left| \frac{\partial\bar\rho}{\partial x_3} \right| \right]^{\frac{1}{2}},$$

where l_1 is the scale of the energy-containing eddies and the last term in square brackets gives the Brunt-Väisälä frequency,

$$R_{\text{b}} \sim (l_1 k)^{\frac{4}{5}}.$$

The second buoyancy subrange model (Shur, 1962; Lumely, 1964) takes, as the controlling parameters in this range, g/ρ_0 and $\partial\bar\rho/\partial x_3$. Somewhat more sophisticated methods were employed in the development of this theory, leading to an interpolation formula that spans the buoyancy and inertial subranges. Nevertheless, in the buoyancy subrange it reduces to the fact that the above two parameters determine the structure. We find

$$E(k) \sim \frac{g}{\rho_0} \left| \frac{\partial\bar\rho}{\partial x_3} \right| k^{-3}$$

                                                                                                           (49)

$$E_\rho(k) \sim \left| \frac{\partial\bar\rho}{\partial x_3} \right|^2 k^{-3},$$

and

$$R_{\text{b}} \sim 1.$$

The most recent analysis of the buoyance subrange (Phillips, 1966) formally follows the approach set out by Lumley. However, it takes note of
the fact that the interpolation formula for $S_{p.e.}(k)$ shows this flux to be essentially constant well down into the buoyancy subrange. Consequently, it
in effect takes for the important parameters the Brunt-Väisälä frequency
and χ_ρ. This gives

$$E(k) \sim \frac{g}{\rho_0} \left| \frac{\partial \bar{\rho}}{\partial x_3} \right| k^{-3}$$

$$E_\rho(k) \sim \chi_\rho \left[\frac{g}{\rho_0} \left| \frac{\partial \bar{\rho}}{\partial x_3} \right| \right]^{-\frac{1}{2}} k^{-1} \,,$$

(50)

and

$$R_b \sim (l_1 k)^2 \,.$$

It is clear, from the necessary condition $R_b \gg 1$, that Phillips' formulation is most promising, whereas Lumley's result for $E_\rho(k)$ must be re-
jected. A possible explanation of Phillips' model may be given as follows.

Within the energy-containing range the motions that produce the density
fluctuations transform almost all of their kinetic energy into potential energy in the process. The velocity field, therefore, has essentially all of its
energy concentrated in a narrow part of the energy-containing range. The
random vorticity (shear) of subsequent of these eddies does strain the density irregularities already produced, the characteristic straining time being simply the Brunt-Väisälä period. Thus in accord with the theory proposed by Bolgiano (1965), in which the development of density fluctuations,

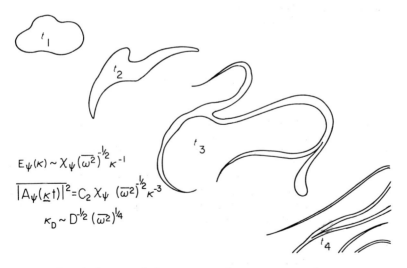

Fig. 4. Quasi-turbulent stirring of a passive irregularity.

once they are in existence, is attributed to the vorticity of the large-scale velocity components, it being assumed those of smaller-scale are too weak to have a significant influence, the present model leads to a k^{-1} form for the spectrum of $\overline{\rho^2}$. This straining, distortion process is depicted in fig. 4.

BIBLIOGRAPHY AND REFERENCES

The following text and monographs are recommended for deeper study in the areas indicated:

Turbulence, General
Batchelor, G.K., 1953, Theory of Homogeneous Turbulence, Cambridge University Press, London, 197.
Hinze, J.O., 1959, Turbulence, McGraw-Hill, New York, 586.

Atmospheric turbulence
Lumley, J.L. and H.A.Panofsky, 1964, The Structure of Atmospheric Turbulence, Interscience Publishers, New York, 239.

References cited in text:
Bolgiano Jr., R., 1959, J. Geophys. Res. 64, 2226.
Bolgiano Jr., R., 1962, J. Geophys. Res. 67, 3015.
Bolgiano Jr., R., 1965, Progress in Radio Science 1960-1963, Elsevier Publishing Co., Amsterdam, II, 80.
Deissler, R.G., 1961, Phys. Fluids 4, 1187.
Lumley, J.L., 1964, J. Atmos. Sci. 21, 99.
Monin, A.S. and A.M. Obouhov. 1954. Trudy Geofiz. Inst. Akad. Nauk SSSR, 24. 151.
Phillips, O.M., 1966, Proc. International Coll. Fine-scale Structure of the Atmosphere, Akad. Nauk SSSR, Moskva.
Shur, G.N., 1962, Trudy Tsentral Aero. Obs. 43, 79.

COMMENTS

Hoult:
1) I have developed a theory of how to distinguish random dispersive waves from turbulence (Phys. Fluids, Aug. 1966) and have applied it to observations made at Arecibo, (Space Sci. Rev. 1966) which show the presence of acoustic waves. By these techniques one can measure the power spectrum of the sources of random dispersive waves.

2) It can be shown that the typical behaviour of a smoke trail in the altitude range 50-100 km is better described by the presence of random dispersive waves rather than turbulence.

Erkmen:
I would like to remark that in the relation of eq. (3), the mean quantities have an analytical definition such that when separating the flow (or other

quantities, such as pressure, density, etc.) into mean flow and disturbance (deviation from the mean flow), the mean flow, for example for the x-component, $\bar{u}$, $(u = \bar{u} + u')$ is given by the following fundamental relation,

$$\bar{u}(t, x_0, y_0, z_0) = \frac{1}{T} \int_{t_0 - \frac{1}{2}T}^{t_0 + \frac{1}{2}T} u \, dt$$

Here:

u = Actual flow in the x-direction
$\bar{u}$ = Mean flow in the x-direction
T = period
t = time
t_0 = time origine
u' = fluctuation (deviation from the mean)

Therefore, $\bar{u}$ is a time mean of the flow u. The whole picture can be demonstrated by the following figure:

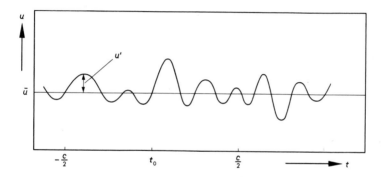

DISCUSSION

Baguette:
    Quelle est la raison pour décomposer par l'analyse de Fourier la partie fluctuante de la vitesse?

Misme:
    Etant donné la complexité des phénomènes, une méthode d'approche est d'étudier un développement en série; la méthode classique de la série de Fourier met en évidence des périodes différentes.
    Quant au spectra, c'est la transformation de Fourier et la fonction d'autocorrélation qu'il faut utiliser.

Bolgiano:
    In addition to M. Misme's response I should like to add the following.

Decomposition of the velocity field into Fourier components provides a convenient method of analysis that displays nicely interactions arising in non-linear terms. This is the same method that is employed in the analysis of signals in communication systems when it is necessary to study the effects of non-linear circuit elements. As is well known, in such cases there is effected a transfer of energy among different frequency components.

Nguyen:

En ce qui concerne les quantités telles que la vitesse U, la pression P, vous les avez divisés en deux parties: une partie représentant la fluctuation et vue partie représentant une valeur moyenne. Quelle est la définition exacte de cette valeur moyenne?

Est-ce une solution stationnaire, est-ce une moyenne prise dans l'espace des phases, ou bien une moyenne prise sur une autre grandeur?

Bolgiano:

It is presumed in the analysis that a stationary solution exists and that the mean values are those of this stationery field. In reality, of course, this is not true; but it may be assumed so without serious error provided the periods of nearly constant local mean values are much longer than those of the turbulence.

Rawer:

Is it possible to replace the term isentropic by adiabatic?

Bolgiano:

Yes, it is possible to demand only that the processes be adiabatic, not isentropic. This, in fact, is implied in assumption (d), page 384. Additional (molecular) terms will then appear on the right-hand-side of eqs. (30) and (34) but in typical atmospheric flows they will be of second order and may thus be neglected in our analysis of the dynamics.

Gille:

I was very interested in Prof. Bolgiano's paper, especially the section on stratified turbulence. The condition that $S_{pe}(k) \gg S_{ke}(k)$ seems to say that the major mechanism damping turbulence is the thermal mechanism that destroy the density variations.

This need not be a diffusive mechanism. As I pointed out yesterday, radiative destruction of temperature perturbations can be much more rapid than destruction by conduction for layer scales. I should like to suggest that in further computations involving the shape of the spectrum, that the radiative dissipation be parametrized and included, rather than a conductive mechanism. In the lower part of the atmosphere this could initiate cut off for scales considerably larger than suggested by conduction.

Spizzichino:

Cette intervention montre qu'au moins dans un cas, il n'existait pas de turbulence entre 50 et 90 km. Que sait-on des régions de l'atmosphère où la turbulence est présent et de celles où elle est absente? Qu'est-ce que les ondes planétaires?

Gille:

If one looks at a map of the jet stream position, one will see that it does not follow a latitude circle, but oscillates in space about some mean latitude. Usually there are three to five such major oscillations around the earth and portions of smaller oscillations such that up to 15 might fit around a latitude circle may usually be recognized. These can be referred to as planetary waves. The maintenance of the oscillatory pattern of these waves depends upon the North-South variation of the Coriolis Parameter.

Spizzichino:

Les équations de base de la théorie des ondes de gravité sont les mêmes que celles utilisées pour la turbulence. Certains termes dont on tient compte pour l'étude de la turbulence sont negligés dans la théorie classique des ondes de gravité (par exemple le terme en $v \cdot \nabla v$ dans l'éq. du moment), mais on devrait en tenir compte pour une théorie plus élaborée des ondes degravité. La méthode d'analyse est la même pour ces deux théories: on procède par analyse de Fourier.

Dans ces conditions, quelle est la différence de nature entre les ondes de gravité et la turbulence?

Bolgiano:

In general analysis the equations governing these two types of motion are the same. Gravity waves are natural modes which are excited by external driving forces and among which internal coupling and transfer of energy do not play a dominant role. The spectral distribution of energy is therefore determined, in the first degree, by the external driving process.

In turbulence, on the other hand, it is believed that strong interaction among the modes occurs so that an equilibrium state is realized in which the spectral distribution of energy is determined primarily by internal energy transfer. Under these circumstances at the high wave-numbers, at least (in the tail of the spectrum), the spectral form is independent of the driving mechanism, only its intensity and viscous cut-off point being determined thereby.

Misme:

Les équations de Navier supposent un fluide impossible. L'introduction de la densité potentielle conduit à une densité variable. Quelle est la zone de validité et son épaisseur?

Bolgiano:

L'introduction de la densité potentielle conduit à negliger un terme, ce qui est possible si le terme négligé est très petit.

Les équations entre les numeros (31) et (32) de la page 386 montrent que l'épaisseur qui pourra ainsi être considérée, sera ≪ que l'échelle de hauteur de la densité potentielle qui est de l'ordre de 100 km dans la troposphère et la mésosphère, et de l'ordre de 10 km de la stratosphère et la thermosphère. Donc une épaisseur de 1 à 10 km (avec la zone) sera toujours acceptable.

Rawer:

Could not your scale height $-\rho_0/(\partial\rho/\partial z)$ be expressed in terms of the atmospheric parameters (in the case of an atmosphere of homogeneous composition but with a vertical temperature gradient). Perhaps one could find then a relation with the parameter kT/mg which we normally call scale height.

Bolgiano:

Yes, as noted on page 389, potential density is closely related to potential temperature. Consequently,

$$\frac{1}{\bar{\rho}}\frac{\partial\bar{\rho}}{\partial z} = -\frac{1}{\bar{\Theta}}\frac{\partial\bar{\Theta}}{\partial z} \approx -\frac{1}{T-\Gamma z}\left[\frac{\partial T}{\partial z}-\Gamma\right],$$

where

$$\Gamma \equiv \frac{\partial T}{\partial z}\bigg|_{\text{adiabatic}} = -\frac{g}{c_p}.$$

Thus, the corresponding scale height of the potential density distribution depends very strongly upon the temperature distribution.

DIFFERENT ASPECTS DE LA TURBULENCE

P. MISME

Ingénieur en chef de la Météorologie détaché au C.N.E.T.,
chargé du G.E.R.M., Paris

Abstract. The author starts by distinguishing the different types of turbulence velocity studied separately: whirls of Bénard, convection, atmospheric layers, irregular turbulence of Obukov. He talks about the radioelectric turbulence which is
determined by the law of the turbulence velocity. He shows the rôle of the turbulence energy and one supposes that this energy is obtained at the beginning of a
radiative atmosphere. The received data agree with the experiment.

Resumé. L'auteur commence par rappeler les différents types de turbulences de vitesse qui ont été étudiées séparément: tourbillons de Bénard, convection, feuilletage atmosphérique, turbulence inorganisée d'Obukov. Puis il signale les caractéristiques de la turbulence radioélectrique et montre que cette dernière suit les
lois de la turbulence de vitesse. On met ensuite en évidence le rôle de l'énergie
mise en jeu par la turbulence et on suppose que cette énergie est obtenue à partir
du bilan radiatif de l'atmosphère. Les ordres de grandeur escomptés sont en bon
accord avec l'expérience.

1. INTRODUCTION

On peut appeler turbulence atmosphérique tout phénomène intéressant une
grandeur X qui peur être représentée de la façon suivante:

$$X = \overline{X} + \Delta X$$

où $\overline{X}$ est la valeur moyenne de X et ΔX une valeur aléatoire.

Une première difficulté de définition surgit au sujet de l'espace et de la
durée qui doivent être considérés comme intervalles à l'intérieur desquels
la moyenne est établie.

De cette définition qui, sans être universelle, en vaut bien une autre, on
peut déduire que pour chaque paramètre variable dans l'atmosphère il
pourra exister une forme de turbulence: turbulence de vitesse, de température, d'indice de réfraction, de densité etc.

De plus, l'instrument qui est utilisé pour mesurer la turbulence ayant
une certaine constante de temps, la différence entre ΔX et $\overline{X}$ ne pourra être
faite que pour un intervalle d'intégration de X beaucoup plus grand que la
constante de temps de l'instrument.

On commencera par rappeler certains types types de turbulences qui, au
cours du temps, ont été étudiés séparément. Puis on essayera de les relier
entre eux afin d'envisager une synthèse de ce qui peut caractériser la turbulence atmosphérique.

2. TOURBILLONS DE BENARD

Ce phénomène peut être mis en évidence en laboratoire de la façon suivante: au-dessus d'une plaque faiblement chauffée on matérialise les mouvements de l'air par de la fumée. On voit alors se former des cellules
tourbillonnaires de dimensions égales. La vitesse de l'air n'est pas aléatoire, une répresentation en est donnée sur la fig. 1. Plusieurs couches de
tourbillons peuvent coexister (Avsec, 1939). L'échange de chaleur entre
les différentes couches ainsi que la dynamique du système a été étudiée
théoriquement (Vernotte, 1946) et on montre ainsi les caractéristiques de
ce mécanisme de turbulence:

1) Le mouvement est entretenu par un apport d'énergie calorifique à la
   base, ou un refroidissement au sommet.
2) Lorsque cet apport d'énergie est trop élevé, le mouvement est désorga-
   nisé et il se forme une turbulence d'origine convective. S'il est trop faible
   les mouvements cessent.
3) Les mouvements de l'air n'existent que pour un nombre de modes limité
   et les cellules dont la coupe horizontale est un triangle équilatéral ou
   hexagone, sont les plus stables.

Les tourbillons de Bénard sont fréquents à tous niveaux dans la troposphère et peuvent être vus lorsque les mouvements verticaux de l'air pro-
voquent, par refroidissement adiabatique, la condensation de la vapeur

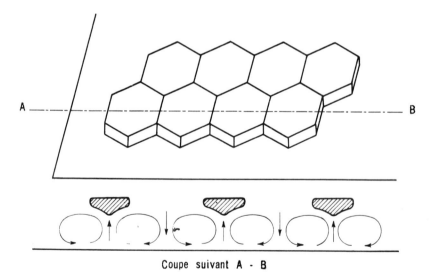

Coupe suivant A - B

Fig. 1. En haut de la figure on montre les tourbillons de Bénard en perspective ca-
valière et on a schématisé par un plan la base chaude de ces tourbillons. En bas de
la figure on a représenté l'écoulement de l'air dans un plan vertical. Au dessus des
mouvements ascendants, les nuages ont été schématisés.

d'eau. On constate alors la formation de petits nuages réguliers qui peuvent exister en plusieurs couches superposées. La dimension de ces tourbillons est de l'ordre de la centaine de mètres, mais leur anisotropie éventuelle a été peu étudiée.

Il est très probable que ce phénomène existe également dans la mésosphère mais l'absence de vapeur d'eau en quantité suffisante ne permet pas de le voir. Aucune mesure cependant ne les a encore mis en évidence, ce qui n'est pas une preuve de leur non existence. Par contre dans la basse ionosphère le gradient positif de la température est défavorable à la formation de ces tourbillons.

3. FEUILLETAGE ATMOSPHÉRIQUE

On peut rappeler ici les grandes lignes de ce qui a conduit à la théorie du feuilletage atmosphérique (Misme, 1964).

Considérons deux points situés sur une même ligne isobare P_0 à une altitude quelconque (pression P_0). On sait par expérience qu'à petite échelle, quelques centaines de mètres, les températures présentent des irrégularités atteignant de 1 à 2 degrés centigrades. Dans une masse d'air homogène, ces variations de température sont produites par des variations d'*albédo* dont les plus importantes proviennent du sol ou des sommets de nuages.

Soit alors deux points P_1 et P_2 situés à la verticale d'un point "chaud" et d'un point "froid", cette différence "chaud", "froid" étant de l'ordre de 1 à 2°C. Il existera alors une différence de pression entre P_1 et P_2. Cette différence peut être chiffrée, elle est égale à

$$\Delta P = P_0 \frac{gz}{R'T_0^2} \Delta T_0 \tag{1}$$

où g = accélération de la pesanteur.

     R' = constante des gaz par unité de masse.

     T_0 = température moyenne des deux points considérés en P_0.

ΔT_0 = écart de température entre ces points.

     z = distance verticale entre P_0 et P_1.

Cette expression a été obtenue en supposant un gradient de température constant.

De (1) on voit que ΔP croît avec l'altitude.

Les particules d'air sont alors soumises à une force de pression horizontale, ce qui crée un mouvement freiné par les forces de viscosité. On peut montrer que lorsque z est suffisamment grand, le mouvement de ces particules devient oscillatoire ce qui a pour effet de donner naissance à une zone turbulente dont les dimensions horizontales sont grandes devant les dimensions verticales. De plus ce brassage homogénéise l'air et donne ainsi naissance à la base d'une couche stable du feuillet. On constate encore dans ce mécanisme que l'energie calorifique responsable de la variation de densité de l'air, donc de la pression, a été transformée en énergie cinétique avant de reprendre la forme calorifique par l'intermédiaire des forces de frottement.

Ce type de turbulence, mis en évidence dans la troposphère, peut exister à n'importe quelle altitude y compris dans la basse ionosphère dans la mesure où des différences de température sont possibles à petite échelle.

4. TURBULENCE INORGANISÉE

On ne fera ici que rappeler brièvement les principes bien connus de la théorie d'Obukov. Supposons un volume composé de deux masses d'air de températures différentes. Si ce milieu est mis en mouvement par une énergie mécanique, il se formera des cellules de températures différentes. On conçoit intuitivement que la plus petite dimension de ces cellules sera fonction de l'énergie mise en jeu. Pour les cellules les plus petites il n'y aura pas de fractionnement mécanique mais une égalisation de la température entre les chaudes et les froides par diffusion de la chaleur. Une analyse thermodynamique de ce mécanisme permet alors d'ecrire que la dimension l des plus petites cellules obtenues mécaniquement est donnée par

$$l^4 = 90 \frac{\nu^3}{\phi} \tag{2}$$

où ν = viscosité cinématique.

ϕ = puissance mécanique mise en jeu par unité de masse.

90 = coefficient sans dimension.

Cette formule confirme que dans un milieu même hétérogène, mais non soumis à une énergie mécanique, il n'y a pas de turbulence puisque l devient infini et que dans ce cas les échanges de chaleur ont lieu par diffusion moléculaire: l'écoulement est laminaire. Un raisonnement image de ce mécanisme est donné en Annexe.

5. CONVECTION

Lorsqu'il existe un apport d'énergie calorifique suffisant en un point de l'atmosphère, l'air est réchauffé. Dans certains cas, étant moins dense que l'air ambiant il peut se déplacer de bas en haut jusqu'à un niveau qui est facilemant calculable. Il se forme alors des "cheminées d'ascendance" auxquels l'air est fourni par des courants descendants plus ou moins voisins. On est exactement au point de vue de la turbulence dans le cas étudié théoriquement par Bolganio (1959): en plus de l'énergie mécanique introduite par Obukov, on considère, dans le cas de la convection, des forces d'*Archimède* ou forces de "flottaison". L'apport initial d'énergie est toujours d'origine thermique, mais la transformation en énergie cinétique est faite par deux mécanismes différents: un mouvement moyen vertical et un mouvement instantané aléatoire.

De par leur formation, les mouvements convectifs prennent naissance plus particulièrement près du sol et peuvent intéresser toute la troposphère. Ils ne semblent pas pouvoir exister dans la stratosphère mais se rencontrent éventuellement dans la mésosphère.

6. TURBULENCE AÉRONAUTIQUE

Dans ce cas il ne s'agit pas d'un mécanisme de turbulence mais d'une méthode d'observation très utilisée pour étudier ce qui a été appelé peut-être improprement, la turbulence en ciel clair* (en Anglais C.A.T., pour Clear Air Turbulence). Il s'agit encore d'une turbulence de vitesse mais la méthode d'observation ne permet pas de distinguer les mouvements de l'air à une échelle inférieure à celle de l'avion. D'ailleurs étant donné la masse de ce dernier et sa vitesse, la plus petite échelle est voisine de 100 m. On ne détecte donc qu'une partie du spectre de turbulence. On peut cependant remarquer que la turbulence paraît très anisotropique. En effet les mouvements verticaux de l'avion sont plus nombreux que les mouvements horizontaux bien que le coefficient C_x de l'avion soit beaucoup plus élevé pour les déplacements verticaux qu'horizontaux.

7. TURBULENCE RADIOÉLECTRIQUE

Dans tout ce qui a été rappelé ci-dessus, il n'a été question que de turbulence de vitesse. La turbulence radioélectrique se manifeste par l'irrégularité de l'indice de réfraction. On sait qu'une des seules méthodes qui existent pour la mesure avec la précision suffisante à ces études, est l'emploi d'un réfractomètre. Un sondage fait avec cet appareil met en évidence une fluctuation quasi constante de l'incidence. Cependant on peut rencontrer des irrégularités plus importantes qui restent pratiquement constantes dans les temps et l'espace. Cette notion de constance étant de l'ordre de quelques heures et quelques dizaines de mètres: il s'agit de feuillets. Il n'apparaît pas, expérimentalement, une grande variation dans l'amplitude de ces fluctuations en fonction de l'altitude jusque vers 20 km. Dans tous les cas la valeur $\Delta N/N$ (où N = coïndice de réfraction**) et ΔN = fluctuation de ce coïndice) n'est pas constante ainsi qu'on l'avait supposé initialement pour les besoins de certains calculs.

8. RELATIONS ENTRE LES TURBULENCES DE VITESSE ET D'INDICE DE RÉFRACTION

Pour les fréquences supérieures à quelques dizaines de MHz, on obtient un ordre de grandeur des variations de l'indice de réfraction ou plutôt du coïndice N par la formule

---

* On ne voit pas en effet pourquoi, en dehors des Cumulonimbus qui sont un cas particulier de la convection, il n'y aurait de la turbulence en ciel clair. Il est probable au contraire que c'est le cas général. On désigne plutôt sous ce vocable étrange la turbulence à haute altitude et en particulier dans la stratosphère.

** Le coindice de refraction, N, est obtenu à partir de l'indice de réfraction, n, par l'équation de définition $N = 10^6 \, (n-1)$.

$$\Delta N = 0.3 \, \frac{\Delta P}{\text{mb}} - \frac{\Delta T}{^{\circ}\text{K}} + 7 \, \frac{\Delta r}{\text{g/kg}} \qquad (3)$$

où ΔP = variation de pression

ΔT = variation de température

Δr = variation du rapport de mélange (gramme de vapeur d'eau par kilogramme d'air sec).

Pour la turbulence radioélectrique la valeur quadratique moyenne de ΔN est de l'ordre de $1 N$. Dans un volume d'air échantillon pris pour évaluer le spectre de turbulence, les altitudes sont quasiment constantes et la contribution de ΔP est insignifiante. Dans la basse stratosphère la contribution de la vapeur d'eau est prépondérante. Lorsque cette dernière a presque complètement disparu, c'est-à-dire au-dessus d'une dizaine de kilomètres les irrégularités de température sont les seules à influer ΔN. La théorie d'Obukov ayant été faite pour les irrégularités de température, on voit qu'elle est directement applicable à la turbulence radioélectrique au-dessus de 10 km. En dessous de ce niveau l'humidité joue un rôle prépondérant. La diffusivité de la vapeur d'eau étant faible dans une atmosphère au repos, la même théorie sera encore utilisable. Pour les fréquences basses pour lesquelles l'ionisation joue le rôle prépondérant, la considération de la diffusion des particules ionisées dans un gaz neutre tend à prouver que cette théorie de turbulence est encore utilisable.

Un autre aspect de la turbulence radioélectrique doit dependant être envisagé. Dans la majorité des applications on est conduit à interpreter le rôle de l'atmosphère sur une liaison radioélectrique fixe par rapport au sol. Le cas des liaisons air-air entre deux appareils soumis à la même turbulence que les ondes radioélectriques est un cas très particulier d'usage restreint.

Certaines formes de la turbulence étudiées ci-dessus sont liées au mouvement général de l'atmosphère, d'autres, telle que la convection, sont liées au sol. On retrouve cette différence analytique entre les méthodes d'Euler et Lagrange utilisées en mécanique des fluides. Ces différences ne sont pas négligeables puisqu'il a été trouvé (Angell, 1964) au même endroit et au même instant des pentes du spectre différentes suivant la méthode d'observation. On sait que de nombreux efforts théoriques ont été faits pour relier ces deux méthodes, mais il ne semble pas que les résultats en soient probants (Gifford, 1953 et 1955; Mickelsen, 1955).

En terminant ce paragraphe on se doit de noter une méthode de mesure indirecte de la turbulence. En admettant que la propagation transhorizon est produite par la diffusion par les éléments turbulents de l'air, on peut déduire une relation entre les caractéristiques du signal reçu et celles de la turbulence. Remarquons que même en admettant la validité des théories de diffusion dans ce cas particulier, le spectre de turbulence ainsi mesuré est une espèce de spectre "équivalent" dans tout le volume commun et ne serait représentatif que si la turbulence était homogène ce qui n'est pas le cas. Lorsqu'il a été possible de mesurer séparément le spectre de turbulence par cette méthode indirecte et directement avec un réfractomètre, les résultats n'ont pas été concordants (Bull, 1966).

9. ORIGINE DE L'ÉNERGIE

On a mis en évidence que dans tous les mécanismes de turbulence les transformations énergétiques étaient les suivantes:

énergie calorifique→énergie mécanique→turbulence→énergie calorifique.

La turbulence apparaît comme intermédiaire entre une partie de l'énergie calorifique fournie par le soleil et l'énergie calorifique utilisée à réchauffer l'atmosphère. Dans les cas des tourbillons de Bénard, de la convection ou du feuilletage, le rôle de l'énergie calorifique est évident, et la transformation de la chaleur en mouvement est produite par l'intermédiaire d'une source chaude perdant sa chaleur au bénéfice d'une source froide. L'ordre de grandeur de la différence de température entre ces deux sources est de l'ordre de quelques degrés, soit ΔT pour une température ambiante T. Par suite l'énergie mécanique disponible sera au maximum la fraction $\Delta T/T$ du bilan radiatif de l'atmosphère. Dans le cas de la turbulence inorganisée (autre que lorsqu'elle est localisée sous un feuillet stable) la source d'énergie mécanique est extérieure au système turbulent: il peut s'agir du vent sur le relief, des différences de vitesse entre deux masses d'air tel que le cisaillement de vent ainsi créé soit générateur de turbulence. Bien que le bilan radiatif soit la source d'énergie, la fraction utilisable est difficile à évaluer puisque la quantité ΔT est inconnue. L'ordre de magnitude de 10^{-2} paraît cependant un maximum.

10. RÉPARTITION DU BILAN RADIATIF EN FONCTION DE L'ALTITUDE

Cette quantité a été mesurée dans l'atmosphère jusque vers 25 km (Kuhm et Suomi, 1960) et calculée au dessus (Murgatroyd et Goody, 1958).

Sur la fig. 2 on a résumé ces deux sources de renseignements et opéré de la façon suivante. Les résultats de mesures ont été obtenus de nuit et correspondent à un refroidissement de l'atmosphère (perte d'énergie). On a supposé que de jour il y aurait eu un réchauffement apportant la même énergie. On a donc tenu compte du rapport de la durée jour/nuit et converti les résultats en unités cohérentes (erg/g.sec). Pour la même saison et la même latitude on a fait correspondre les valeurs calculées entre 30 et 100 km. On notera que les deux courbes sont dans le prolongement l'une de l'autre.

Dans le paragraphe précédent on a évalué le pourcentage d'énergie utilisable: il est au maximum de 10^{-2}. On peut alors calculer la fraction d'énergie qui sera transformée en mouvement et en déduire par exemple la dimension des particules les plus petites à l'aide de la formule (2). On aura ainsi un ordre de grandeur, mais rappelons que ce bilan radiatif est très variable en fonction du temps et de l'altitude. Dans le cas particulier signalé ici on voit par exemple l'existence d'une zone sans turbulence puisque $\phi = 0$ vers 12 km d'altitude.

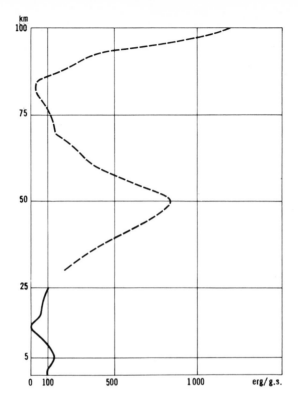

Fig. 2. Bilan radiatif de l'atmosphère d'après les références Kuhm et Suomi (1960) et Murgatroyd et Goody (1958).

11. CONCLUSION

En essayant d'obtenir une vue plus synthétique de ces problèmes, on est conduit à conclure que dans la majorité des cas, les turbulences de vitesse et d'indice de réfraction sont représentées par des spectres analogues. Une des méthodes numérique consiste à introduire le bilan radiatif de l'atmosphère considéré comme la source d'énergie qui sera transformée en chaleur par l'intermédiaire de mouvement.

12. ANNEXE

Pour certains, les textes originaux présentent une abstraction qui nuit à leur compréhension.

Un raisonnement imagé qui ne prétend pas être d'une grande rigeur scientifique, permettra peut-être de mieux saisir ce mécanisme:

Considérons une machine à laver à l'intérieur de laquelle on met deux fluides de densités différentes: de l'air chaud et de l'air froid. On pourrait rendre le phénomène visible avec des fluides de couleurs différentes que l'on appellera ici: bleu, le plus froid et le plus dense, et rouge, le plus chaud et le moins dense. En l'absence de brassage, donc de puissance mécanique, ces deux fluides seront superposés, le bleu restera au fond de la machine et le rouge au dessus. La diffusion moléculaire ne les mélangera que dans un temps très long.

Mettons la machine en action en fournissant une faible puissance au moteur. Les deux fluides seront grossièrement mélangés: on verra se former de gros tourbillons bleus et de gros tourbillons rouges. Si la puissance augmente ces tourbillons seront plus petits. Leurs dimensions est donc une fonction décroissante de la puissance mise en jeu (Certains auteurs utilisent la notion d'énergie par unité de temps ce qui complique les notions simples).

Cependant il existe de plus la diffusion moléculaire de "quelque chose" dans un milieu. Ce "quelque chose", dans l'exemple choisi, sera la chaleur. La vitesse de cette diffusion dépendra de la surface en contact et du gradient de température. En résumé, la puissance mécanique mise en jeu homogénéise le milieu en morcelant les grands tourbillons en de petits jusqu'à une limite au-dessous de laquelle l'homogénéisation est faite par la diffusion de la chaleur. On a donc deux familles de tourbillons représentées par deux lois statistiques différentes. Pour une dimension intermédiaire entre les grands et les petits, les deux mécanismes auront la même importance. Cette dimension critique sera uniquement fonction de la puissance et du coefficient de diffusivité. Il est intéressant de remarquer que pour la chaleur ce coefficient a les mêmes dimensions que la viscosité et que ces deux quantités sont reliées par le nombre de Prandtl. On utilisera donc la viscosité cinématique qui est également introduite dans la turbulence de vitesse.

Tous calculs faits, cette dimension intermédiaire l est donnée par:

$$l^4 = 90 \frac{\nu^3}{\phi}$$

avec: 90 = nombre sans dimensions

$\quad\quad \nu$ = viscosité cinématique

$\quad\quad \phi$ = puissance mise en jeu par unité de masse du fluide.

On retrouve ainsi le fait que si la puissance est nulle, cette dimension est infinie, c'est-à-dire qu'il y a uniquement diffusion moléculaire de la chaleur: l'écoulement est laminaire.

Plusieurs remarques sont à faire:

1) Lorsque ϕ est très différent de 0, l est peu variable avec ϕ, c'est le cas le plus souvent étudié.

2) Le nombre 90 provient du produit de l'inverse de nombre de Prandtl par 2 coefficients sans dimensions dont l'un est mal déterminé. On a ainsi pour l un ordre de grandeur plutôt qu'une mesure précise.

3) Si on étudie la turbulence de vitesse (Kolmogorov) et non plus de température, ce nombre 90 ne serait plus le même mais les différents auteurs ne sont pas d'accord sur sa valeur.

4) La puissance mise en jeu ϕ peut être calculée (voir l'article ci-dessus) et mesurée. En effet on a admis dans le raisonnement précédent que pour les grands tourbillons le mouvement ne se transforme pas en chaleur (on rappelle qu'il y a un simple morcellement mécanique). Pour la turbulence de vitesse il suffit donc de mesurer l'énergie cinétique des tourbillons d'une dimension prédéterminée. Cette quantité est appelée le taux de dissipation et notée en général par ϵ. Il y a identité entre ϕ et ϵ. Dans le cas de la turbulence de vitesse il est d'usage d'employer ϵ plutôt que ϕ. (Voir les discussions de l'article de Spizzichino pour la mesure de ϵ).

Dans le cas de la turbulence de température ϕ est conservé par les grands tourbillons et restitué en chaleur dans les petits. On peut donc encore mesurer ϕ.

RÉFÉRENCES

Angell, J.K., 1964, J. Royal Meteorol. Soc. 90, 57.
Avsec, D., 1939, Tourbillons thermo-convectifs dans l'air, P.S.T., Ministère de l'Air, No. 155.
Bolganio, R., 1959, J. Geophys. Res. 64, 2226.
Bull, G., 1966, J. Atmos. Terrest. Phys. 28, 513.
Gifford, F., 1953, 1955, Monthly Weather Res. 81, 179; Monthly Weather Rev. 83, 293.
Kuhm. P.M. and W.E.Suomi, 1960, J. Geophys. Res. 65, 2116.
Mickelsen, W.R., 1955, NACA. Tech. Note 3570, Washington D.C.
Misme, P., 1964, Ann. Télécomm. 19, 49.
Murgatroyd, R.J. and R.M.Goody, 1958, J. Royal Meteorol. Soc. 84, 361.
Vernotte, P., 1946, Thermocinétique, P.S.T., No. 224, Ministère de l'Air.

DISCUSSION

Maenhout:
At what latitude was the radiative budget in your figure measured, and when: summer or winter, day or night?

Misme:
Les mesures de Kuhm et Suomi ont été faites la nuit au mois de juillet vers 45⁰ de la latitude Nord. Afin de trouver un ordre de grandeur, on les a transformées en mesures de jour: réchauffement au lieu de refroidissement et durée du jour plus grande que celle de la nuit. On les a complétées par les calculs de Murgatroyd pour le jour à la même latitude et pour la même saison. Cette présentation ne prétend donner qu'un ordre de grandeur.

Rawer:

Le profile du bilan radiatif donné correspond aux conditions de jour. De nuit apparaîtront certainement des niveaux à bilan négatif, c.à.d. de re-froidissement. Donc la position des niveaux aux conditions stables (apport d'énergie presque nul) va être différente de jour et de nuit, ainsi que la turbopause. Or, les observations de cette dernière ont été effectuées sur-tout par la méthode des trainées de sodium qui s'applique seulement au crépuscule. Ainsi les données d'expérience actuelles ne concernent que les conditions très particulières entre nuit et jour; elles ne sont donc pas re-présentatives du jour ou de la nuit.

Misme:
d'accord

Robert:

Les calculs de Murgatroyd semblant montrer une croissance du bilan calorifique avec l'altitude au delà de 85 km, comment peut-on conclure à la présence d'une turbopause au niveau de 85 km?

Misme:

Il y a deux problèmes à considérer.
1) Dans la théorie que l'on a exposée sur le rôle de l'apport d'énergie, on voit que les dimensions minimales des tourbillons sont proportionnelles à la puissance $\frac{1}{4}$ du rapport ν^3/ϕ. Or ϕ augmente moins vite que ν^3, c'est une des raisons supposées de la turbopause.
2) L'énergie mécanique n'est qu'une faible partie de l'énergie calorifique. Si le milieu est presque homogène du point de vue de la température, il n'y aura pas de transformation de l'énergie calorifique en énergie mé-canique. C'est peut être cet aspect qui est prépondérant à la turbopause. En effet il n'y a pas ou peu de cause de variation de l'*albédo* dans le plan horizontal à partir d'une centaine de km.

Rawer:
Comment on ionospheric refraction and turbulence

A direct relation between the spectrum of turbulent speeds, Δv, and radio observations is only to be expected when the Doppler enlargement of the transmitted frequency is observed. If intensity measurements of echoes are made, the spectrum of the frequency fluctuations, Δf, is probably better related. It is, however, not always clear whether this relation is simple, particularly in cases where reactions (chemical or electrical) occur in the medium. For example: condensation of water vapor, attachment of elec-trons, recombination, dissociation etc.

A recent result seems to be important in this context: With pumped mass spectrometers, scientists of the US Air Force have stated that rather thin layers occur, where metallic ions reach a high percentage of the total ionization. It seems that Es-layers be of this type.

Misme:

Il y a là un résultat de Bolganio: on peut avoir couches laminaires stables dans un milieu turbulent. En effet, on trouve beaucoup de similtude entre des couches turbulentes dans un milieu stratifié, et des couches stratifiées dans un milieu turbulent!

Revah:

My question concerns the rate of dissipation of turbulence from meteor observations.

Misme:

Validité de la mesure du taux de dissipation de la turbulence par la méthode des deux points de reflexion sur une même traînée météorique. (Méthode de Greenhow et Neufeld d'une part, et celle de Roper et Elford d'autre part.)

Spizzichino:
Problème des composantes NS et verticale à l'observation des météores.

Réponse à la question: observe-t-on des variations du vent dûes à la turbulence à petite échelle avec le radar de Garchy?
1) Pendant la durée d'un écho météorique (< 1 sec), le vent mesuré reste rigoureusement constant.
2) Des mesures de vent faites à la même altitude et à des instants très voisins semblent indiquer une faible variabilité du vent mesuré. Cette variabilité pourrait être due à des mouvements à plus petite échelle, mais elle peut avoir d'autres causes:
   a) l'influence d'un vent Nord-Sud
   b) l'influence d'un gradient du vent Est-Ouest
   c) l'influence d'une composante verticale du vent.
   Une étude plus approfondie des vents mesurés serait nécessaire pour évaluer l'importance relative de ces différents effets. Les bases théoriques d'une telle étude sont données dans la Note Technique CNET/CDS: "Résultats d'une première campagne de mesure des vents au moyen d'un radar météorique" par Revah et Spizzichino (1966).

Question:
Onde de gravité dans un milieu turbulent. Peut-on reconnaître l'onde de gravité dans le spectre?

Misme:

Le mouvement vertical d'une particule dans une onde de gravité est de l'ordre de 1 m/s (voir Dr. Gille). Considérons un réfractomêtre descendant verticalement. Au dépouillement, peut-on éliminer cette composante du spectre obtenu?

Bolganio:

In an attempt to clarify the question of the ability to interpret short (2 min) records of dropsondes in terms of turbulence and gravity waves I asked Dr. Gille to describe the spatial distribution of the velocity field of the assumed gravity wave. He noted that in the troposphere the most common type of wave would be a Lamb-wave at a sharp temperature inversion, decaying exponentially in both upward and downward directions, and propagating horizontally.

Neubauer:

Is there any influence of the turbulent Reynolds-stresses on the dynamics of prevailing winds?

Bolganio:

Eddy stress is mostly small and negligible, but at 100 km we do not know enough and nonlinear terms might be more important that the Coriolis term.

Stilke:

This is a comment concerning the amplitude of (the vertical component of) orbital movement in gravity waves. Our measurements in the very low troposphere and calculations for the lower troposphere should allow the assumption, that in the troposphere the amplitude of the vertical motion might be up to one tenth of the height above ground.

SECOND GENERAL DISCUSSION
ON TURBULENCE AND WAVES

Rawer:

In this discussion some of us are mainly interested in consequences of these phenomena concerning radio wave propagation. For others the emphasis may be on the interpretation of radio propagational observations in terms of atmospheric physics or meteorology.

We may subdivide the subject in that of turbulence in the usual sense and that of 'mechanical' waves, i.e. identifiable acoustic or gravity waves. Thus our discussion could have the following sections:

1. Turbulence
2. Acoustic and gravity waves.

1. TURBULENCE

Rawer:

Years ago radio propagation people were thinking in terms of isotropic turbulence. It is the merit of Prof. Bolgiano to have shown to radio people that atmospheric turbulence is essentially anisotropic. May I first ask whether this anisotropy is more due to wind shears or to the effect of gravity without shearing?

Bolgiano:

Wind shears are essential for turbulence.

Misme:

As an example we may consider the motion of an aeroplane. When flying you feel very often vertical acceleration and motion; the horizontal accelerations, however, are quite small. This observation shows that the atmospheric turbulence elements have quite large horizontal dimensions as compared with their vertical thickness. The ratio is of the order 10:1. There may also exist combinations of gravity waves with turbulence. Fig. 1 shows how turbulence could be linked with a gravity wave.

As to the second possibility it might be interesting to draw surfaces of constant correlation for the different model cases, see fig. 2.

It is clear that in the absence of shearing and of gravitational forces these surfaces must be concentric spheres (i.e. circles in our fig. 2). Now shearing is stratification along the vertical axis. Neglecting all other con-

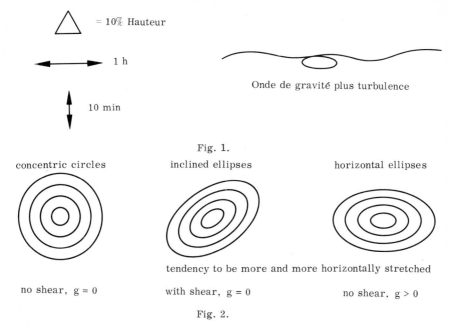

Fig. 1.

concentric circles   inclined ellipses   horizontal ellipses

tendency to be more and more horizontally stretched

no shear, g = 0   with shear, g = 0   no shear, g > 0

Fig. 2.

sequences of gravity ($g = 0$) but admitting a wind shear we obtain *inclined* ellipsoids (i.e. ellipses in a vertical plane see our fig. 2), because the correlation between points of different height depends now on the shearing. With increasing shearing these ellipsoids become more elongated and more horizontally stretched. On the other hand the case of negligible shear but non-negligible gravitational effect must result in horizontally stretched ellipsoids (see fig. 2).

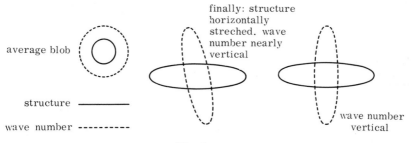

Fig. 3.

It is important to know that the structure itself and the description of turbulence by a spectrum (i.e. by a wave number distribution) must be clearly distinguished. Fig. 3 shows the average shape of the blobs (full lines) and the corresponding average wave number distribution (with the elevation angle, broken lines). With increasing shear while the blob shape is stretched more and more horizontally, the wave number ellipse is at right angle to it so that its elongation axis approaches more and more the vertical (fig. 3).

2. WAVES

Rawer:
I shall now put a certain number of questions concerning acoustic and gravity waves. *The first question concerns the relation of acoustic waves and turbulence.* Are they found in the same frequency range?

Gille:
Advective terms are neglected in turbulence description. So acoustic waves are not contained in the equations, only the energy input provoked by them.

Rawer:
The second question is that after the origin (energy source and height) *of acoustic waves.*

Gille:
Acoustic waves are clearly generated by thunderstorms, tornadoes and surf. The wind passing over obstacles or irregularities is also a powerful natural source of acoustic waves. (The jet stream would radiate lower frequencies, thus provoke gravity waves.)

Stilke:
A nearly continuous source of acoustic waves seems to be the waved sea surface (or the breaking of oceanic waves at the coast); that at least in winter time may be measured almost continuously with periods of about 5 sec. This was shown by sensitive microbarovariographs (when there is no strong turbulence near the recording station) at Hamburg and in Switzerland[*]. Other sources seem to be tornados in the USA and hurricanes. When recording thunderstorms with microbarovariographs, one finds the 'pressure noses' superimposed and followed by wave like pressure variations with periods between 5 and 10 min. But I do not know, whether these are acoustic waves, gravity waves or just oscillations with Brunt's period.

Bolgiano:
Acoustic waves overlap in both frequency and wave number the turbulence portion of the spectrum. They may be generated atmospherically by intense turbulence, ocean surface waves, small intense storms and lightning strokes. While much of this acoustic energy will be reflected at alti-

---

[*] Saxer. L.. 1954. Archiv. Meteorol. Geophys. Bioklim.. A. VI. 451.

tudes below 50 km, some of it appears to penetrate at least to the lower thermosphere. Lightning strokes are sometimes heard 20 miles away. This proves that the corresponding acoustic wave goes high up.

Gille:

Large explosions have been observed at much larger distances by re-fraction in the ozone layer. It can be expected that a part of the wave ener-gy penetrates to higher altitudes.

Rawer:

These explosions have been heard at more than 100 km distance. Thus low audible frequencies from ground come rather high up.

May I now come to the *third question after the origin* (energy source and height) *of gravity waves.*

Stilke:

As to acoustic waves with long periods (about 5 sec), there exists an es-timation of the energy transfer from aceanic waves into acoustic waves in the air [*].

So we come finally to the more general question: Is it possible, and to which extent, that the energy inherent in turbulence of long periods (for ex-ample convection due to solar irradiation) is transferred into acoustic or gravity waves in a larger range at the earth's surface? A model for such excitation is a large diaphragm with ordered oscillation in limited ranges only; oscillation periods had to be up to 10 min and longer.

Gille:

Waves with periods from 5 min to 3 h are the main gravity waves. The meteorological disturbances mentioned above would also generate gravity waves.

The geostrophic adjustment of the jet stream and the wind systems of meteorological disturbances presumably radiate gravity waves. Lee waves of mountains are also thought to be sources and it appears that earthquakes may excite such waves. The sources of acoustic waves may also make a contribution to these long period waves.

Neubauer:

The time-statistics of thunderstorms should then be apparent.

Gille:

One believes that atmospheric electricity is maintained through the sum of all thunderstorms. An analogue could eventually be valid for the excita-tion of gravity waves.

Rawer:

But then these waves should mainly come from the equatorial belt, with

[*] Daniels. F. B., 1952. J. Acoust. Soc. Amer. 24. 83.

important diurnal variation of the location of origin.

Spizzichino:

After Hines, a polar jet stream in winter should be the source of *travelling disturbances*.

Gille:

One must consider the filtering mechanisms. It is difficult to say whether the causes of gravity waves have large latitudinal variation, or whether observed variations come from the filtering effect of variable wind profiles as used in Hines's recent theory.

Rawer:

The occurrence of travelling disturbances, called 'transitoria' at vertical ionospheric sounding has a very important day-to-night variation. Is there any source of gravity waves known which acts only during daytime?

Stilke:

A mechanism depending on the time of day for giving rise to gravity waves might be 'turbulent' motions caused by convection (heating of the ground). Records of wind speed (three components u, v, w) and temperature at a height of 250 m above ground (tall antenna mast) show strong fluctuations at noon with periods of 5 to 10 min (and smaller), beginning in clear summer days with sunrise, and nearly absent in calm nights.

Neubauer:

In considering the sources of gravity-waves in the troposphere it is necessary to take into account that the waves have to travel long horizontal distances until they get to ionospheric heights. Hence the correlation of the source and its ionospheric effects is difficult.

Bolgiano:

With 30 m/s phase velocity 24 h are needed to reach the 300 km level. Even with acoustic speeds (which are not probable) at least 3 h time difference are to be expected.

Rawer:

As the observed transitoria start shortly after sunrise and stop after sunset it seems that it is perhaps difficult to explain them with an energy feed near ground level. One should then consider whether excitation of gravity waves in the atmosphere is possible, for example in the mesosphere.

Gille:

Solar radiation probably changes the ducting conditions more than the mechanism of excitation.

Ilias:

Observations on large scale irregularities (order of 60 km) of the electron content taken by satellite signals in Athens during 1964-1965, indicate some interesting features which probably can be useful if some-one is looking at the origin of the gravity waves (provided that those irregularities result from gravity waves).

1) In contrast with the earlier mentioned h' disturbances which are a day-time phenomenon, the electron content large scale irregularities are day and night phenomena as well.

2) The latitudinal distribution of the amplitude of these irregularities indicates a clear maximum towards the equator.

3) No significant influence of the geomagnetic activity was found, but a seasonal effect (from the one year data) indicates an amplitude maximum during winter.

It seems to me that the above observations are in favour of an equatorial origin of the cause of these irregularities and consequently of the gravity waves - if in fact these irregularities are the result of gravity waves.

Rawer:

Going to always longer periods may I now as *fourth question ask after the origin* (energy and level of excitation) *of tidal waves.*

Gille:

These propagate as gravity waves, only that the Coriolis force and the earth' curvature must be considered and have some slightly modifying influence on propagation.

Rawer:

Resonance phenomena in the earth's atmosphere have been considered as decisive for the excitation rate by Wilkes. I wonder whether this is really so. In that case only full wave solutions could be accepted. I wonder whether geometrical acoustics is not good enough for computing a large part of the data obtained for example by Pfeffer. In that range, where geometrical acoustics applies, resonance phenomena should be negligible.

Gille:

Pfeffer's results in the whole range for periods between 10 sec and 1000 sec depend critically on the period, so that really a wave solution is needed.

Spizzichino:

The rather large amplitude of the 12 h period has been explained in past literature by a resonance effect. Is this theory always considered to be the right answer to the problem?

Gille:

The large amplitude of the 12 h tidal wave can not only be a resonance effect because it concerns only the solar not the lunar wave and this means

that the resonant cavity should have an extremely sharp resonance which is
not acceptable.

Spizzichino:
    It is easily understood that in the case of the semidiurnal tide an oscilla-
tion of large wavelength be excited in the cavity around the earth. Could it
be similar with the diurnal tide for which the theoretical modes have a
smaller (vertical) wavelength such that the small irregularities of the shape
of the cavity could probably destroy resonance effects.

Neubauer:
    Butler and Small[*] have published a new theory. They argue that the di-
urnal tide has a vertical wavelength much smaller than the semidiurnal
tide, so that the matching between the distribution with height of the heat
source in the ozone layer and the altitude distribution of the tidal wave is
good for the semidiurnal tide and poor for the diurnal tide. Or in other
words, the diurnal tide is excited at different heights in opposite sense and
so nearly cancelled because of its small wavelength compared to the extent
of the heat source. This is not true for the semidiurnal tide, which has a
much longer vertical wavelength. As to the different amplitudes of the solar
and lunar semidiurnal tide, heating in the ozone layer is an additional energy source for the 12 h tide, whilst the lunar one is only fed by gravity force.

Stilke:
    We must distinguish here between gravity waves in the strict sense and
related waves which are propagating along an interphase and may be called
'interphase gravity waves'. Fig. 4 gives examples which apply to the troposphere.

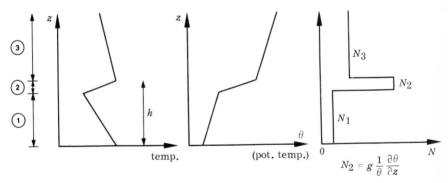

Fig. 4.

The condition for gravity waves to be excitable is:

$$\omega < N \ (\text{i.e.}: \omega < N_1, \ N_2, \ N_3) \ .$$

This condition could also be written using Brunt's period ($\tau_{Br.} = 2\pi/N$)

$$\tau > \tau_{Br}\ 1, 2, 3\ .$$

On the other side the condition for 'interphase gravity waves' is:

$$\omega < N_{Max} \equiv \sqrt{g} \cdot d\ \ln\theta/dz_{Max}\ ,\ \text{i.e.}\ \omega < N_2$$

which means

$$\tau > \tau_{Br}\ 2$$

Thus gravity waves with long enough period may coexist in all three layers at the same time. Interphase gravity waves, however, could exist in layer 2 only, provided that their period is rather short, this is the case $\omega > N_1$, N_3, but $\omega < N_2$. Under these conditions evanescent waves only appear in layers 1 and 3 (with exponentional or nearly exponential decrease of amplitude with distance from the interphase). If the thickness of layer 2 is small (against its height above ground, and against the vertical wavelength) the (phase) velocity, v, of the interphase waves is given by

$$v^2 \approx \frac{g}{k}\frac{\Delta\rho}{\rho} = \frac{g}{k}\frac{\Delta\theta}{\theta}\ ,$$

and for small h (see fig. 4)

$$v^2 \approx gh\frac{\Delta\rho}{\rho} = gh\frac{\Delta\theta}{\theta}$$

Wind and windshears are, of course, neglected in these equations.